Chp. 1 all ex p 22/23

Chp 2 p 48-69

Chp 3 p 76-81 leave out

99- ... clone

... cyclone

add 83-9...

p. 85-90

hurricanes

Chp 4 - 112-115

PRENTICE HALL

Teacher's SCIENCE EXPLORER Edition

Weather and Climate

PRENTICE HALL
Needham, Massachusetts
Upper Saddle River, New Jersey
Glenview, Illinois

ISBN 0-13-434559-2
4 5 6 7 8 9 10   05 04 03 02 01 00

PRENTICE HALL
SCIENCE EXPLORER
GET READY FOR A CONTENT-RICH, HANDS-ON EXPLORATION!
PRENTICE HALL SCIENCE EXPLORER Earth's Waters
PRENTICE HALL SCIENCE EXPLORER Motion, Forces and Energy
PRENTICE HALL SCIENCE EXPLORER Animals
15 Books In All

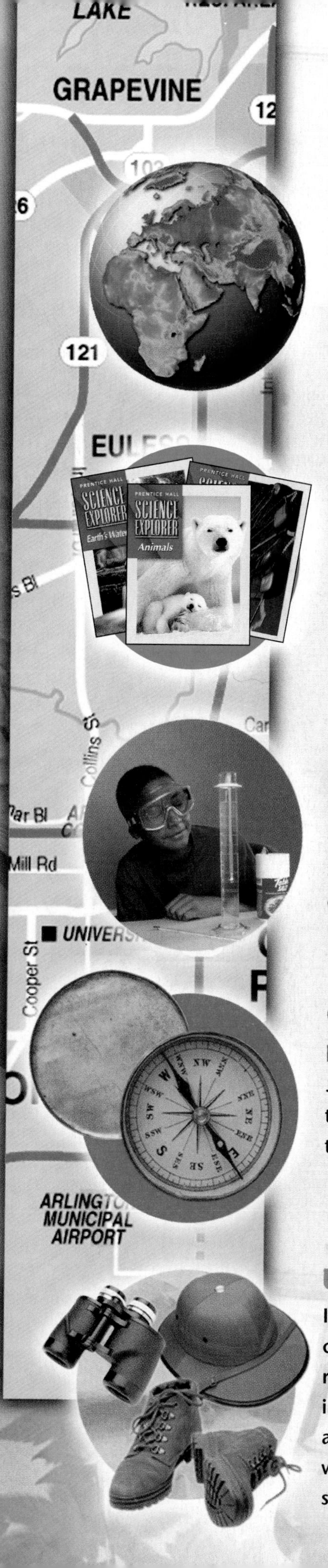

Chart your own course.

15 motivational hardcover books make it easy for you to create your own curriculum; meet local, state, and national guidelines; and teach your favorite topics in depth.

Prepare your students with rich, motivating content...

Science Explorer is crafted for today's middle grades student, with accessible content and in-depth coverage of all the important concepts.

...and a wide variety of inquiry activities.

Motivational student- and teacher-tested activities reinforce key concepts and allow students to explore science concepts for themselves.

Check your compass regularly.

Science Explorer gives you more ways to regularly check student performance than any other program available.

Utilize a variety of tools.

Integrated science sections in every chapter and Interdisciplinary Explorations in every book allow you to make in-depth connections to other sciences and disciplines. Plus, you will find a wealth of additional tools to set your students on a successful course.

Chart the course you want with 15 motivating books that easily match your curriculum.

Each book in the series contains:

- Integrated Science sections in every chapter
- Interdisciplinary Explorations for team teaching at the end of each book
- Comprehensive skills practice and application—assuring that you meet the National Science Education Standards and your local and state standards

For custom binding options, see your local sales representative.

EXPLORATION TOOLS: BASIC PROCESS SKILLS

Observing

Measuring

Calculating

Classifying

Predicting

Inferring

Graphing

Creating data tables

Communicating

LIFE SCIENCE TITLES

From Bacteria to Plants
1 Living Things
2 Viruses and Bacteria
3 Protists and Fungi
4 Introduction to Plants
5 Seed Plants

Animals
1 Sponges, Cnidarians, and Worms
2 Mollusks, Arthropods, and Echinoderms
3 Fishes, Amphibians, and Reptiles
4 Birds and Mammals
5 Animal Behavior

Cells and Heredity
1 Cell Structure and Function
2 Cell Processes and Energy
3 Genetics: The Science of Heredity
4 Modern Genetics
5 Changes Over Time

Human Biology and Health
1 Healthy Body Systems
2 Bones, Muscles, and Skin
3 Food and Digestion
4 Circulation
5 Respiration and Excretion
6 Fighting Disease
7 The Nervous System
8 The Endocrine System and Reproduction

Environmental Science
1 Populations and Communities
2 Ecosystems and Biomes
3 Living Resources
4 Land and Soil Resources
5 Air and Water Resources
6 Energy Resources

Integrated Science sections in every chapter

EXPLORATION TOOLS: ADVANCED PROCESS SKILLS

Posing questions

Forming operational definitions

Developing hypotheses

Controlling variables

Interpreting data

Interpreting graphs

Making models

Drawing conclusions

Designing experiments

EARTH SCIENCE TITLES

Inside Earth
1 Plate Tectonics
2 Earthquakes
3 Volcanoes
4 Minerals
5 Rocks

Earth's Changing Surface
1 Mapping Earth's Surface
2 Weathering and Soil Formation
3 Erosion and Deposition
4 A Trip Through Geologic Time

Earth's Waters
1 Earth: The Water Planet
2 Fresh Water
3 Freshwater Resources
4 Ocean Motions
5 Ocean Zones

Weather and Climate
1 The Atmosphere
2 Weather Factors
3 Weather Patterns
4 Climate and Climate Change

Astronomy
1 Earth, Moon, and Sun
2 The Solar System
3 Stars, Galaxies, and the Universe

PHYSICAL SCIENCE TITLES

Chemical Building Blocks
1 An Introduction to Matter
2 Changes in Matter
3 Elements and the Periodic Table
4 Carbon Chemistry

Chemical Interactions
1 Chemical Reactions
2 Atoms and Bonding
3 Acids, Bases, and Solutions
4 Exploring Materials

Motion, Forces, and Energy
1 Motion
2 Forces
3 Forces in Fluids
4 Work and Machines
5 Energy and Power
6 Thermal Energy and Heat

Electricity and Magnetism
1 Magnetism and Electromagnetism
2 Electric Charges and Current
3 Electricity and Magnetism at Work
4 Electronics

Sound and Light
1 Characteristics of Waves
2 Sound
3 The Electromagnetic Spectrum
4 Light

Integrated Science sections in every chapter

Place your students in the role of science explorer through a variety of inquiry activities.

Motivational student- and teacher-tested activities reinforce key concepts and allow students to explore science concepts for themselves. More than 350 activities are provided for each book in the Student Edition, Teacher's Edition, Teaching Resources, Integrated Science Lab Manual, Inquiry Skills Activity Book, Interactive Student Tutorial CD-ROM, and *Science Explorer* Web Site.

STUDENT EDITION ACTIVITIES

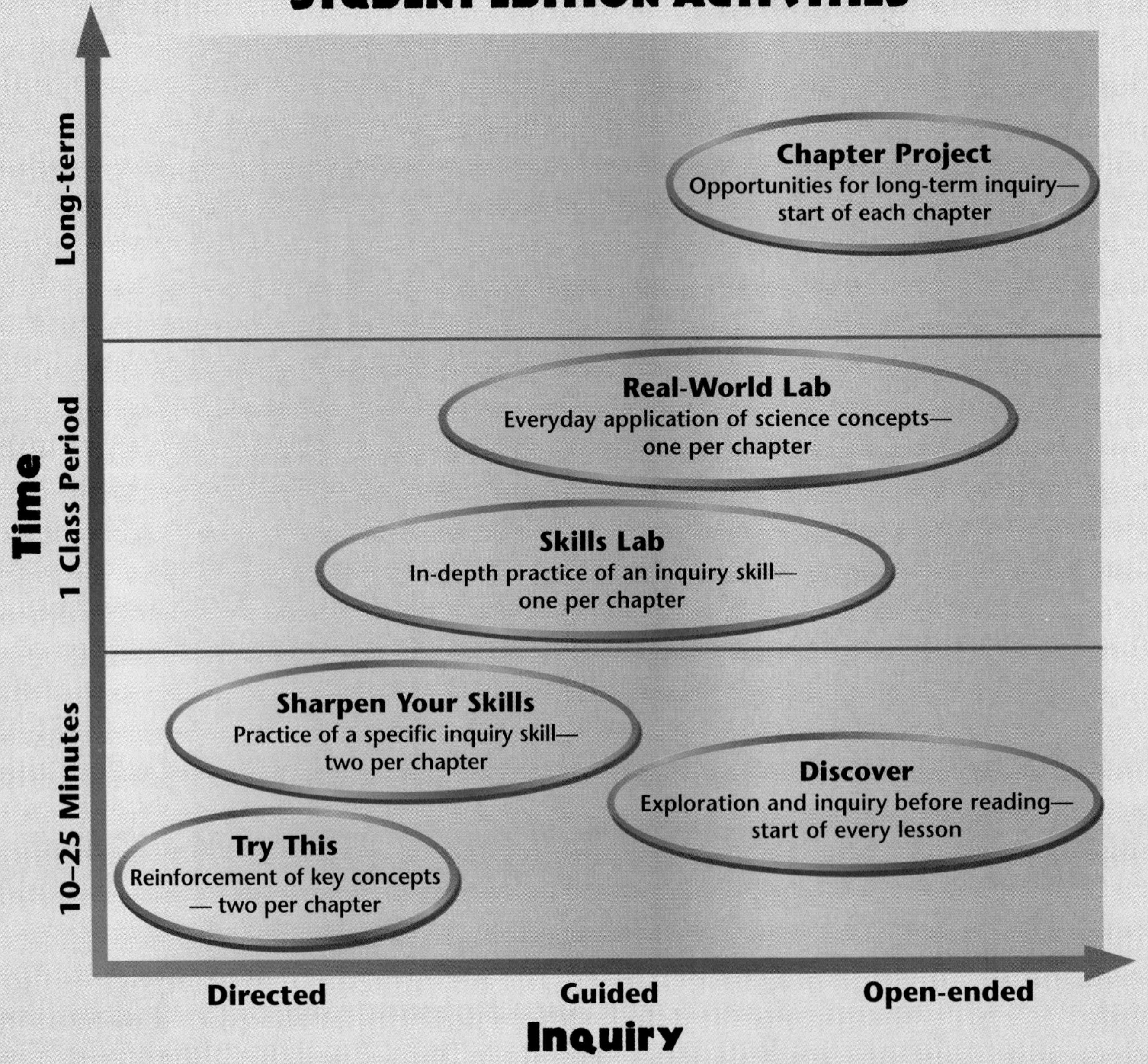

Check your compass regularly with integrated assessment tools.

Prepare for state exams with traditional and performance-based assessment.

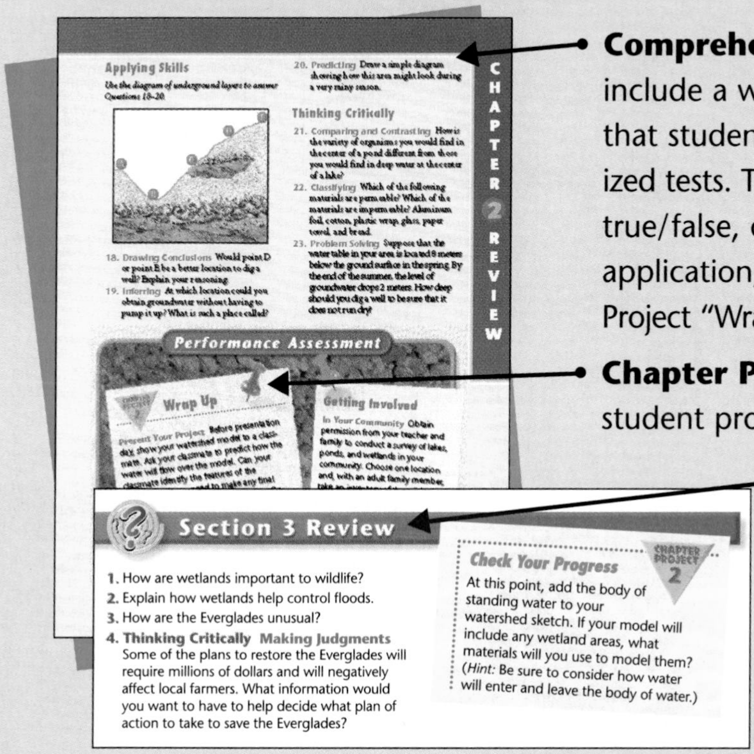

Applying Skills

Use the diagram of underground layers to answer Questions 18–20.

18. Drawing Conclusions Would point D or point E be a better location to dig a well? Explain your reasoning.
19. Inferring At which location could you obtain groundwater without having to pump it up? What is such a place called?
20. Predicting Draw a simple diagram showing how this area might look during a very rainy season.

Thinking Critically

21. Comparing and Contrasting How is the variety of organisms you would find in the center of a pond different from those you would find in deep water at the center of a lake?
22. Classifying Which of the following materials are permeable? Which of the materials are impermeable? Aluminum foil, cotton, plastic wrap, glass, paper towel, and bread.
23. Problem Solving Suppose that the water table in your area is located 8 meters below the ground surface in the spring. By the end of the summer, the level of groundwater drops 2 meters. How deep should you dig a well to be sure that it does not run dry?

CHAPTER 2 REVIEW

Performance Assessment

Wrap Up

Present Your Project Before presentation day, show your watershed model to a classmate. Ask your classmate to predict how the water will flow over the model. Can your classmate identify the features of the ...

Getting Involved

In Your Community Obtain permission from your teacher and family to conduct a survey of lakes, ponds, and wetlands in your community. Choose one location and, with an adult family member, ...

Section 3 Review

1. How are wetlands important to wildlife?
2. Explain how wetlands help control floods.
3. How are the Everglades unusual?
4. **Thinking Critically Making Judgments** Some of the plans to restore the Everglades will require millions of dollars and will negatively affect local farmers. What information would you want to have to help decide what plan of action to take to save the Everglades?

Check Your Progress

CHAPTER PROJECT 2

At this point, add the body of standing water to your watershed sketch. If your model will include any wetland areas, what materials will you use to model them? (*Hint:* Be sure to consider how water will enter and leave the body of water.)

Comprehensive Chapter Reviews include a wide range of question types that students will encounter on standardized tests. Types include multiple choice, enhanced true/false, concept mastery, visual thinking, skill application, and critical thinking. Also includes Chapter Project "Wrap Up."

Chapter Projects contain rubrics that allow you to easily assess student progress.

Section Reviews provide "Check your Progress" opportunities for the Chapter Project, as well as review questions for the section.

Additional *Science Explorer* assessment resources:

- **Assessment Resources with CD-ROM**
- **Resource Pro® with Planning Express® CD-ROM**
- **Standardized Test Practice Book**
- **On-line review activities** at www.phschool.com

See page T9 for complete product descriptions.

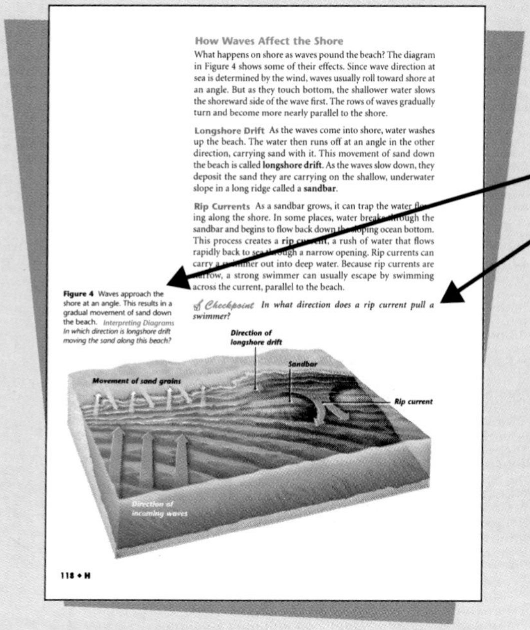

How Waves Affect the Shore

What happens on shore as waves pound the beach? The diagram in Figure 4 shows some of their effects. Since wave direction at sea is determined by the wind, waves usually roll toward shore at an angle. But as they touch bottom, the shallower water slows the shoreward side of the wave first. The rows of waves gradually turn and become more nearly parallel to the shore.

Longshore Drift As the waves come into shore, water washes up the beach. The water then runs off at an angle in the other direction, carrying sand with it. This movement of sand down the beach is called **longshore drift**. As the waves slow down, they deposit the sand they are carrying on the shallow, underwater slope in a long ridge called a **sandbar**.

Rip Currents As a sandbar grows, it can trap the water flowing along the shore. In some places, water breaks through the sandbar and begins to flow back down the sloping ocean bottom. This process creates a **rip current**, a rush of water that flows rapidly back to sea through a narrow opening. Rip currents can carry a swimmer out into deep water. Because rip currents are narrow, a strong swimmer can usually escape by swimming across the current, parallel to the beach.

✓ *Checkpoint In what direction does a rip current pull a swimmer?*

Figure 4 Waves approach the shore at an angle. This results in a gradual movement of sand down the beach. *Interpreting Diagrams In which direction is longshore drift moving the sand along this beach?*

118 • H

Self-assessment opportunities help students keep themselves on course.

- **Caption Questions** throughout the text assess critical thinking skills.
- **Checkpoint Questions** give students an immediate content check as new concepts are presented.
- **Interactive Student Tutorial CD-ROM** provides students with electronic self-tests, review activities, and Exploration activities.
- **Got It! Video Quizzes** motivate and challenge students with engaging animations and interactive questions.
- **www.science-explorer.phschool.com** provides additional support and on-line test prep.

Utilize a wide variety of tools.

Easy-to-manage, book-specific teaching resources

15 Teaching Resource Packages, each containing a Student Edition, Teacher's Edition, Teaching Resources with Color Transparencies, Guided Reading Audiotape, Materials Kit Order form, and Correlation to the National Science Education Standards.

15 Teacher's Editions with a three-step lesson plan—*Engage/Explore, Facilitate,* and *Assess*—that is ideal for reaching all students. Chapter planning charts make it easy to find resources, as well as to plan for block scheduling and team teaching.

15 Teaching Resource Books with Color Transparencies offer complete support organized by chapter to make it easy for you to find what you need—when you need it.

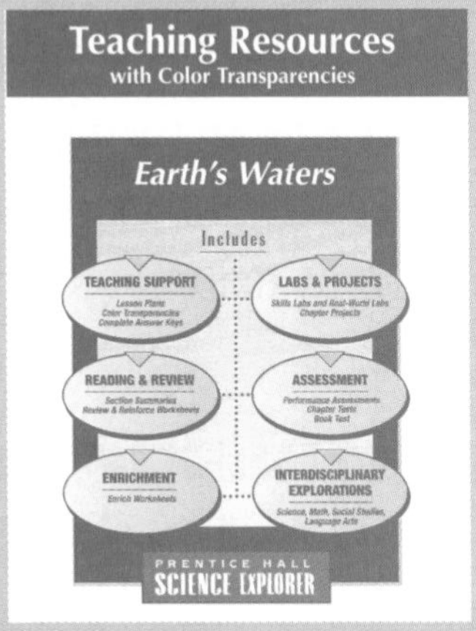

15 Guided Reading Audiotapes (English and Spanish) provide section summaries for students who need additional support.

15 Explorer Videotapes allow students to explore concepts through spectacular short videos containing computer animations. Available in Spanish.

Program-wide print resources

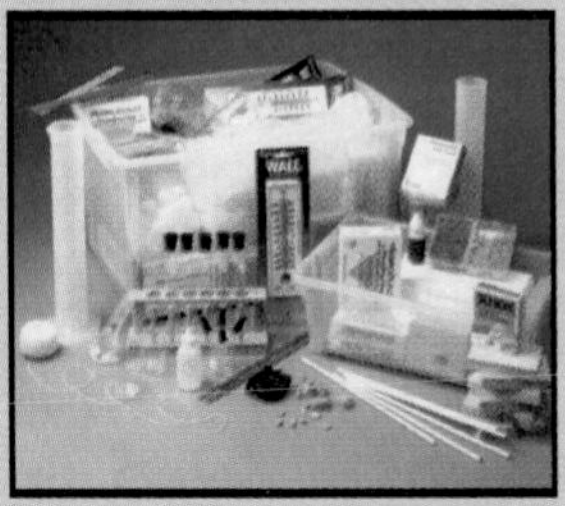

1

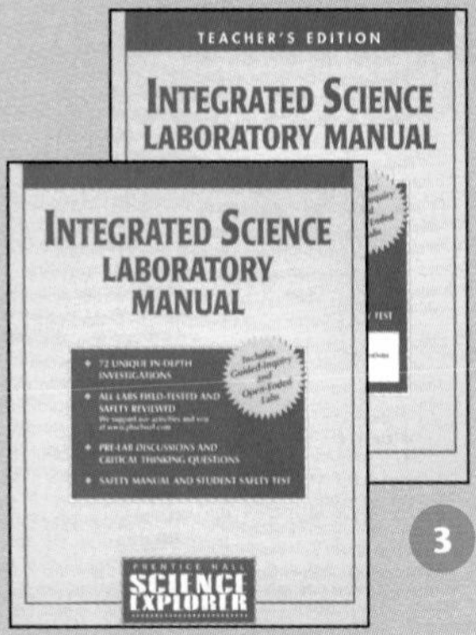

2 3

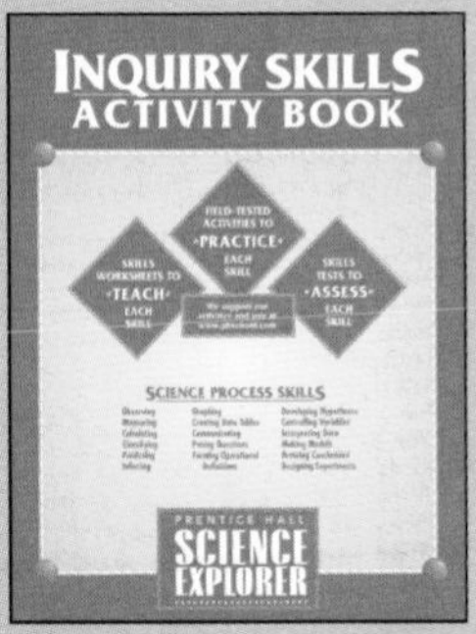

4

5

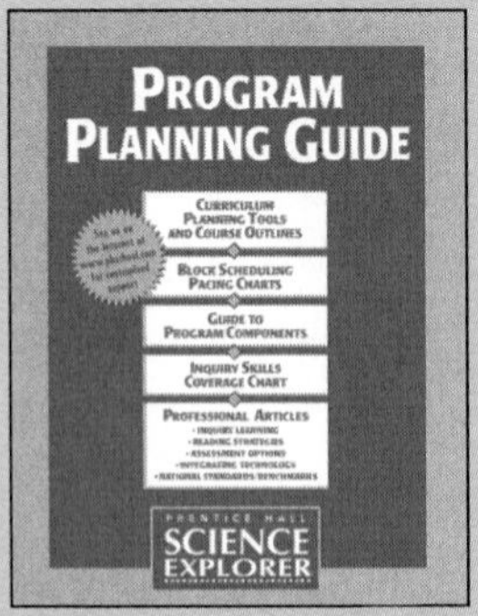

6

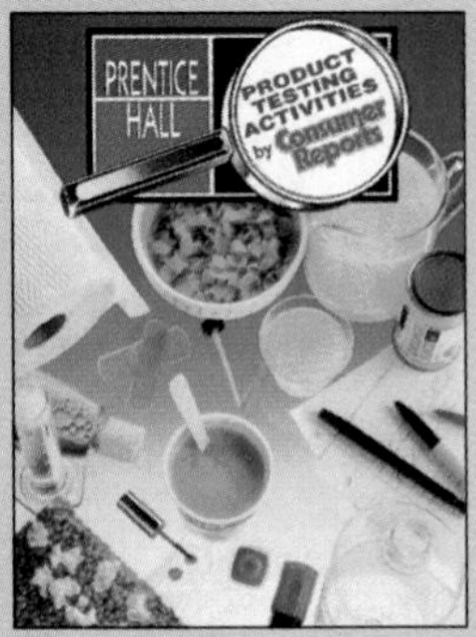

7

1. **Materials Kits**—Prentice Hall and Science Kit, Inc. have collaborated to develop a Consumable Kit and Nonconsumable Kit for each book. Ordering software makes it easy to customize!

2&3. **Integrated Science Laboratory Manual with Teacher's Edition**—74 in-depth labs covering the entire curriculum, with complete teaching support.

4. **Inquiry Skills Activity Book**—additional activities to teach, practice, and assess a wide range of inquiry skills.
5. **Student-Centered Science Activities**—five activity books for the Northeast, Southeast, Midwest, Southwest, and West.
6. **Program Planning Guide**—course outlines, block scheduling pacing charts, correlations, and more.
7. **Product Testing Activities by *Consumer Reports***—19 student-oriented testing activities turn students into real-world explorers.

Additional print resources...

8. **Reading in the Content Area**—with Literature Connections
9. **Standardized Test Practice**—review and self-tests to prepare for statewide exams.
10. **15 Prentice Hall Interdisciplinary Explorations**
11. **How to Assess Student Work**
12. **How to Manage Instruction in the Block**
13. ***Cobblestone, Odyssey, Calliope,* and *Faces* Magazines**

Program-wide technology resources

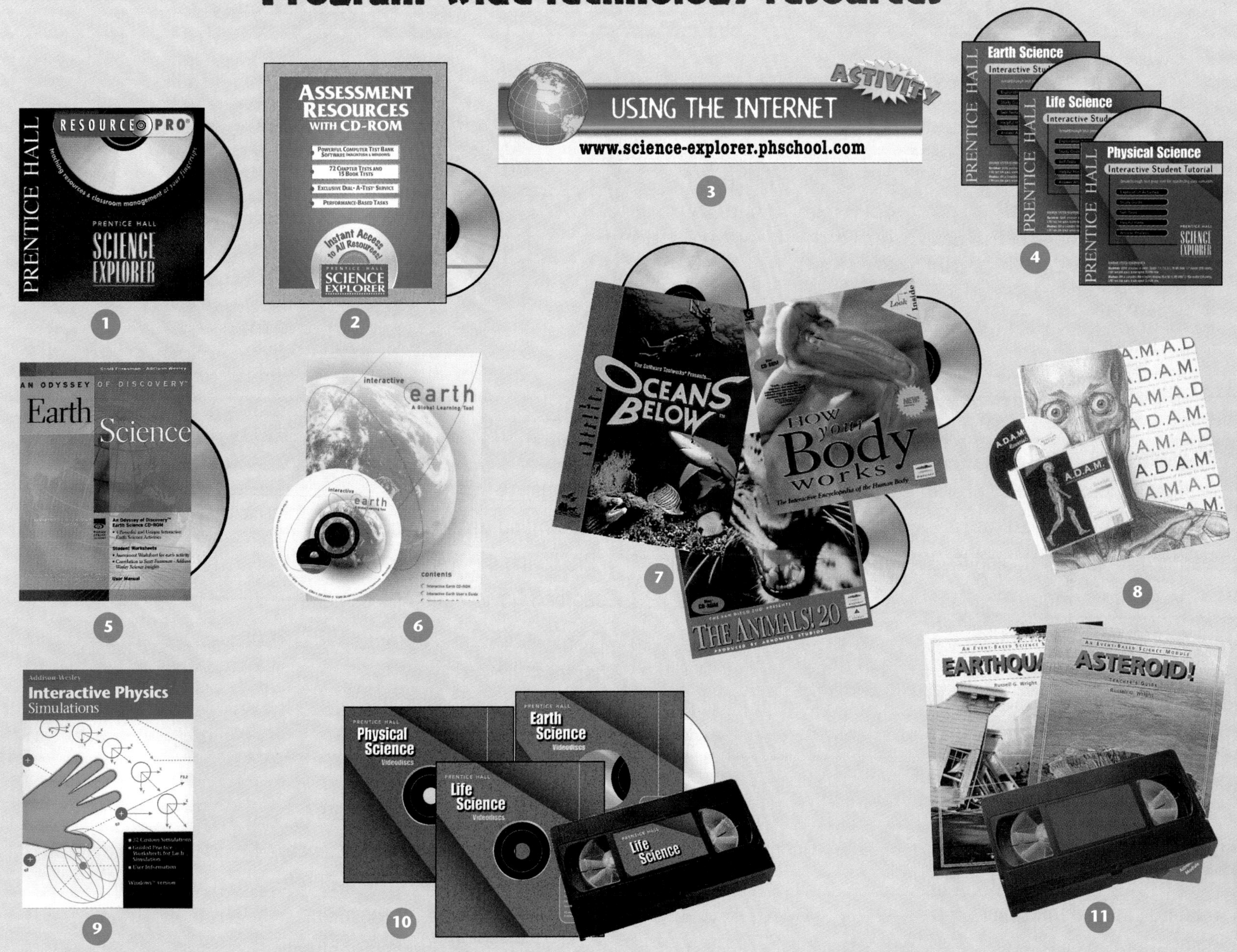

1. **Resource Pro® CD-ROM**—the ultimate management tool with easy access to blackline masters and lab activities for all 15 books. Planning Express® software lets you customize lesson plans by day, week, month, and year. Also includes Computer Test Bank software.
2. **Assessment Resources with CD-ROM**—*Computer Test Bank* software with Dial-A-Test® provides you with unparalleled flexibility in creating tests.
3. ***Science Explorer* Web Site**—activities and teaching resources for every chapter at www.science-explorer.phschool.com
4. **Interactive Student Tutorial CD-ROMs**—provide students with self-tests, helpful hints, and Explorations. Tests are scored instantly and provide complete explanations to all answers.
5. **An Odyssey of Discovery CD-ROMs**—interactive labs encourage students to hypothesize and experiment. (Life and Earth Science).
6. **Interactive Earth CD-ROM**—explore global trends, search the media library, and zoom in on a 3-D globe.
7. **Mindscape CD-ROMs**—*The Animals!™, Oceans Below,* and *How Your Body Works* bring science alive with compelling videoclips, 3-D animations, and interactive databases.
8. **A.D.A.M. The Inside Story**—take an entertaining tour of each body system, designed for middle grades students.
9. **Interactive Physics**—explore physics concepts with computer simulations that encourage what-if questions.
10. **Explorer Videotapes and Videodiscs**—explore and visualize concepts through spectacular short documentaries containing computer animations (Spanish audio track).
11. **Event-Based Science**—series of NSF-funded modules that engage students with inquiry-based projects. Includes video.

Options for Pacing *Weather and Climate*

The Pacing Chart below suggests one way to schedule your instructional time. The ***Science Explorer*** program offers many other aids to help you plan your instructional time, whether regular class periods or **block scheduling.** Refer to the Chapter Planning Guide before each chapter to view all program resources with suggested times for Student Edition activities.

Pacing Chart

	Days	Blocks
Nature of Science: Eyes on Earth	1	$\frac{1}{2}$
Chapter 1 The Atmosphere		
Chapter 1 Project Watching the Weather	Ongoing	Ongoing
1 The Air Around You	3–4	$1\frac{1}{2}$–2
2 Integrating Environmental Science: Air Quality	2–3	1–2
3 Air Pressure	3–4	$1\frac{1}{2}$–2
4 Layers of the Atmosphere	2–3	1–2
Chapter 1 Review and Assessment	1	$\frac{1}{2}$
Chapter 2 Weather Factors		
Chapter 2 Project Your Own Weather Station	Ongoing	Ongoing
1 Energy in the Atmosphere	3–4	$1\frac{1}{2}$–2
2 Integrating Physics: Heat Transfer	1–2	$\frac{1}{2}$–1
3 Winds	3–4	$1\frac{1}{2}$–2
4 Water in the Atmosphere	2–3	1–$1\frac{1}{2}$
5 Precipitation	1–2	$\frac{1}{2}$–1
Chapter 2 Review and Assessment	1	$\frac{1}{2}$
Chapter 3 Weather Patterns		
Chapter 3 Project The Weather Tomorrow	Ongoing	Ongoing
1 Air Masses and Fronts	2–3	1–$1\frac{1}{2}$
2 Storms	4–5	2–$2\frac{1}{2}$
3 Integrating Health: Floods	1–2	$\frac{1}{2}$–1
4 Predicting the Weather	2–3	1–$1\frac{1}{2}$
Chapter 3 Review and Assessment	1	$\frac{1}{2}$
Chapter 4 Climate and Climate Change		
Chapter 4 Project Investigating Microclimates	Ongoing	Ongoing
1 What Causes Climate?	4–5	2–$2\frac{1}{2}$
2 Climate Regions	4–5	2–$2\frac{1}{2}$
3 Long-Term Changes in Climate	2	1
4 Integrating Environmental Science: Global Changes in the Atmosphere	2	1
Chapter 4 Review and Assessment	1	$\frac{1}{2}$
Interdisciplinary Exploration: Antarctica	2–3	1–$1\frac{1}{2}$

RESOURCE PRO®

The Resource Pro® CD-ROM is the ultimate scheduling and lesson planning tool. Resource Pro® allows you to preview all the resources in the *Science Explorer* program, organize your chosen materials, and print out any teaching resource. You can follow the suggested lessons or create your own, using resources from anywhere in the program.

Thematic Overview of *Weather and Climate*

The chart below lists the major themes of *Weather and Climate*. For each theme, the chart supplies a big idea, or concept statement, describing how a particular theme is taught in a chapter.

	Chapter 1	Chapter 2	Chapter 3	Chapter 4
Energy	Photochemical smog is caused by the action of sunlight on chemicals. Earth's atmosphere is heated by the sun.	Nearly all the energy in Earth's atmosphere comes from the sun. The energy transferred from a hotter object to a cooler one is referred to as heat.	A storm is a violent disturbance in the atmosphere.	Students investigate how the angle of light affects the rate of temperature change. Global warming is a gradual increase in the temperature of Earth's atmosphere.
Patterns of Change	Students use weather observations to predict the weather. Air pressure and density decrease as altitude increases.	Students look for patterns in weather data and investigate wind patterns around a building.	As an air mass moves into an area, it changes the weather there. Meteorologists interpret weather data to prepare weather forecasts.	Major climate changes could be caused by variations in the position of Earth relative to the sun, changes in the sun's energy output, and the movement of continents.
Scale and Structure	Earth's atmosphere is made up of various gases and is divided into four main layers.		An air mass is a huge body of air that has similar temperature, humidity, and air pressure throughout.	Earth has three main temperature zones and five main climate regions.
Systems and Interactions	Earth's atmosphere makes conditions on Earth suitable for living things. Most air pollution is caused by burning fossil fuels.	Winds are caused by the unequal heating of Earth and its atmosphere. Water moves between Earth's atmosphere and surface in the water cycle.	Four major types of air masses influence the weather in North America. El Niño affects global weather.	Students relate microclimates to the organisms found there. The seasons are caused by the tilt of Earth's axis.
Unity and Diversity		Heat is transferred by radiation, conduction, and convection. Rain, sleet, hail, and snow are types of precipitation.	Air masses are classified as tropical, polar, maritime, or continental and fronts as cold, warm, stationary, or occluded.	
Stability	The layers of the atmosphere are classified by their characteristic temperatures.			Climate regions are determined on the basis of average temperature and precipitation.
Modeling		Students create a weather station.		

Inquiry Skills Chart

The Prentice Hall *Science Explorer* program provides comprehensive teaching, practice, and assessment of science skills, with an emphasis on the process skills necessary for inquiry. The chart lists the skills covered in the program and cites the page numbers where each skill is covered.

	Student Text: Projects and Labs	Student Text: Activities	Student Text: Caption and Review Questions	Teacher's Edition: Extensions
Basic Process SKILLS				
Observing	12–13, 28–29, 40–41	20, 23, 45, 53, 83, 99, 112, 152	69, 89, 101, 130	43, 49, 53, 68, 80, 84, 97, 115, 127, 140, 152
Inferring	28–29, 120–121	14, 27, 48, 67, 95, 115, 127, 134, 139, 152	21, 23, 48, 117	16, 23, 32, 43, 60, 64, 66, 79, 90, 96, 114, 116, 136, 152
Predicting	40–41, 74–75, 92–93	22, 31, 152	16, 26, 30, 39, 60, 64, 66, 98, 105, 138	22, 26, 27, 78, 103, 140, 152–153
Classifying		81, 129, 131, 153	39, 66, 73, 82, 109, 131	129, 153
Making Models	28–29, 40–41, 54–55	52, 153	109	15, 35, 50, 57, 62, 79, 81, 85, 101, 116, 130, 136, 153
Communicating	12–13, 40–41, 74–75, 110–111	11, 15, 30, 35, 58, 66, 73, 87, 89, 91, 96, 109, 137, 145, 151, 153	38, 72, 108, 144	23, 33, 60, 81, 85, 98, 102, 105, 125, 143, 153
Measuring	18–19, 28–29, 40–41, 46–47, 54–55, 110–111, 120–121	42, 148, 154–155	49, 145	26, 63, 69, 154–155
Calculating	46–47, 132–133	69, 84, 118, 155	39, 73	27, 49, 69, 104, 155
Creating Data Tables	12–13, 18–19, 28–29, 40–41, 46–47, 54–55, 110–111, 120–121	162		125, 131, 162
Graphing	40–41, 46–47, 92–93, 110–111, 120–121, 132–133	148, 162–164	39, 73	32, 162–164
Advanced Process SKILLS				
Posing Questions		156–157	109	156–157
Developing Hypotheses	46–47, 110–111	16, 61, 76, 156–157	119	156–157
Designing Experiments	18–19, 120–121	39, 156–157		156–157
Controlling Variables	18–19, 120–121	148, 156–157		50, 100, 156–157

Advanced Process SKILLS (continued)				
	Student Text: Projects and Labs	Student Text: Activities	Student Text: Caption and Review Questions	Teacher's Edition: Extensions
Forming Operational Definitions	12–13, 46–47	122, 156–157	56	65, 156–157
Interpreting Data	12–13, 18–19, 28–29, 40–41, 46–47, 54–55, 74–75, 92–93, 106, 110–111, 120–121, 132–133	50, 63, 102, 149, 156–157	15, 109, 145	63, 103, 156–157
Drawing Conclusions	46–47, 54–55, 106, 132–133	25, 141, 148, 156–157	36, 73	127, 135, 156–157
Critical Thinking SKILLS				
Comparing and Contrasting	40–41, 74–75, 132–133	142, 148, 149, 158	73, 126, 128, 145	77, 128, 158
Applying Concepts	18–19, 46–47, 54–55, 92–93, 106, 132–133	158	17, 32, 39, 45, 51, 58, 60, 70, 77, 84, 91, 97, 109, 114, 131, 140	22, 77, 104, 115, 129, 158
Interpreting Diagrams, Graphs Photographs, and Maps	74–75, 106	158	20, 39, 43, 57, 80, 82, 88, 91, 104, 109, 113, 138, 145	105, 136, 158
Relating Cause and Effect	28–29	159	39, 73, 109, 123, 145	81, 119, 159
Making Generalizations	110–111	159		159
Making Judgments		159	109, 145	159
Problem Solving		24, 94, 159	73	89, 114, 159
Information Organizing SKILLS				
Concept Maps		160	38, 72, 144	21, 160
Compare/ Contrast Tables		160	108	70, 91, 160
Venn Diagrams		160		161
Flowcharts		147, 160		161
Cycle Diagrams		160		51, 161

The *Science Explorer* program provides additional teaching, reinforcement, and assessment of skills in the Inquiry Skills Activities Book and the Integrated Science Laboratory Manual.

Materials Kits

Throughout the *Science Explorer* program, every effort has been made to keep the materials and equipment *affordable, reusable,* and *easily accessible.*

The ***Science Explorer*** program offers an abundance of activity options so you can pick and choose those activities that suit your needs. To help you order supplies at the beginning of the year, the Master Materials List cross-references the materials by activity. If you prefer to create your list electronically,use the electronic order forms at:
www.science–explorer.phschool.com

There are two kits available for each book of the ***Science Explorer*** program, a Consumable Kit and a Nonconsumable Kit. These kits are produced by **Science Kit and Boreal Laboratories,** the leader in providing science kits to schools. Prentice Hall and Science Kit collaborated throughout the development of ***Science Explorer*** to ensure that the equipment and supplies in the kits precisely match the requirements of the program activities.

The kits provide an economical and convenient way to get all of the materials needed to teach each book. For each book, Science Kit also offers the opportunity to buy equipment and safety items individually. For a current listing of kit offerings or additional information about materials to accompany ***Science Explorer***, please, contact Science Kit at:
1-800-828-7777
or at their Internet site at:
www.sciencekit.com

Science Kit® & Boreal® Laboratories

Equipment			
*	Description	Quantity per class	Textbook Section(s)
SS	Apron, lab	30	1-1 (TT) 3-1 (DIS)
SS	Balance	5	1-3 (DIS)
SS	Calculator	5	4-2 (Lab)
SS	Goggles, chemical splash, class set	1	1-1 (DIS) 1-1 (TT) 1-2 (DIS) 2-1 (Lab) 2-5 (DIS) 4-2 (TT)
SS	Hot plate	5	2-2 (DIS)
SS	Microscope	5	1-1 (Lab)
SS	Mitt, oven	5	1-1 (DIS) 1-2 (DIS)
SS	Support base with rod	5	2-1 (Lab)
SS	Support ring with clamp	5	2-1 (Lab)

KEY: **DIS**: Discover; **SYS**: Sharpen Your Skills; **TT**: Try This; **Lab**: Lab
* Items designated **C** are in the Consumable Kit, **NC** are in the Nonconsumable Kit, and **SS** are School Supplied.

PRENTICE HALL
SCIENCE EXPLORER

Weather and Climate

Program Resources

Student Edition
Annotated Teacher's Edition
Teaching Resources Book with Color Transparencies
Weather and Climate Materials Kits

Program Components

Integrated Science Laboratory Manual
Integrated Science Laboratory Manual, Teacher's Edition
Inquiry Skills Activity Book
Student-Centered Science Activity Books
Program Planning Guide
Guided Reading English Audiotapes
Guided Reading Spanish Audiotapes and Summaries
Product Testing Activities by Consumer Reports™
Event-Based Science Series (NSF funded)
Prentice Hall Interdisciplinary Explorations
Cobblestone, Odyssey, Calliope, and *Faces* Magazines

Media/Technology

Science Explorer Interactive Student Tutorial CD-ROMs
Odyssey of Discovery CD-ROMs
Resource Pro® (Teaching Resources on CD-ROM)
Assessment Resources CD-ROM with Dial-A-Test®
Internet site at www.science-explorer.phschool.com
Life, Earth, and Physical Science Videodiscs
Life, Earth, and Physical Science Videotapes

Science Explorer Student Editions

From Bacteria to Plants
Animals
Cells and Heredity
Human Biology and Health
Environmental Science
Inside Earth
Earth's Changing Surface
Earth's Waters
Weather and Climate
Astronomy
Chemical Building Blocks
Chemical Interactions
Motion, Forces, and Energy
Electricity and Magnetism
Sound and Light

Staff Credits

The people who made up the *Science Explorer* team—representing editorial, editorial services, design services, field marketing, market research, marketing services, on-line services/multimedia development, product marketing, production services, and publishing processes—are listed below. Bold type denotes core team members.

Kristen E. Ball, **Barbara A. Bertell,** Peter W. Brooks, **Christopher R. Brown, Greg Cantone,** Jonathan Cheney, **Patrick Finbarr Connolly,** Loree Franz, Donald P. Gagnon, Jr., **Paul J. Gagnon, Joel Gendler,** Elizabeth Good, Kerri Hoar, **Linda D. Johnson,** Katherine M. Kotik, Russ Lappa, Marilyn Leitao, David Lippman, **Eve Melnechuk, Natania Mlawer,** Paul W. Murphy, **Cindy A. Noftle,** Julia F. Osborne, Caroline M. Power, Suzanne J. Schineller, **Susan W. Tafler,** Kira Thaler-Marbit, Robin L. Santel, Ronald Schachter, **Mark Tricca,** Diane Walsh, Pearl B. Weinstein, Beth Norman Winickoff

Acknowledgment for pages 150–151: Excerpt from *Alone* by Richard E. Byrd, reprinted by arrangement with Island Press. Copyright ©1938 by Richard E. Byrd, ©renewed 1986.

ISBN 0-13-434494-4
5 6 7 8 9 10   03 02 01 00

Cover: Lightning flashes over Tucson, Arizona.

Teacher's Edition ISBN 0-13-434559-2

Program Authors

Michael J. Padilla, Ph.D.
Professor
Department of Science Education
University of Georgia
Athens, Georgia

Michael Padilla is a leader in middle school science education. He has served as an editor and elected officer for the National Science Teachers Association. He has been principal investigator of several National Science Foundation and Eisenhower grants and served as a writer of the National Science Education Standards.

As lead author of *Science Explorer,* Mike has inspired the team in developing a program that meets the needs of middle grades students, promotes science inquiry, and is aligned with the National Science Education Standards.

Ioannis Miaoulis, Ph.D.
Dean of Engineering
College of Engineering
Tufts University
Medford, Massachusetts

Martha Cyr, Ph.D.
Director, Engineering Educational Outreach
College of Engineering
Tufts University
Medford, Massachusetts

Science Explorer was created in collaboration with the College of Engineering at Tufts University. Tufts has an extensive engineering outreach program that uses engineering design and construction to excite and motivate students and teachers in science and technology education.

Faculty from Tufts University participated in the development of *Science Explorer* chapter projects, reviewed the student books for content accuracy, and helped coordinate field testing.

CHAPTER PROJECT

Book Author

Barbara Brooks Simons
Science Writer
Boston, Massachusetts

Contributing Writers

Alfred B. Bortz, Ph.D.
School of Education
Duquesne University
Pittsburgh, Pennsylvania

Emery Pineo
Science Teacher
Barrington Middle School
Barrington, Rhode Island

Karen Riley Sievers
Science Teacher
Callanan Middle School
Des Moines, Iowa

Sharon M. Stroud
Science Teacher
Widefield High School
Colorado Springs, Colorado

Reading Consultant

Bonnie B. Armbruster, Ph.D.
Department of Curriculum and Instruction
University of Illinois
Champaign, Illinois

Interdisciplinary Consultant

Heidi Hayes Jacobs, Ed.D.
Teacher's College
Columbia University
New York, New York

Safety Consultants

W. H. Breazeale, Ph.D.
Department of Chemistry
College of Charleston
Charleston, South Carolina

Ruth Hathaway, Ph.D.
Hathaway Consulting
Cape Girardeau, Missouri

I ◆ 3

Tufts University Program Reviewers

Behrouz Abedian, Ph.D.
Department of Mechanical Engineering

Wayne Chudyk, Ph.D.
Department of Civil and Environmental Engineering

Eliana De Bernardez-Clark, Ph.D.
Department of Chemical Engineering

Anne Marie Desmarais, Ph.D.
Department of Civil and Environmental Engineering

David L. Kaplan, Ph.D.
Department of Chemical Engineering

Paul Kelley, Ph.D.
Department of Electro-Optics

George S. Mumford, Ph.D.
Professor of Astronomy, Emeritus

Jan A. Pechenik, Ph.D.
Department of Biology

Livia Racz, Ph.D.
Department of Mechanical Engineering

Robert Rifkin, M.D.
School of Medicine

Jack Ridge, Ph.D.
Department of Geology

Chris Swan, Ph.D.
Department of Civil and Environmental Engineering

Peter Y. Wong, Ph.D.
Department of Mechanical Engineering

Content Reviewers

Jack W. Beal, Ph.D.
Department of Physics
Fairfield University
Fairfield, Connecticut

W. Russell Blake, Ph.D.
Planetarium Director
Plymouth Community Intermediate School
Plymouth, Massachusetts

Howard E. Buhse, Jr., Ph.D.
Department of Biological Sciences
University of Illinois
Chicago, Illinois

Dawn Smith Burgess, Ph.D.
Department of Geophysics
Stanford University
Stanford, California

A. Malcolm Campbell, Ph.D.
Assistant Professor
Davidson College
Davidson, North Carolina

Elizabeth A. De Stasio, Ph.D.
Associate Professor of Biology
Lawrence University
Appleton, Wisconsin

John M. Fowler, Ph.D.
Former Director of Special Projects
National Science Teacher's Association
Arlington, Virginia

Jonathan Gitlin, M.D.
School of Medicine
Washington University
St. Louis, Missouri

Dawn Graff-Haight, Ph.D., CHES
Department of Health, Human Performance, and Athletics
Linfield College
McMinnville, Oregon

Deborah L. Gumucio, Ph.D.
Associate Professor
Department of Anatomy and Cell Biology
University of Michigan
Ann Arbor, Michigan

William S. Harwood, Ph.D.
Dean of University Division and Associate Professor of Education
Indiana University
Bloomington, Indiana

Cyndy Henzel, Ph.D.
Department of Geography and Regional Development
University of Arizona
Tucson, Arizona

Greg Hutton
Science and Health Curriculum Coordinator
School Board of Sarasota County
Sarasota, Florida

Susan K. Jacobson, Ph.D.
Department of Wildlife Ecology and Conservation
University of Florida
Gainesville, Florida

Judy Jernstedt, Ph.D.
Department of Agronomy and Range Science
University of California, Davis
Davis, California

John L. Kermond, Ph.D.
Office of Global Programs
National Oceanographic and Atmospheric Administration
Silver Spring, Maryland

David E. LaHart, Ph.D.
Institute of Science and Public Affairs
Florida State University
Tallahassee, Florida

Joe Leverich, Ph.D.
Department of Biology
St. Louis University
St. Louis, Missouri

Dennis K. Lieu, Ph.D.
Department of Mechanical Engineering
University of California
Berkeley, California

Cynthia J. Moore, Ph.D.
Science Outreach Coordinator
Washington University
St. Louis, Missouri

Joseph M. Moran, Ph.D.
Department of Earth Science
University of Wisconsin–Green Bay
Green Bay, Wisconsin

Joseph Stukey, Ph.D.
Department of Biology
Hope College
Holland, Michigan

Seetha Subramanian
Lexington Community College
University of Kentucky
Lexington, Kentucky

Carl L. Thurman, Ph.D.
Department of Biology
University of Northern Iowa
Cedar Falls, Iowa

Edward D. Walton, Ph.D.
Department of Chemistry
California State Polytechnic University
Pomona, California

Robert S. Young, Ph.D.
Department of Geosciences and Natural Resource Management
Western Carolina University
Cullowhee, North Carolina

Edward J. Zalisko, Ph.D.
Department of Biology
Blackburn College
Carlinville, Illinois

4 ◆ I

Teacher Reviewers

Stephanie Anderson
Sierra Vista Junior High School
Canyon Country, California

John W. Anson
Mesa Intermediate School
Palmdale, California

Pamela Arline
Lake Taylor Middle School
Norfolk, Virginia

Lynn Beason
College Station Jr. High School
College Station, Texas

Richard Bothmer
Hollis School District
Hollis, New Hampshire

Jeffrey C. Callister
Newburgh Free Academy
Newburgh, New York

Judy D'Albert
Harvard Day School
Corona Del Mar, California

Betty Scott Dean
Guilford County Schools
McLeansville, North Carolina

Sarah C. Duff
Baltimore City Public Schools
Baltimore, Maryland

Melody Law Ewey
Holmes Junior High School
Davis, California

Sherry L. Fisher
Lake Zurich Middle School North
Lake Zurich, Illinois

Melissa Gibbons
Fort Worth ISD
Fort Worth, Texas

Debra J. Goodding
Kraemer Middle School
Placentia, California

Jack Grande
Weber Middle School
Port Washington, New York

Steve Hills
Riverside Middle School
Grand Rapids, Michigan

Carol Ann Lionello
Kraemer Middle School
Placentia, California

Jaime A. Morales
Henry T. Gage Middle School
Huntington Park, California

Patsy Partin
Cameron Middle School
Nashville, Tennessee

Deedra H. Robinson
Newport News Public Schools
Newport News, Virginia

Bonnie Scott
Clack Middle School
Abilene, Texas

Charles M. Sears
Belzer Middle School
Indianapolis, Indiana

Barbara M. Strange
Ferndale Middle School
High Point, North Carolina

Jackie Louise Ulfig
Ford Middle School
Allen, Texas

Kathy Usina
Belzer Middle School
Indianapolis, Indiana

Heidi M. von Oetinger
L'Anse Creuse Public School
Harrison Township, Michigan

Pam Watson
Hill Country Middle School
Austin, Texas

Activity Field Testers

Nicki Bibbo
Russell Street School
Littleton, Massachusetts

Connie Boone
Fletcher Middle School
Jacksonville Beach, Florida

Rose-Marie Botting
Broward County School District
Fort Lauderdale, Florida

Colleen Campos
Laredo Middle School
Aurora, Colorado

Elizabeth Chait
W. L. Chenery Middle School
Belmont, Massachusetts

Holly Estes
Hale Middle School
Stow, Massachusetts

Laura Hapgood
Plymouth Community Intermediate School
Plymouth, Massachusetts

Sandra M. Harris
Winman Junior High School
Warwick, Rhode Island

Jason Ho
Walter Reed Middle School
Los Angeles, California

Joanne Jackson
Winman Junior High School
Warwick, Rhode Island

Mary F. Lavin
Plymouth Community Intermediate School
Plymouth, Massachusetts

James MacNeil, Ph.D.
Concord Public Schools
Concord, Massachusetts

Lauren Magruder
St. Michael's Country Day School
Newport, Rhode Island

Jeanne Maurand
Glen Urquhart School
Beverly Farms, Massachusetts

Warren Phillips
Plymouth Community Intermediate School
Plymouth, Massachusetts

Carol Pirtle
Hale Middle School
Stow, Massachusetts

Kathleen M. Poe
Kirby-Smith Middle School
Jacksonville, Florida

Cynthia B. Pope
Ruffner Middle School
Norfolk, Virginia

Anne Scammell
Geneva Middle School
Geneva, New York

Karen Riley Sievers
Callanan Middle School
Des Moines, Iowa

David M. Smith
Howard A. Eyer Middle School
Macungie, Pennsylvania

Derek Strohschneider
Plymouth Community Intermediate School
Plymouth, Massachusetts

Sallie Teames
Rosemont Middle School
Fort Worth, Texas

Gene Vitale
Parkland Middle School
McHenry, Illinois

Zenovia Young
Meyer Levin Junior High School (IS 285)
Brooklyn, New York

I ◆ 5

PRENTICE HALL SCIENCE EXPLORER

Prepare your students with rich, motivating content

Science Explorer **is crafted for today's middle grades student, with accessible content and in-depth coverage. Integrated Science Sections support every chapter and the Interdisciplinary Exploration provides an engaging final unit.**

Contents

Weather and Climate

Draw upon the world around you.

Interdisciplinary Activities connect to every discipline and give science a meaningful, real-world context.

Activities

Inquiry Activities

CHAPTER PROJECT

Opportunities for long-term inquiry

DISCOVER

Exploration and inquiry before reading

Sharpen your Skills

Practice of specific science inquiry skills

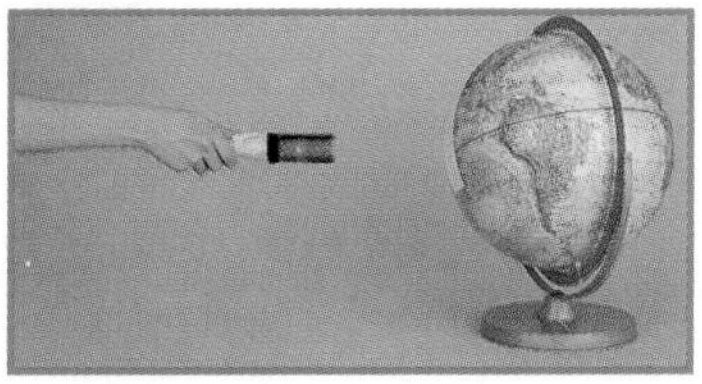

TRY THIS

Reinforcement of key concepts

Skills Lab

In-depth practice of inquiry skills

Real-World Lab

Everyday application of science concepts

Interdisciplinary Activities

Science and History

Science and Society

Connection

Check your compass — regularly assess student progress.

Self-assessment tools are built right into the student text and **on-going assessment** is woven throughout the Teacher's Edition. You'll find a wealth of **assessment technology** in the Resource Pro®, Interactive Student Tutorial, and Assessment Resources CD-ROMs.

Guide your students to become science explorers.

A wide range of **student-tested** activities, **from guided to open-ended,** with options for **short- and long-term** inquiry.

Eyes on Earth

Focus on Meteorology

This four-page feature provides students with an insider's view of the process of scientific inquiry. It introduces a young research meteorologist who studies severe storms, including hurricanes. The feature describes how he became interested in meteorology, attained his career goals, and now uses sophisticated technology to gather and analyze weather data in order to predict severe storms.

In Chapter 3 of this book, students learn about storms, including hurricanes, and how meteorologists predict the weather. However, students do not need to read Chapter 3 to appreciate the content of this feature.

Scientific Inquiry

- Before students read the feature, have them preview the photos and captions on pages 8 and 9. Then ask: **What is meteorology?** *(The correct response is "the study of weather." Some students may logically think that meteorology is "the study of meteors.")* Inform students that both *meteor* and *meteorology* have the same Greek root, which means "atmosphere." Explain that weather is caused by disturbances in the atmosphere. Finally, introduce the feature by telling students that it is about a meteorologist, or scientist who studies the weather.
- Call students' attention to the paragraph that opens the feature, then ask: **Besides satellite launches, what are some reasons people might want to know what the weather will be in the future?** *(Responses might include: in order to make outdoor plans and plan what to wear.)* Point out that predicting severe weather is especially important because knowledge of an approaching storm often prevents loss of life and property. Add that some severe storms in the past have killed thousands of people and caused billions of dollars worth of damage. Conclude by saying that better weather prediction is one of the main goals of meteorological research.

Nature of Science

Eyes On EARTH

At the Kennedy Space Center on the east coast of Florida, a crew prepares to launch a satellite into space. They know that a thunderstorm may be moving toward them. Should they launch the mission or delay? Before deciding, the crew contacts meteorologists for the latest weather forecast.

The Kennedy Space Center is about 100 kilometers east of the center of the state. More summer thunderstorms occur in central Florida than nearly any other area in the world. Predicting when severe storms will develop and where they will move is one of the most demanding jobs for a meteorologist. One of the best people at this job is J. Marshall Shepherd.

J. Marshall Shepherd
The son of two school principals, J. Marshall Shepherd was born in 1969 and raised in the small town of Canton, Georgia. Today he works for NASA as a research meteorologist for Mission to Planet Earth. He's an expert on the development of powerful thunderstorms. He studied meteorology at Florida State University.

Background

The Greek philosopher Aristotle is given credit for coining the term *meteorology.* His manuscript titled *Meteorologica,* written around 340 B.C., is the oldest known description of weather phenomena. One of the first people to study weather using scientific methods was Galileo. In 1593, he invented a device called a thermoscope for measuring temperature. Throughout the next three centuries, many advances in meteorological theory were made, and a number of new instruments for measuring weather factors were invented, including the barometer for measuring air pressure and the hygrometer for measuring relative humidity. However, the history of modern weather technology didn't really begin until 1949, when radar was first used to gather weather data. Then technology advanced rapidly, and by 1960 the first weather satellite had been launched.

Hurricane Fran roars over the Caribbean Sea near Florida and the island of Cuba. White clouds swirl around the "eye" at the center of the hurricane (upper right).

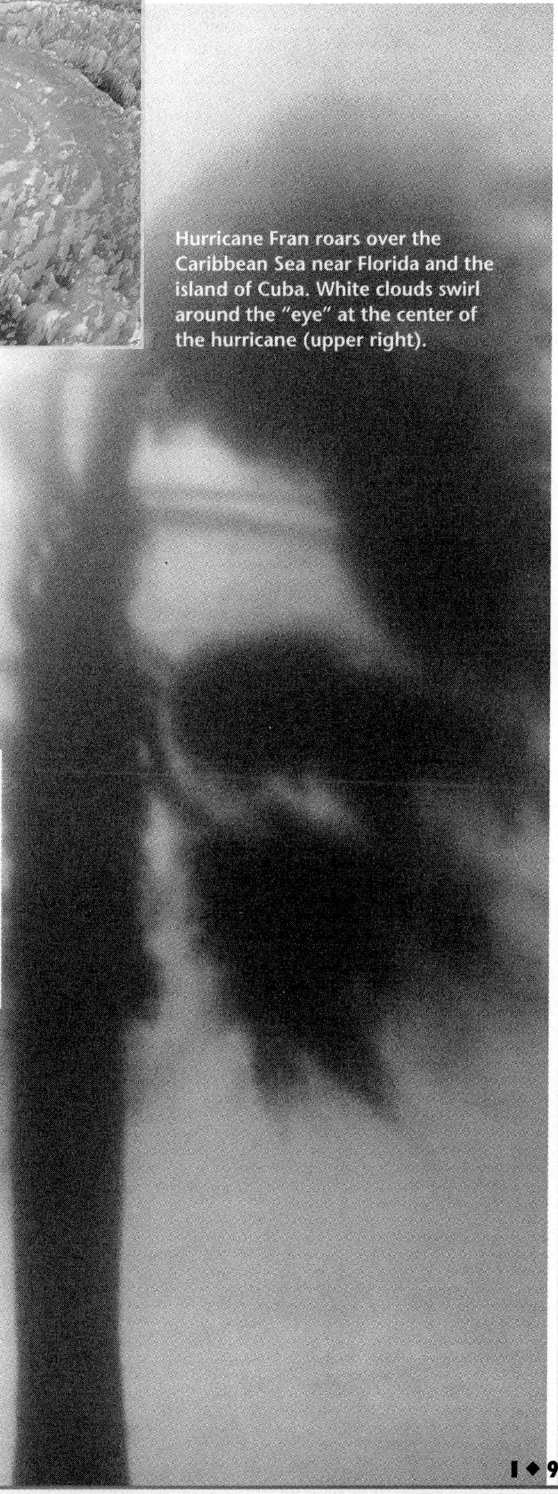

Getting Started at a Science Fair

Marshall Shepherd is an "old hand" at predicting the weather. He's been at it since sixth grade, when his teacher suggested that he enter a science fair. Marshall titled his science project "Can a Sixth-Grader Predict the Weather?" First he toured the local TV station in Atlanta to see what instruments meteorologists use to measure basic weather variables.

> **"The shape of Florida is part of the reason that so many storms form here."**

"Then I did a little background reading and decided I could build some of those instruments out of basic materials around the house," he recalls.

Using household materials and a few inexpensive items at supply stores, Marshall Shepherd built everything he needed for his project. He constructed a weather station with an anemometer to measure wind speed, a wind vane to measure wind direction, a barometer to measure air pressure, a hair hygrometer to measure humidity, and a rain gauge.

I ◆ 9

Background

The goal of NASA's Mission to Planet Earth (MTPE) is to collect the data needed to study planet-wide environmental problems, such as ozone depletion, deforestation, and global warming. MTPE, in turn, includes several different projects and programs. The Upper Atmosphere Research Satellite (UARS), for example, collects data on the chemistry of the upper atmosphere. The space shuttle's Atmospheric Laboratory for Applications and Science (ATLAS) investigates how solar radiation and pollution affect the upper atmosphere. The Earth Probes program involves several specialized satellites, including the Tropical Rainfall Measuring Mission (TRMM) satellite described on page 10. In 1998, the Earth Observing System (EOS) program began launching a total of 17 spacecraft, each of which will study a different aspect of climate change.

- Emphasize that Marshall Shepherd's sixth-grade science fair project was the initial impetus for his interest in meteorology. Ask: **Did any of your strong interests develop in a similar way, that is, because of a single positive experience? Explain what happened.** *(Students may say, for example, that they developed an interest in cooking or horses through a 4-H project, an interest in sports through playing on an intramural team or watching the Olympic games on television, or an interest in camping through their first scout camp experience.)* **How did Shepherd's science fair experience change his life?** *(From then on, he did science projects in school and, by the end of high school, he knew that he wanted to be a research scientist at NASA, a goal he pursued and accomplished.)*
- Tell students that, when they study Chapter 2 of this book, they will have an opportunity to make and use simple instruments for measuring wind speed, wind direction, air pressure, humidity, and rainfall, just as Marshall Shepherd did in his sixth-grade science fair project.
- Point out to students that, starting with his first science project and continuing through his present job as a NASA research meteorologist, Marshall Shepherd has been interested in collecting weather data. Use this fact to introduce students to the importance of data collection in scientific inquiry. Tell students that scientists depend on data to test and either confirm or reject hypotheses. To make this point clearer, relate the following example to the class. In 1856, an American meteorologist named William Ferrel hypothesized, on theoretical grounds alone, that winds in the Northern Hemisphere blow in a counterclockwise direction around areas of low air pressure and in a clockwise direction around areas of high air pressure (students will read about these high and low pressure systems in Chapter 3). Then, just a few months later, a Dutch meteorologist named Buys Ballot collected the data on wind direction and air pressure needed to test Ferrel's hypothesis. The data confirmed the hypothesis, and it is now known as Buys Ballot's law.

◆ Have students examine the illustration of TRMM, a satellite that gathers the tropical rainfall data Marshall Shepherd helps analyze. Also have students read the caption under the illustration. Then contrast the TRMM satellite with a geostationary weather satellite. Explain that a geostationary satellite orbits Earth at the same speed as Earth's rotation. Because of this, it stays over the same spot on Earth each day, which is why it is called *geostationary.* TRMM, in contrast, passes over many different places on Earth each day, providing a wealth of information on rainfall. You may want to share with students the additional information about the TRMM satellite at the bottom of page 11. Emphasize that measuring tropical rainfall, as TRMM does, is crucial to understanding and predicting global climate.

◆ Encourage students to share what they may already know about hurricanes. Ask: **What is a hurricane?** *(A kind of storm that produces very high winds)* **Where do hurricanes usually occur in the United States?** *(In Florida and other southeastern states bordering on the Atlantic Ocean)* Point out that hurricanes develop over the ocean and then usually move rather slowly toward the coast. Add that it often is possible to predict in advance where a hurricane will strike land. This is important so people can prepare themselves for the storm by boarding up windows, trimming dead tree branches, and taking other steps to secure property. If necessary, they also can temporarily leave the area to prevent injury and loss of life. Tell students they will learn more about hurricanes and other types of severe storms and how to keep safe in them in Chapter 3. Also tell students they will have a chance to track a hurricane, as Marshall Shepherd did when he was in college, if they do the Real-World Lab in Chapter 3.

◆ Remind students that Marshall Shepherd works at NASA where he contributes to Mission to Planet Earth. Share with students the additional information about Mission to Planet Earth on the bottom of page 9. Point out that Marshall Shepherd's specialty is "remote sensing." Ask: **Why is Marshall Shepherd's specialty so relevant to Mission to Planet Earth?** *(Because Mission to Planet Earth focuses on collecting and analyzing weather observations from remote places—high in the atmosphere and space—using satellites and spacecraft)*

◆ After students have read Looking Ahead, ask: **What does Marshall Shepherd plan to do after Mission to Planet Earth?** *(From the ground, he wants to conduct Earth-directed meteorological research from the international space station. He also wants "to reach out, inspire, and expose students to science.")*

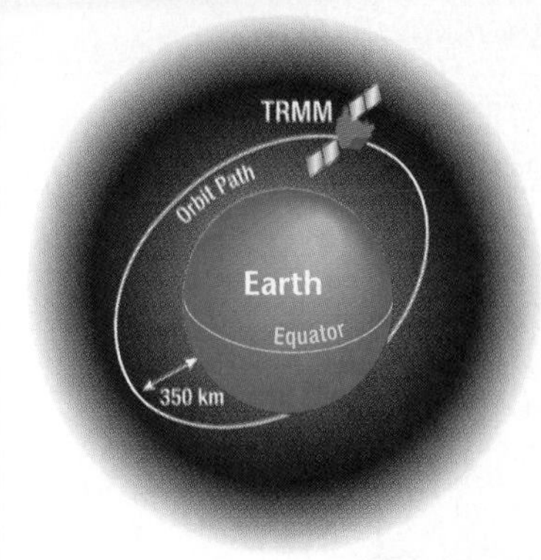

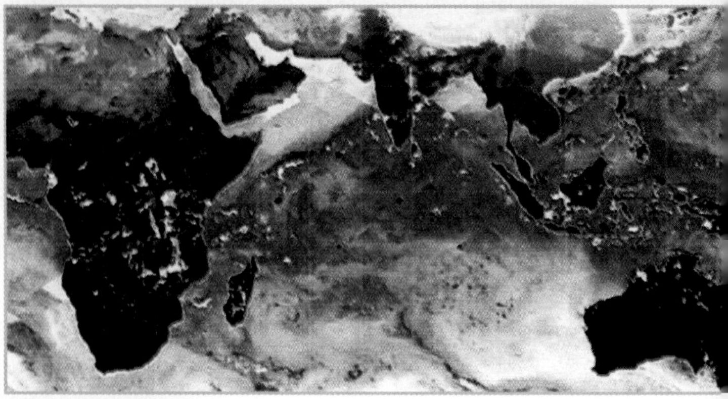

▲ TRMM, a device that records weather conditions from space, orbits Earth at an altitude of 350 kilometers. It flies over each position on Earth at a different time each day.

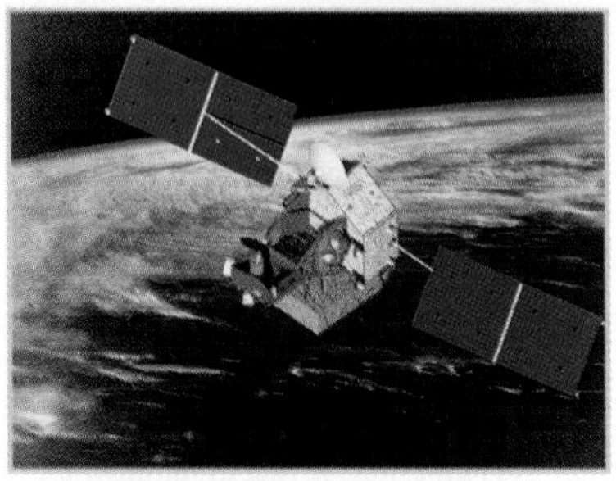

TRMM observatory is about the size of a small room and weighs as much as a medium-sized truck. It contains two solar panels and instruments to record weather data.

"From these basic instruments, I took weather observations around my neighborhood," he explains. "I developed a model of day-to-day weather over a six-month period and found some very interesting and accurate results." Marshall's instruments and scientific work on this project won prizes for him at local, district, and state science fairs.

"From that point on, I was involved with science projects," he recalls. By the time he graduated from high school, he had a definite goal. "One day, I planned to be a research scientist at NASA (National Aeronautics and Space Administration)," he stated.

Predicting Severe Storms

Hurricane Andrew—the most powerful hurricane ever to strike Florida—swept through Southern Florida and Louisiana in 1992. Marshall was in college at the time. "My college research paper was on hurricane tracking using radar. I actually did some work with Hurricane Andrew," he says. "That's how I got interested in tropical weather."

In graduate school, Marshall Shepherd investigated the way powerful thunderstorms form and move, especially those in central Florida. The long, narrow shape of Florida is part of the reason that so many storms form there. "When you have land heating faster than water, you get something called sea-breeze circulation," he explains. "On a typical summer day, a sea-breeze forms on both the west coast and the east coast of Florida. They tend to move toward the center. When they collide, you get intense thunderstorm development."

Designing New Instruments

Now Marshall Shepherd works at NASA, where his projects contribute to NASA's Mission to Planet Earth.

Master Materials List

Consumable Materials

*	Description	Quantity per class	Textbook Section(s)
SS	Bag, plastic, small sandwich	15	4-4 (TT)
C	Bag, plastic, zip lip, 1 qt.	5	1-4 (DIS) 2-1 (DIS)
C	Balloons, 15" round, pkg. of 5	2	1-3 (DIS) 1-3 (Lab)
C	Battery, size D	10	4-1 (DIS)
SS	Bulb, incandescent, 100 watt	5	2-1 (Lab))
C	Candle, warming	5	1-1 (DIS) 1-2 (DIS) 2-2 (DIS)
SS	Cardboard, corrugated, 10 × 20 cm	10	3-1 (DIS) 2-3 (Lab)
SS	Cardboard, white 8 1/2" × 11"	5	1-3 (Lab)
C	Clay, modeling, water-resistant, 1 lb.	1	1-1 (DIS) 1-3 (TT) 1-3 (Lab) 1-2 (DIS)
C	Cup, plastic clear, 300 mL	5	1-1 (TT) 3-3 (DIS)
C	Detergent, household, 14.7 oz.	1	3-2 (DIS)
SS	Filters, coffee, pkg. of 100	1	1-1 (Lab)
C	Food coloring, blue, 30 mL	1	3-1 (DIS)
C	Food coloring, dark red, 30 mL	1	3-1 (DIS)
SS	Glue, white, 4 oz.	1	1-3 (Lab)
SS	Graph paper, single sheet	30	2-1 (Lab) 2-2 (TT) 4-1 (Lab) 4-2 (Lab)
SS	Ice cubes	5	2-4 (DIS)
C	Limewater solution, 1 L, (calcium hydroxide)	1	1-1 (TT)
SS	Map, U.S., with city names and latitude lines	5	4-2 (Lab)
C	Matches, wood safety, pkg. of 30	5	1-1 (DIS) 1-2 (DIS)
SS	Paper	5	2-1 (DIS)
SS	Paper, construction, black, pkg. of 15	1	2-3 (TT) 4-1 (Lab) 4-4 (DIS)
SS	Pen	5	2-3 (Lab)
SS	Pen, felt tip marker, black, soluble	5	2-3 (DIS)
SS	Pencil	5	1-3 (Lab) 2-3 (DIS) 2-3 (TT) 4-1 (Lab)
SS	Pencils, colored, pkg. of 12	5	3-2 (Lab) 4-2 (Lab)
SS	Pie plate, aluminum	5	2-2 (DIS)
C	Plastic wrap, 50-sq. ft. roll	1	4-2 (TT) 4-4 (DIS)
C	Salt, non-iodized, 737 g	1	2-5 (DIS) 3-1 (DIS)
C	Sand, fine, 2.5 kg	1	2-1 (Lab)
SS	Shoebox	10	4-4 (DIS)
C	Splints, wooden, 15 cm, pkg. of 25	1	2-3 (Lab)
C	Straws, plastic, pkg. of 50	1	1-1 (TT) 1-3 (TT) 1-3 (Lab) 2-3 (TT)
C	String, cotton, 200 ft.	1	2-1 (Lab)
SS	Sunscreen	2	4-4 (TT)
C	Sunprint kit refill, 12 sheets	1	4-4 (TT)
C	Tape, adding machine, 100-ft. roll	1	4-1 (DIS)
SS	Tape, clear, roll	1	4-1 (Lab)
SS	Tape, masking, 3/4" × 60 yd.	1	1-3 (Lab) 2-3 (DIS) 2-3 (TT) 2-3 (Lab) 4-1 (DIS)
SS	Thread, spool	1	2-2 (DIS)
C	Toothpicks, round, pkg. of 250	1	2-3 (Lab)
SS	Tube, cardboard	5	4-1 (DIS)

KEY: **DIS**: Discover; **SYS**: Sharpen Your Skills; **TT**: Try This; **Lab**: Lab **Quantities based on 5 lab groups per class.**

* Items designated **C** are in the Consumable Kit, **NC** are in the Nonconsumable Kit, and **SS** are School Supplied.

Master Materials List

Nonconsumable Materials

*	Description	Quantity per class	Textbook Section(s)
NC	Ball, inflatable (beach ball)	5	2-3 (DIS)
NC	Beaker, pyrex, 400 mL	10	2-1 (Lab) 2-5 (DIS)
SS	Books, thick	30	4-1 (Lab)
SS	Bottle, plastic, 2 L	5	1-3 (TT) 2-4 (DIS)
NC	Bowl, plastic translucent, 16 oz.	10	4-2 (TT)
NC	Container, clear plastic w/lid, 11 3/4" × 6" × 3 1/4"	5	3-1 (DIS) 3-3 (DIS)
NC	Flashlight, plastic	5	4-1 (DIS)
NC	Funnel, plastic, 3.25"	5	2-5 (SYS) 3-3 (DIS)
SS	Globe	5	4-1 (DIS)
NC	Jar, wide mouth, 12 oz. polystyrene	5	3-2 (DIS) 2-5 (SYS)
NC	Jar, specimen, wide mouth, 16 oz. flint glass	5	1-1 (DIS) 1-3 (Lab) 1-4 (DIS)
NC	Jar, specimen, wide mouth, 4 oz. flint glass	5	1-1 (DIS) 1-2 (DIS)
NC	Lid, jar, white metal for 12 oz. jar	5	3-2 (DIS)
SS	Light socket	5	2-1 (Lab) 4-3 (DIS)
NC	Marbles, 9/16", pkg. of 6	1	3-2 (DIS)
NC	Meter stick	5	2-2 (TT) 2-3 (Lab)
NC	Pan, aluminum foil, 22.5 cm diameter	5	1-1 (DIS) 1-2 (DIS)
NC	Pins, straight steel, pkg. of 150	1	2-3 (TT)
SS	Protractor	5	4-1 (Lab)
NC	Rubber band, #31, pkg. of 52	1	1-1 (Lab) 1-3 (Lab) 1-4 (DIS) 4-2 (TT)
SS	Ruler, plastic	5	1-3 (Lab) 2-1 (Lab) 3-2 (Lab) 4-2 (Lab)
SS	Scissors	5	1-3 (Lab) 2-2 (DIS) 2-3 (TT) 4-1 (Lab) 4-4 (DIS)
SS	Stopwatch	5	1-1 (DIS) 2-1 (Lab) 4-1 (Lab)
NC	Test tube, 18 × 150 mm, 27 mL	5	2-5 (DIS)
NC	Thermometer, low temp., −40°C to 50°C	10	1-1 (Lab) 2-1 (DIS) 2-1 (Lab) 2-2 (TT) 4-4 (DIS)
SS	Vacuum cleaner with intake hose	1	1-1 (Lab)
SS	Wind vane	5	2-3 (Lab)

KEY: **DIS**: Discover; **SYS**: Sharpen Your Skills; **TT**: Try This; **Lab**: Lab

* Items designated **C** are in the Consumable Kit, **NC** are in the Nonconsumable Kit, and **SS** are School Supplied.

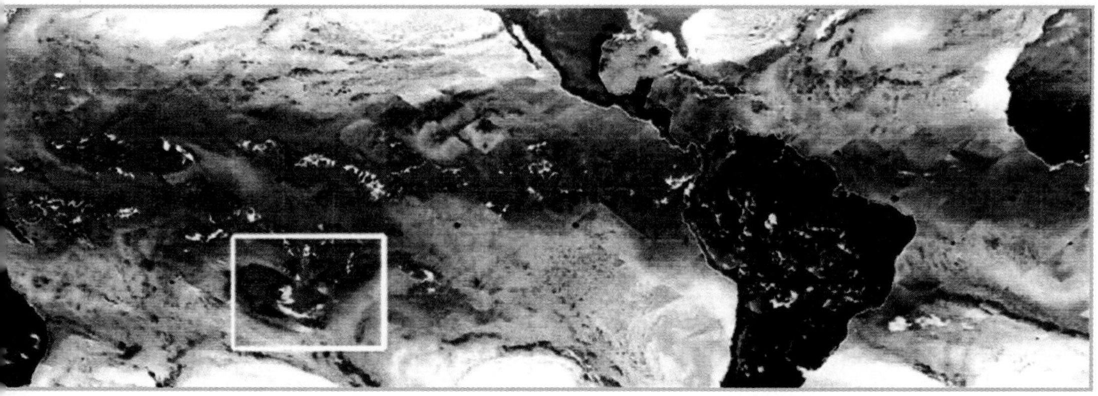

This map was generated by TRMM. The white rectangle identifies a cyclone.

This long-term program uses information from satellites, aircraft, and ground studies to explore environmental changes around the world.

Marshall Shepherd's knowledge of thunderstorms is especially valuable in interpreting data from TRMM (Tropical Rainfall Measuring Mission), a device that measures tropical and subtropical rainfall. Rainfall cycles in tropical regions affect weather throughout the world.

Marshall Shepherd's work involves both observation and calculation. As he did in sixth grade, he designs and builds instruments. But now his devices are some of the most advanced in the world. He no longer takes his instruments into a neighborhood to measure weather conditions directly. Instead, his specialty is "remote sensing"—making observations of weather conditions (rainfall, water vapor, and so on) from a distance.

After collecting data, Marshall uses a computer to analyze it. He and others have designed a computer program that uses the data to predict the development of severe storms. So when a crew at the Kennedy Space Center must decide whether or not to launch a rocket, they rely on predictions from programs similar to ones that Marshall Shepherd has worked on.

Looking Ahead

Marshall Shepherd's personal goals go beyond Mission to Planet Earth. "With the upcoming international space station, scientists are going to have the opportunity to do research from space. My goal is to conduct Earth-directed meteorological research from the space station as well as from the ground. I'll use some of the new instruments we are currently developing." He describes another important goal back home on Earth—"to reach out, inspire, and expose students to science."

In Your Journal

Marshall Shepherd credits his success to having detailed goals. "I always write down goals, and check them off as they happen," he says. Think of an important task that you would like to accomplish over the next year. Identify the steps and note target dates you will need to meet in order to reach your goal. How do those steps help bring you closer to achieving your goal?

In Your Journal Help students focus on the writing activity by asking: **What goal did Marshall Shepherd set for himself when he was a teen?** *(By the time he graduated from high school, he had the definite goal of being a research scientist at NASA.)* **What steps did he take to reach his goal?** *(To reach his goal, he studied meteorology in college and graduate school.)* Advise students to select a goal that is fairly specific. Doing so will make it easier to outline the steps required to reach the goal. Also advise students to make their goal and the steps they must take to reach it as reasonable as possible.

Introducing Weather and Climate

Tell students that they do not need a degree in meteorology or a job at NASA like Marshall Shepherd in order to know a lot about the weather. Point out to students that, when they read this book, they will learn what causes weather, how to measure weather factors such as temperature and wind speed, and even how to predict what the weather will be like tomorrow based on the weather today. They also will learn how the weather varies in general from one part of the world to another. To help motivate student interest in learning about weather, ask: **What are some ways the weather is important to you?** *(Students may say the weather influences how they get to school, what they wear, and what they do for recreation, among many other possible ways.)*

Background

The Tropical Rainfall Measuring Mission, or TRMM, is run by the Goddard Space Flight Center in Maryland for NASA. The TRMM satellite orbits Earth between 35°N and 35°S latitude and measures tropical and subtropical rainfall.

Why is measuring tropical rainfall so important? Tropical rainfall makes up more than two thirds of global rainfall, and it is the main heat source that drives global air circulation. Variation in tropical rainfall can affect the weather in places thousands of kilometers away. The best known influence of tropical weather on global weather is El Niño, which students will read about in Chapter 3. Despite the importance of tropical rainfall patterns, until TRMM our knowledge of tropical rainfall, especially over the oceans, was very limited.

CHAPTER 1 The Atmosphere

Sections	Time	Student Edition Activities	Other Activities
CHAPTER PROJECT 1 **Watching the Weather** p. 13	Ongoing (2 weeks)	Check Your Progress, p. 17 Check Your Progress, p. 36 Wrap Up, p. 39	
1 The Air Around You pp. 14–19 ◆ State how the atmosphere is important to living things. ◆ Identify the gases that are present in Earth's atmosphere.	3–4 periods/ $1\frac{1}{2}$–2 blocks	**Discover** How Long Will the Candle Burn?, p. 14 **Try This** Breathe In, Breathe Out, p. 16 **Real-World Lab: You and Your Environment** How Clean Is the Air?, pp. 18–19	**TE** Building Inquiry Skills: Inferring, p. 16
2 *Integrating Environmental Science* **Air Quality** pp. 20–24 ◆ Name the main sources of air pollution. ◆ Explain how photochemical smog and acid rain form.	2–3 periods/ 1–2 blocks	**Discover** What's On the Jar?, p. 20 **Sharpen Your Skills** Predicting, p. 22 **Science at Home,** p. 23	**TE** Demonstration, p. 21 **TE** Integrating Chemistry, p. 22 **TE** Inquiry Challenge, p. 22 **IES** "Metropolis," pp. 35–36 **ISLM** I-1, "Examining Acid Rain"
3 Air Pressure pp. 25–30 ◆ Identify some of the properties of air. ◆ Name instruments that are used to measure air pressure. ◆ Explain how increasing altitude affects air pressure and density.	3–4 periods/ $1\frac{1}{2}$–2 blocks	**Discover** Does Air Have Mass?, p. 25 **Try This** Soda-Bottle Barometer, p. 27 **Skills Lab: Measuring** Working Under Pressure, pp. 28–29 **Science at Home,** p. 30	**TE** Including All Students, p. 26 **TE** Including All Students, p. 27 **TE** Real-Life Learning, p. 26 **PTA** "Testing Food Wraps," pp. 1–8
4 Layers of the Atmosphere pp. 31–36 ◆ Describe the characteristics of the main layers of the atmosphere.	2–3 periods/ 1–2 blocks	**Discover** Is Air There?, p. 31	**TE** Exploring Layers of the Atmosphere, p. 33 **TE** Building Inquiry Skills: Modeling, p. 35 **IES** "Wagons West," p. 41
Study Guide/Chapter Review pp. 37–39	1 period/ $\frac{1}{2}$ block		**ISAB** Provides teaching and review of all inquiry skills

For Standard or Block Schedule The Resource Pro® CD-ROM gives you maximum flexibility for planning your instruction for any type of schedule. Resource Pro® contains Planning Express®, an advanced scheduling program, as well as the entire contents of the Teaching Resources and the Computer Test Bank.

CHAPTER PLANNING GUIDE

Program Resources	Assessment Strategies	Media and Technology
TR Chapter 1 Project Teacher Notes, pp. 6–7 **TR** Chapter 1 Project Student Materials, pp. 8–11 **TR** Chapter 1 Project Scoring Rubric, p. 12	**SE** Performance Assessment: Chapter 1 Project Wrap Up, p. 39 **TE** Check Your Progress, pp. 17, 36 **TR** Chapter 1 Project Scoring Rubric, p. 12	Science Explorer Internet Site
TR 1-1 Lesson Plan, p. 13 **TR** 1-1 Section Summary, p. 14 **TR** 1-1 Review and Reinforce, p. 15 **TR** 1-1 Enrich, p. 16 **TR** Real-World Lab blackline masters, pp. 29–31 **SES** Book E, *Environmental Science,* Chapter 2	**SE** Section 1 Review, p. 17 **SE** Analyze and Conclude, p. 19 **TE** Ongoing Assessment, p. 15 **TE** Performance Assessment, p.17 **TR** 1-1 Review and Reinforce, p. 15	Exploring Earth Science Videodisc, Unit 2 Side 2, "Air Today, Gone Tomorrow" Audiotapes, English-Spanish Summary 1-1 Transparency 1, "Gases in Dry Air" Interactive Student Tutorial CD-ROM I-1
TR 1-2 Lesson Plan, p. 17 **TR** 1-2 Section Summary, p. 18 **TR** 1-2 Review and Reinforce, p. 19 **TR** 1-2 Enrich, p. 20 **SES** Book E, *Environmental Science,* Chapter 5	**SE** Section 2 Review, p. 23 **TE** Ongoing Assessment, p. 21 **TE** Performance Assessment, p. 23 **TR** 1-2 Review and Reinforce, p. 19	Exploring Earth Science Videodisc, Unit 6 Side 2, "Caution: Breathing May Be Hazardous to Your Health" Audiotapes, English-Spanish Summary 1-2 Transparency 2, "Effects of Air Pollutants on Humans" Interactive Student Tutorial CD-ROM, I-1
TR 1-3 Lesson Plan, p. 21 **TR** 1-3 Section Summary, p. 22 **TR** 1-3 Review and Reinforce, p. 23 **TR** 1-3 Enrich, p. 24 **TR** Skills Lab blackline masters, pp. 32–33 **SES** Book K, *Chemical Building Blocks,* Chapter 2	**SE** Analyze and Conclude, p. 29 **SE** Section 3 Review, p. 30 **TE** Ongoing Assessment, p. 27 **TE** Performance Assessment, p. 30 **TR** 1-3 Review and Reinforce, p. 23	Exploring Physical Science Videodisc, Unit 1 Side 1, "Racing Hot Air Balloons" Audiotapes, English-Spanish Summary 1-3 Transparency 3, "Density of Air at Two Altitudes" Interactive Student Tutorial CD-ROM I-1
TR 1-4 Lesson Plan, p. 25 **TR** 1-4 Section Summary, p. 26 **TR** 1-4 Review and Reinforce, p. 27 **TR** 1-4 Enrich, p. 28	**SE** Section 4 Review, p. 36 **TE** Ongoing Assessment, pp. 33, 35 **TE** Performance Assessment, p. 36 **TR** 1-4 Review and Reinforce, p. 27	Exploring Earth Science Videodisc, Unit 2 Side 2, "A Trip Through the Earth" Audiotapes, English-Spanish Summary 1-4 Transparency 4, Layers of the Atmosphere" Interactive Student Tutorial CD-ROM, I-1
TR Chapter 1 Performance Assessment, pp. 134–136 **TR** Chapter 1 Test, pp. 137–140	**SE** Chapter 1 Review, pp. 37–39 **TR** Chapter 1 Performance Assessment, pp. 134–136 **TR** Chapter 1 Test, pp. 137–140 **CTB** Chapter 1 Test	Interactive Student Tutorial CD-ROM, I-1 Computer Test Bank, Chapter 1 Test

Key: **SE** Student Edition
CTB Computer Test Bank
ISAB Inquiry Skills Activity Book
TE Teacher's Edition
SES Science Explorer Series Text
PTA Product Testing Activities by *Consumer Reports*
TR Teaching Resources
ISLM Integrated Science Laboratory Manual
IES Interdisciplinary Explorations Series

Meeting the National Science Education Standards and AAAS Benchmarks

National Science Education Standards	Benchmarks for Science Literacy	Unifying Themes
Science As Inquiry (Content Standard A) ◆ **Design and conduct a scientific investigation** Students investigate particles in air. *(Real-World Lab)* ◆ **Use the appropriate tools and techniques to gather, analyze, and interpret data** Students use a barometer to measure air pressure. *(Skills Lab)* ◆ **Develop descriptions, explanations, predictions, and models using evidence** Students gather and interpret weather data and predict weather conditions. *(Chapter Project)* **Physical Science** (Content Standard B) ◆ **Properties and changes of properties in matter** Some gases in air are chemically active. Smog and acid rain form when certain substances in the air combine. Density and pressure are two properties of air. *(Sections 1, 2, 3)* **Earth and Space Science** (Content Standard D) ◆ **Structure of the Earth system** Earth's atmosphere is a mixture of gases and is in four layers. *(Sections 1, 4)* **Science and Technology** (Content Standard E) ◆ **Design a solution or product** Students consider the issue of air polluted by cars. *(Science and Society)*	**1B Scientific Inquiry** Students gather and interpret weather data and predict weather. Students investigate particles in air. *(Chapter Project; Real-World Lab)* **3A Technology and Science** Students use a barometer to measure air pressure. Technology has helped scientists explore the atmosphere. *(Skills Lab; Science & History)* **3C Issues in Technology** Some human activities cause air pollution. Students consider the issue of air polluted by cars. *(Section 2; Science and Society)* **4B The Earth** Earth's atmosphere is a mixture of various gases and is divided into four main layers. *(Sections 1, 4)* **4D Structure of Matter** Earth's atmosphere is made up of molecules of various gases. Smog and acid rain form when certain substances in the air combine. Density and pressure are two properties of air. *(Sections 1, 2, 3)* **4E Energy Transformation** Earth's atmosphere is heated by the sun. *(Section 4)* **8C Energy Sources and Use** Most air pollution is caused by burning fossil fuels. *(Section 2; Science and Society)* **12D Communication Skills** Students create drawings, graphs, and tables to summarize their weather observations. *(Chapter Project)*	◆ **Energy** Fossil fuels are an important source of energy. Photochemical smog is caused by the action of sunlight on chemicals. Earth's atmosphere is heated by the sun. *(Sections 2, 4; Science and Society)* ◆ **Patterns of Change** Students use their weather observations to predict weather conditions. Weather factors affect the number of particles in the air. Air pressure and density decrease as altitude increases. Students construct a barometer and use it to measure air pressure. *(Chapter Project; Real-World Lab; Section 3; Skills Lab)* ◆ **Scale and Structure** Earth's atmosphere is made up of nitrogen, oxygen, and various other gases and is divided into four main layers. *(Sections 1, 4)* ◆ **Stability** The composition of the atmosphere remains fairly constant. The layers of the atmosphere are classified by their characteristic temperatures. *(Sections 1, 4)* ◆ **Systems and Interactions** Earth's atmosphere makes conditions on Earth suitable for living things. Most air pollution is caused by burning fossil fuels. Cars add to air pollution. *(Sections 1, 2; Science and Society)*

Media and Technology

Exploring Earth Science Videodiscs

◆ **Section 1** "Air Today, Gone Tomorrow" examines the composition of the atmosphere.

◆ **Section 2** "Caution: Breathing May Be Hazardous To Your Health" illustrates the effects of air pollution on breathing.

◆ **Section 4** "A Trip Through the Earth" takes viewers from outer space to the center of Earth.

Exploring Physical Science Videodiscs

◆ **Section 3** "Racing Hot Air Balloons" relates the properties of gases to a hot-air balloon.

Interactive Student Tutorial CD-ROM

◆ **Chapter Review** Interactive questions help students self-assess their mastery of key chapter concepts.

Student Edition Connection Strategies

◆ **Section 1** **Language Arts Connection,** p. 15
Integrating Life Science, p. 16

◆ **Section 2** **Integrating Environmental Science,** pp. 20–24
Integrating Health, p. 21
Integrating Chemistry, p. 22
Science and Society, p. 24

◆ **Section 3** **Integrating Life Science,** p. 30

◆ **Section 4** **Integrating Space Science,** p. 34
Science & History, pp. 34–35
Integrating Technology, p. 36

ACTIVITY

USING THE INTERNET

www.science-explorer.phschool.com

Visit the Science Explorer internet site to find an up-to-date activity for Chapter 1 of *Weather and Climate*.

ACTIVITY	Time (minutes)	Materials Quantities for one work group	Skills
Section 1			
Discover, p. 14	15	**Consumable** modeling clay, short candle, matches **Nonconsumable** aluminum pie pan, small glass jar, stopwatch or watch with second hand, large glass jar	Inferring
Try This, p. 16	10	**Consumable** limewater, straw **Nonconsumable** glass	Developing Hypotheses
Real World Lab, pp. 18-19	20,10,10, 10,10	**Consumable** coffee filters **Nonconsumable** vacuum cleaner with intake hose (1 per class), rubber band, thermometer, low-power microscope	Measuring, Interpreting Data
Section 2			
Discover, p. 20	10	**Consumable** modeling clay, aluminum foil, candle, matches **Nonconsumable** glass jar	Observing
Sharpen Your Skills, p. 22	10	No special materials are required.	Predicting
Science at Home, p. 23	home	**Nonconsumable** flashlight	Observing
Section 3			
Discover, p. 25	10	**Consumable** balloon **Nonconsumable** balance	Drawing Conclusions
Try This, p. 27	15	**Consumable** water, long straw, modeling clay **Nonconsumable** 2-liter soda bottle	Inferring
Skills Lab, pp. 28-29	40,10,10	**Consumable** large rubber balloon, white glue, 12- to 15-cm drinking straw, modeling clay, 10 cm x 25 cm cardboard strip, tape **Nonconsumable** blunt scissors, wide-mouthed glass jar, rubber band, metric ruler, pencil	Measuring, Observing, Inferring
Science at Home, p. 30	home	**Consumable** tap water **Nonconsumable** glass, piece of heavy cardboard	Communicating
Section 4			
Discover, p. 31	10	**Nonconsumable** heavy rubber band, plastic bag, wide-mouthed glass jar	Predicting

A list of all materials required for the Student Edition activities can be found on pages T14–T15. You can order Materials Kits by calling 1-800-828-7777 or by accessing the Science Explorer internet site at **http://www.science-explorer.phschool.com.**

CHAPTER PROJECT 1

Watching the Weather

Most people make observations about the weather almost every day of their lives, but they might not be very aware of specific weather conditions and how they change. Of course they notice when a storm is raging, but they might not notice the red clouds at sunset that may indicate a storm is coming. Most students may not think much about the conditions that make up the weather. If they think about the weather at all, they may just think of it as good or bad.

Purpose In this project, students will become more aware of the weather and the variables such as temperature, precipitation, and wind speed that make up weather conditions. Students also will develop ways of observing weather variables.

Skills Focus Students will be able to
- ◆ design and implement a plan for observing and recording daily weather conditions;
- ◆ look for patterns in their observations that will help them understand the weather and how it changes;
- ◆ create data tables and other means of displaying their observations for the rest of the class.

Project Time Line The entire project will take a minimum of two weeks. The longer students make and record weather observations, the more likely they are to see trends in their data. On the first day, allow class time for introducing the project and brainstorming how students can use their senses to describe the weather. Students should decide as soon as possible which weather variables they will observe and how they will observe them. Students also must devise a way to record their observations. Additional class time will be necessary during the two-week period to monitor students' progress and give extra guidance to students who are having difficulty. At the end of the project, students will need time to review and organize their data and present their results to the rest of the class. For more detailed information on planning and supervising the chapter project, see Chapter 1 Project Teacher Notes, pages 6–7 in Teaching Resources.

CHAPTER 1

The Atmosphere

WHAT'S AHEAD

SECTION 1 The Air Around You
- Discover **How Long Will the Candle Burn?**
- Try This **Breathe In, Breathe Out**
- Real-World Lab **How Clean Is the Air?**

Integrating Environmental Science

SECTION 2 Air Quality
- Discover **What's On the Jar?**
- Sharpen Your Skills **Predicting**

SECTION 3 Air Pressure
- Discover **Does Air Have Mass?**
- Try This **Soda-Bottle Barometer**
- Skills Lab **Working Under Pressure**

12 ◆ I

Suggested Shortcuts To reduce the amount of time students spend on the project, you may assign each student or group of students just one weather variable, such as temperature or precipitation, to monitor. Then, at the end of the project, students can pool their results and the whole class can work together to look for patterns in the data.

Possible Materials Each student will need a log for recording his or her observations, but no other materials or equipment are needed. In fact, you should stress to students that they are to rely only on their senses and not instruments such as thermometers or wind vanes. However, students will need to depend on various materials in their environment, such as the school flag or the clothes people are wearing, to observe weather conditions. Urge students to be creative in the materials they use for their observations. Smoke rising from chimneys, for example, can reveal the direction and speed of the wind as well as flags flying from poles can.

PROJECT 1

Watching the Weather

The air is cool and clear—just perfect for a trip in a hot-air balloon. As you rise, a fresh breeze begins to move you along. Where will it take you? Hot-air balloon pilots need to know about the weather to plot their course.

In this chapter, you will learn about the air around you. As you learn about the atmosphere, you will use your senses to collect information about weather conditions. Even without scientific instruments it is possible to make many accurate observations about the weather.

Your Goal To observe weather conditions without using instruments and to look for hints about tomorrow's weather in the weather conditions today.

Your completed project must

- ◆ include a plan for observing and describing a variety of weather conditions over a period of two to three weeks
- ◆ show your observations in a daily weather log
- ◆ display your findings about weather conditions

Get Started Begin by discussing what weather conditions you can observe. Brainstorm how to use your senses to describe the weather. For example, can you describe the wind speed by observing the school flag? Can you describe the temperature based on what clothes you need to wear outside? Be creative.

Check Your Progress You'll be working on this project as you study this chapter. To keep your project on track, look for Check Your Progress boxes at the following points.

Section 1 Review, page 17: Collect and record observations.

Section 4 Review, page 36: Look for patterns in your data.

Wrap Up At the end of the chapter (page 39), use your weather observations to prepare a display for the class.

Hot-air balloons soar into the atmosphere at a balloon festival in Snowmass, Colorado.

SECTION 4 Layers of the Atmosphere

Discover Is Air There?

Launching the Project To help students start thinking of weather variables they might observe, hand out copies of newspaper weather reports. On the chalkboard, have a volunteer list the weather variables given in the reports, such as temperature, humidity, barometric pressure, and wind speed and direction. Then challenge students to think of ways these weather variables could be observed without instruments. For example, ask: **If a thin skin of ice forms on puddles during the day, what does that tell you about the temperature?** *(It has fallen below the freezing point of water.)* **If the school flag is flying straight out from its pole, what does that tell you about the wind?** *(It is blowing at a high speed.)* Urge students to think of other observations that could give them information about weather conditions.

Program Resources

- ◆ **Teaching Resources** Chapter 1 Project Teacher Notes, pp. 6–7; Chapter 1 Project Student Materials, pp. 8–11; Chapter 1 Project Scoring Rubric, p. 12

Performance Assessment

The Chapter 1 Project Scoring Rubric on page 12 in Teaching Resources will help you evaluate how well students complete the Chapter 1 Project. You may wish to share the scoring rubric with your students so they know what will be expected of them. Students will be assessed on

- ◆ how thoroughly they collect and record observations of a variety of different weather conditions;
- ◆ how accurately they interpret their data to predict weather conditions and identify weather trends;
- ◆ how complete and creative their presentation of results are;
- ◆ if they work in groups, how much they contribute to their group's effort.

SECTION 1 The Air Around You

Objectives

After completing the lesson, students will be able to
- ◆ state how the atmosphere is important to living things;
- ◆ identify the gases that are present in Earth's atmosphere.

Key Terms weather, atmosphere, ozone, water vapor

1 Engage/Explore

Activating Prior Knowledge

Ask students to recall the fire triangle, which many will have learned about in fire safety demonstrations. After drawing a large triangle on the chalkboard, ask: **What is the fire triangle?** *(A triangle representing the three components needed for fire to burn: fuel, heat, and air)* As students explain, label the sides of the triangle on the chalkboard. Then relate the fire triangle to the composition of air by asking: **What is in air that fire needs to burn?** *(oxygen)* Point out that living things also need oxygen, and oxygen is just one of the components of air they will learn about in this section.

DISCOVER ACTIVITY

Skills Focus inferring
Materials *modeling clay, aluminum pie pan, short candle, matches, small glass jar, stopwatch or watch with second hand, large glass jar*
Time 15 minutes
Tips You can use beakers instead of jars for this activity. You may wish to have students practice using stopwatches before they begin the activity.
Expected Outcome Students should observe that the candle quickly burns out under the small jar and that it burns somewhat longer under the large jar.
Think It Over The gas needed for the candle to burn is oxygen. The candle burned longer under the large jar because the large jar contained more oxygen.

SECTION 1 The Air Around You

DISCOVER ACTIVITY

How Long Will the Candle Burn?

1. Put on your goggles.
2. Stick a small piece of modeling clay onto an aluminum pie pan. Push a short candle into the clay. Carefully light the candle.
3. Hold a small glass jar by the bottom. Lower the mouth of the jar over the candle until the jar rests on the pie pan. As you do this, start a stopwatch or note where the second hand is on a clock.
4. Watch the candle carefully. How long does the flame burn?
5. Wearing an oven mitt, remove the jar. Relight the candle and then repeat Steps 3 and 4 with a larger jar.

Think It Over
Inferring How would you explain any differences between your results in Steps 4 and 5?

GUIDE FOR READING

- ◆ How is the atmosphere important to living things?
- ◆ What gases are present in Earth's atmosphere?

Reading Tip **Before you read, preview Figure 2. As you read, write a sentence about each of the major gases in the atmosphere.**

As you walk home from school, the air is warm and still. The sky is full of thick, dark clouds. In the distance you see a bright flash. A few seconds later, you hear a crack of thunder. As you turn the corner onto your street, raindrops start to fall. You begin to run and reach your home just as the downpour begins. That was close! From the shelter of the entrance you pause to catch your breath and watch the storm.

Importance of the Atmosphere

Does the weather where you live change frequently, or is it fairly constant from day to day? **Weather** is the condition of Earth's atmosphere at a particular time and place. But what is the atmosphere? Earth's **atmosphere** (AT muh sfeer) is the layer of gases that surrounds the planet. To understand the relative size of the atmosphere, imagine that the planet Earth is the size of an apple.

Figure 1 When seen from space, Earth's atmosphere appears as a thin layer near the horizon. The atmosphere makes life on Earth possible.

READING STRATEGIES

Reading Tip Make sure students understand how the two parts of Figure 2 are related by pointing out that the table shows the gases that make up the tiny wedge of the circle that is not nitrogen or oxygen. After students have read the section and written their sentences, suggest that they form pairs, read their sentences to each other, and try to identify which gas each sentence describes. Also urge them to work together to resolve any factual errors they detect in each other's sentences.

Study and Comprehension Before students read the section, have them use the main headings and subheadings to make an outline. Be sure they understand which headings are main headings and which are subheadings. Then, as they read the section, have them write down at least one important fact under each heading on their outline.

If you breathe on the apple, a thin film of water will form on its surface. Earth's atmosphere is like that water on the apple—a thin layer of gases on Earth's surface.

Earth's atmosphere makes conditions on Earth suitable for living things. The atmosphere contains oxygen and other gases that you and other living things need to live. In turn, living things affect the atmosphere. The atmosphere is constantly changing, with atoms and molecules of gases moving around the globe and in and out of living things, the land, and the water.

Living things also need warmth and liquid water. By trapping energy from the sun, the atmosphere keeps most of Earth's surface warm enough for water to exist as a liquid. In addition, Earth's atmosphere protects living things from dangerous radiation from the sun. It also prevents Earth's surface from being hit by most meteoroids, or chunks of rock from outer space.

☑ *Checkpoint* *What would conditions on Earth be like without the atmosphere?*

Language Arts CONNECTION

The word *atmosphere* comes from two Greek words: *atmos*, meaning "vapor," and *sphaira*, meaning "ball," or "globe." So the atmosphere is the vapors or gases surrounding a globe—in this case, Earth.

In Your Journal

As you read this chapter, write down all the words that end in *-sphere*. Look up the roots of each word in a dictionary. How does knowing the roots of each word help you understand its meaning?

Composition of the Atmosphere

The atmosphere is made up of a mixture of atoms and molecules of different kinds of gases. An atom is the smallest unit of a chemical element that can exist by itself. Molecules are made up of two or more atoms. **Earth's atmosphere is made up of nitrogen, oxygen, carbon dioxide, water vapor, and many other gases, as well as particles of liquids and solids.**

Nitrogen As you can see in Figure 2, nitrogen is the most abundant gas in the atmosphere. It makes up a little more than three fourths of the air we breathe. Each nitrogen molecule consists of two nitrogen atoms.

Gases in Dry Air

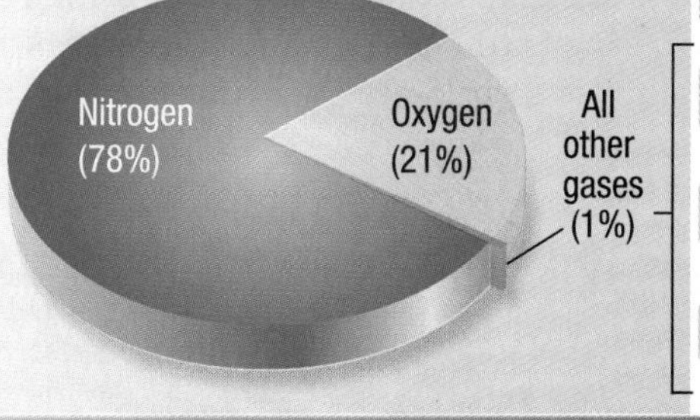

Other Gases	Percentage by Volume
Argon	0.93
Carbon dioxide	0.036
Neon	0.0018
Helium	0.00052
Methane	0.00015
Krypton	0.00011
Hydrogen	0.00005

Figure 2 Dry air in the lower atmosphere always has the same composition of gases. *Interpreting Data* *What two gases make up most of the air?*

Program Resources

◆ **Teaching Resources** 1-1 Lesson Plan, p. 13; 1-1 Section Summary, p. 14

Media and Technology

Audiotapes English-Spanish Summary 1-1

Transparencies "Gases in Dry Air," Transparency 1

Answers to Self-Assessment

☑ *Checkpoint*

Water could not exist as a liquid on Earth's surface. Earth would also be exposed to meteoroids and dangerous radiation from the sun. There would be no life on Earth without the oxygen and other gases that living things need.

Caption Question

Figure 2 Nitrogen and oxygen

2 Facilitate

Importance of the Atmosphere

Language Arts CONNECTION

Point out that many scientific terms are based on Greek words. Ask: **Why do you think English borrowed many scientific terms from Greek?** *(The Greeks were among the first Western people to study and write about the natural world. The words they used were passed on to people throughout Europe.)*

In Your Journal Other words ending in *-sphere* are terms for the layers of the atmosphere. For each term, have students write the meaning of the prefix. **learning modality: verbal**

Composition of the Atmosphere

Building Inquiry Skills: Making Models

Earth's atmosphere is composed largely of just a few gases, but even gases present in small amounts may be important to life. Also, the gases in Earth's atmosphere are present in the same proportions below about 80 kilometers. To reinforce these concepts, invite students to explain how a cake models the composition of the atmosphere. Provide a simple cake recipe first. Ask: **In what ways are the ingredients in a cake like the gases in Earth's atmosphere?** *(A cake is made up largely of just a few ingredients, especially flour. Ingredients, such as baking powder, included in small amounts may be essential for the cake. The ingredients in the cake are always in the same proportions.)* **learning modality: logical/mathematical**

Ongoing Assessment

Oral Presentation Call on students at random to state ways that the atmosphere contributes to life on Earth.

Composition of the Atmosphere, continued

Integrating Life Science

The text gives just a short summary of the nitrogen cycle. Divide the class into groups and challenge each group to research the nitrogen cycle further and then make an illustrated flowchart of it. Each student in the group should take responsibility for learning about and illustrating one part of the cycle. Urge groups to share their flowcharts and work together to resolve any discrepancies. Display their best efforts in the classroom. **cooperative learning**

Building Inquiry Skills: Inferring

Materials *tall glass jar, large cake pan, clean steel wool, water, tape*

ACTIVITY

Time 5 minutes one day; 5 minutes the next day

Estimate the amount of oxygen in the atmosphere by having students follow these instructions: Fill a cake pan almost full of water. Push steel wool down into the bottom of a tall glass jar so it will not fall out when the jar is turned over. (**CAUTION:** Remind students to handle glass carefully.) Fill the jar with water, cover the mouth with a hand, and place the jar upside down in the cake pan. Remove the hand and tilt the jar slightly to let out enough water so that the water level in the jar is just above the water level in the pan. Mark the water level in the jar with a piece of tape and leave the jar where it is. Have students check the water level the next day. It should be about one fifth higher than it was. Explain that oxygen in the air combines with iron in steel wool to form rust. Ask: **From this experiment, how can you tell how much oxygen there is in air?** *(About one fifth of the air is used up, so the air must be about one fifth oxygen.)* **learning modality: logical/mathematical**

TRY THIS

Breathe In, Breathe Out ACTIVITY

How can you detect carbon dioxide in the air you exhale?

1. Put on your goggles.
2. Fill a glass or beaker halfway with limewater.

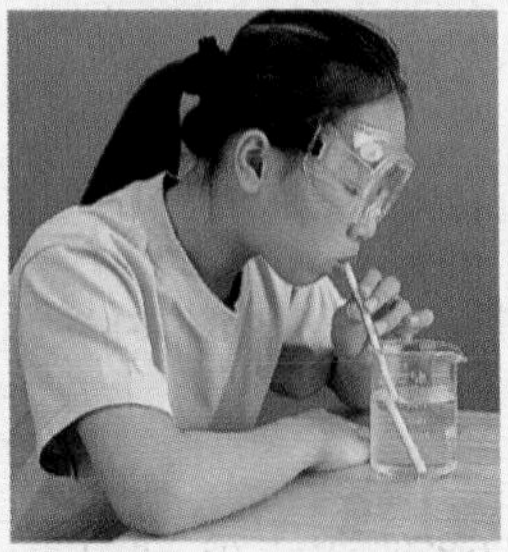

3. Using a straw, slowly blow air through the limewater for about a minute. **CAUTION:** *Do not suck on the straw or drink the limewater.*
4. What happens to the limewater?

Developing Hypotheses What do you think would happen if you did the same experiment after jogging for 10 minutes? If you tried this, what might the results tell you about exercise and carbon dioxide?

INTEGRATING LIFE SCIENCE Nitrogen is essential to living things. Proteins and other complex chemical substances in living things contain nitrogen. You and all other organisms must have nitrogen in order to grow and to repair body cells.

Most living things cannot obtain nitrogen directly from the air. Instead, some bacteria convert nitrogen into substances called nitrates. Plants then absorb the nitrates from the soil and use them to make proteins. To obtain proteins, animals must eat plants or other animals.

Oxygen Most oxygen molecules have two oxygen atoms. Even though oxygen is the second-most abundant gas in the atmosphere, it makes up less than one fourth of the volume. Plants and animals take oxygen directly from the air and use it to release energy from food in a usable form.

Oxygen is also involved in other important processes. Any fuel you can think of, from the gasoline in a car to the candles on a birthday cake, uses oxygen as it burns. Without oxygen, a fire will go out. Burning uses oxygen rapidly. During other processes, oxygen is used slowly. For example, steel in cars and other objects reacts slowly with oxygen to form iron oxide, or rust.

Have you ever noticed a pungent smell in the air after a thunderstorm? This is the odor of ozone, which forms when lightning interacts with oxygen in the air. **Ozone** is a form of oxygen that has three oxygen atoms in each molecule instead of the usual two.

Carbon Dioxide Each molecule of carbon dioxide has one atom of carbon and two atoms of oxygen. Even though the atmosphere contains only a small amount of carbon dioxide, it is essential to life. Plants must have carbon dioxide to produce food. Animals, on the other hand, give off carbon dioxide as a waste product.

When fuels such as coal and gasoline are burned, they release carbon dioxide. Burning these fuels increases the amount of carbon dioxide in the atmosphere. Rising carbon dioxide levels may be raising Earth's temperature. The issue of Earth's rising temperature, or global warming, is discussed in Chapter 4.

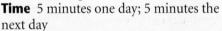

Figure 3 To burn, these candles need oxygen, one of the gases in the atmosphere. ***Predicting*** *What would happen if the candles used up all of the oxygen around them?*

Background

History of Science Scientists began searching for the components of air more than 300 years ago. In the 1600s, an English scientist named Robert Boyle discovered that air contains a substance needed for life when he noted that living things died if deprived of air. He called this substance "vital air." We now call it oxygen.

Almost 100 years later, Joseph Black, a Scottish medical student, found that limestone mixed with acid gives off a substance that puts out flames. He called it "fixed air." We now know it as carbon dioxide.

About 15 years later, one of Black's students, Daniel Rutherford, used a liquid to absorb vital air and fixed air. The substance that remained he called "noxious air," because it put out flames and killed living things. We now know it as nitrogen.

Other Gases Oxygen and nitrogen together make up 99 percent of dry air. Carbon dioxide and argon make up most of the other one percent. The remaining gases are called trace gases because only small amounts of them are present.

Water Vapor The composition of the air discussed so far has been for dry air. In reality, air is not dry because it contains water vapor. **Water vapor** is water in the form of a gas. Water vapor is invisible—it is not the same thing as steam, which is made up of tiny droplets of liquid water. Each water molecule contains two atoms of hydrogen and one atom of oxygen.

The amount of water vapor in the air varies greatly from place to place and from time to time. Air above a desert or polar ice sheet may contain almost no water vapor. In tropical rain forests, on the other hand, as much as five percent of the air may be water vapor.

Water vapor plays an important role in Earth's weather. Clouds form when water vapor condenses out of the air to form tiny droplets of liquid water or crystals of ice. If these droplets or crystals become large enough, they can fall as rain or snow.

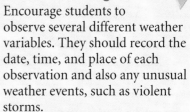

Figure 4 This lush vegetation grows in a rain forest in Costa Rica. The percentage of water vapor in the air in a rain forest may be as high as five percent.

Particles Pure air contains only gases. But pure air exists only in laboratories. In the real world, air also contains tiny solid and liquid particles of dust, smoke, salt, and other chemicals. Sometimes you can see particles in the air around you, but most of them are too small to see.

Section 1 Review

1. Describe two ways in which the atmosphere is important to life on Earth.
2. What are the four most common gases in dry air?
3. Why are the amounts of gases in the atmosphere usually shown as percentages of dry air?
4. **Thinking Critically Applying Concepts** How would the amount of carbon dioxide in the atmosphere change if there were no plants? If there were no animals?

CHAPTER PROJECT 1

Check Your Progress

Have you determined *how*, *where*, and *when*, you will make your observations? Organize a notebook to record them. Think of ways to compare weather conditions from day to day. Make your observations without weather instruments or TV weather reports. (*Hint:* You can estimate how much of the sky is covered by clouds.) For your own safety, do not try to make observations during storms.

TRY THIS

ACTIVITY

Skills Focus developing hypotheses
Materials *glass, limewater, straw*
Time 10 minutes
Tips Make sure students are careful not to splash or ingest any of the limewater.
Expected Outcome Students should observe that the limewater becomes cloudy when they blow into it because of carbon dioxide in their breath. After exercise, more carbon dioxide is exhaled, causing the limewater to get cloudier.
Extend Invite students to detect carbon dioxide in carbonated water by adding some of it to the limewater. **learning modality: kinesthetic**

3 Assess

Section 1 Review Answers

1. *Any two:* Provides oxygen and other gases living things need, traps energy from the sun to keep Earth's surface warm, and protects from meteoroids and radiation from the sun
2. Nitrogen, oxygen, argon, carbon dioxide
3. Because the amount of water vapor in air varies greatly
4. Without plants there would be less oxygen and more carbon dioxide; without animals there would be less carbon dioxide and more oxygen.

CHAPTER PROJECT 1

Check Your Progress

Encourage students to observe several different weather variables. They should record the date, time, and place of each observation and also any unusual weather events, such as violent storms.

Media and Technology

Interactive Student Tutorial CD-ROM I-1

Exploring Earth Science Videodisc Unit 2, Side 2, "Air Today, Gone Tomorrow"

Chapter 2

Answers to Self-Assessment

Caption Question

Figure 3 Their flames would go out.

Program Resources

- **Teaching Resources** 1-1 Review and Reinforce, p. 15; 1-1 Enrich, p. 16
- **Science Explorer Series** *Environmental Science,* Chapter 2, explains the nitrogen cycle.

Performance Assessment

Writing Have students write a paragraph identifying the three most important gases in air for living things, the percentage of each, and why the gas is important.

Real-World Lab

You and Your Environment

How Clean Is the Air?

Preparing for Inquiry

Key Concept The number of particles in air is affected by the weather.

Skills Objectives Students will be able to

- measure the number of particles in samples collected from the air;
- interpret how the number of particles is affected by weather factors.

Time 20 minutes the first day; 10 minutes a day for four days

Advance Planning If possible, students should collect particle samples outside. If they do, the vacuum cleaner may need an extension cord. However, they should not collect samples outside in wet weather. Instead, have students collect the samples as soon as possible after a rainfall. If you use only one vacuum cleaner, plan sufficient time for each group of students to use it.

Alternative Materials A portable vacuum cleaner is easier to carry outside than a regular vacuum cleaner. Instead of coffee filters, you can use paper towels for filters, but they are less effective because they let more particles pass through. Avoid using facial tissues because they are too fragile.

Guiding Inquiry

Invitation To help students focus on the key concept, ask: **What does air contain besides gases?** *(particles)* **How do you think weather conditions might affect the number of particles in the air?** *(Rain might wash particles out of the air, and wind might either stir them up or blow them away.)* Save their predictions so students can compare them with their results.

Introducing the Procedure

Have students read through the complete procedure and copy the data table in their notebook. Then ask: **Why do people in some occupations, such as wood-working, wear protective masks?** *(Because they work where there are high levels of particles in the air, and protective masks trap the particles so they do not breathe them in)* Mention some devices students may be familiar with, including motor vehicles and furnaces, that have filters to trap particles in the air that flows through them. You might want to ask the school custodian to show students how air in the classrooms is filtered or the industrial arts teacher to show them how wood and dust particles are filtered from the air in the shop. Tell students that in this lab they will trap particles in the air by running a vacuum cleaner with a paper filter placed over the end of the hose.

Troubleshooting the Experiment

- If possible, have students run the vacuum cleaner for 30 minutes each time. However, if the air is very dirty, 20 minutes each time may be enough.
- Because a vacuum cleaner is noisy, it may be necessary to run it outside of class time.

Real-World Lab

You and Your Environment

How Clean Is the Air?

Sometimes you can actually see the atmosphere! How? Since air is normally transparent, it can only be visible because it contains particles. In this activity, you will use a vacuum cleaner to gather particles from the air.

Problem

How do weather factors affect the number of particles in the air?

Skills Focus

measuring, interpreting data

Materials

coffee filters
rubber band
thermometer
low-power microscope
vacuum cleaner with intake hose (1 per class)

Procedure

1. Predict what factors will affect the number of particles you collect. How might different weather factors affect your results?
2. In your notebook, make a data table like the one below.
3. Place the coffee filter over the nozzle of the vacuum cleaner hose. Fasten the coffee filter securely to the hose with a rubber band. Make sure the air passes through the coffee filter before entering the vacuum cleaner.
4. You will take air samples in the same place each day for five days. If possible, find a place outdoors. Otherwise, you can run the vacuum cleaner out a classroom window. **CAUTION:** *Do not use the vacuum cleaner outdoors on wet or rainy days.* If it is wet or rainy, collect the sample as soon as possible after it stops raining.
5. Hold the vacuum nozzle at least one meter above the ground each time you use the vacuum. Turn on the vacuum. Run the vacuum for 30 minutes. Shut off the vacuum.

DATA TABLE

Date and Time	Temperature	Amount of Precipitation	Wind Direction	Wind Speed	Number of Particles

18 ◆ I

6. While the vacuum is running, observe the weather conditions. Measure the temperature. Estimate the amount of precipitation, if any, since the previous observation. Note the direction from which the wind, if any, is blowing. Also note whether the wind is heavy, light, or calm. Record your observations.
7. Remove the coffee filter from the nozzle. Label the filter with the place, time, and date. Draw a circle on the filter to show the area that was over the vacuum nozzle.
8. Place the coffee filter on the stage of a microscope (40 power). Be sure that the part of the filter that was over the vacuum nozzle is directly under the microscope lens. Without moving the coffee filter, count all the particles you see. Record the number in your data table.
9. Repeat Steps 3–8 each clear day.

Analyze and Conclude

1. Was there a day of the week when you collected more particles?
2. What factors changed during the week that could have caused changes in the particle count?
3. Did the weather have any effect on your day-to-day results? If so, which weather factor do you think was most important?
4. Make a list of some possible sources of the particles you collected. Are these sources natural, or did the particles come from manufactured products?
5. How could you improve your method to get more particles out of the air?
6. **Apply** Identify areas in or around your school where there may be high levels of dust and other particles. What can people do to protect themselves in these areas?

Design an Experiment

Do you think time of day will affect the number of particles you collect? Develop a hypothesis and a plan for testing it. Could you work with other classes to get data at different times of the day? Before carrying out your plan, get your teacher's approval.

Sample Data Table

Date and Time	Temp.	Amt. of Precipitation	Wind Direction	Wind Speed	# of Particles
Oct. 1, 2 P.M.	18°C	none	SW	calm	60
Oct. 2, 2 P.M.	19°C	none	SW	light breeze	55
Oct. 3, 2 P.M.	11°C	1 cm	W	moderate wind	18
Oct. 4, 2 P.M.	12°C	5 cm	W	strong wind	10
Oct. 5, 2 P.M.	13°C	5 cm	W	strong wind	11

Program Resources

- **Teaching Resources** Real-World Lab blackline masters, pp. 29–31

Safety

Emphasize the importance of not using the vacuum cleaner around water because of electrical shock. Review the safety guidelines in Appendix A.

- Explain the importance of controlling other variables besides weather conditions that might influence the number of particles collected, such as proximity to a dusty playing field. Stress that samples should be taken in the same place each day to help control these other variables.

Expected Outcome
Using the microscope, students should be able to see and count the particles collected on the filters. The number of particles may vary greatly from one sample to another.

Analyze and Conclude
1. The particle count may vary from day to day depending on human activities and the weather.
2. The particle count is likely to be higher later in the week as particles given off by motor vehicles and factories and produced by other human activities accumulate in the air. Changing weather conditions also may cause changes in the particle count.
3. Weather factors most likely to affect day-to-day results are wind speed and recent precipitation.
4. Particles can come from many different sources. Natural sources include flowering plants, bare ground, and forest fires. Manufactured products that produce particles include motor vehicles, factories, and power plants.
5. Possible ways to get more particles out of the air include using a more powerful vacuum cleaner or a vacuum cleaner with a wider hose, running the vacuum cleaner longer each time, and using a finer filter.
6. **Apply** The cafeteria, gymnasium, and shop may have more particles than the classrooms. Playing fields and parking lots may have more particles than lawn areas. Wearing dust masks and using special air filters can help protect people from high levels of particles in the air.

Extending the Inquiry

Design an Experiment Students may hypothesize that more particles will be collected later in the day as particles accumulate in the air. They can test their hypothesis by comparing samples collected at different times of day.

Integrating Environmental Science

Section 2 Air Quality

Objectives

After completing the lesson, students will be able to

- ◆ name the main sources of air pollution;
- ◆ explain how photochemical smog and acid rain form.

Key Terms pollutant, photochemical smog, acid rain

1 Engage/Explore

Activating Prior Knowledge

Guide students in recalling weather reports they may have seen or heard that included an air quality index or pollen count. Alternatively, share copies of newspaper weather reports that include these measures. Then ask: **Why do weather reports include warnings about air pollution and pollen in the air?** *(Because high levels of pollution and pollen in the air can make people sick)* **What is the source of pollen in the air?** *(plants)* **What are some sources of pollution in the air?** *(cars and factories)*

Discover Activity

Skills Focus observing
Materials *modeling clay, aluminum foil, candle, matches, glass jar*
Time 10 minutes
Tips Before students light their candles, be sure the candles are firmly in place in the modeling clay. When students put their jars near the flame, caution them to avoid touching the wax or wick.
Expected Outcome Students should see black powder collect on the part of the jar just above the flame. In addition to soot, students may see condensation form on the jar from water vapor in the air.
Think It Over The black powder on the jar is soot, which came from the incomplete burning of the wax candle.

Integrating Environmental Science

Section 2 Air Quality

Discover Activity

What's On the Jar?

1. Put on your goggles.
2. Put a small piece of modeling clay on a piece of aluminum foil. Push a candle into the clay. Light the candle.
3. Wearing an oven mitt, hold a glass jar by the rim so that the bottom of the jar is just above the flame.

Think It Over

Observing What do you see on the jar? Where did it come from?

Guide for Reading

- ◆ What are the main sources of air pollution?
- ◆ How do photochemical smog and acid rain form?

Reading Tip **As you read, look for evidence to support this statement: Most air pollution is caused by human activities. What facts support this statement? What facts do not support it?**

One hundred years ago, the city of London, England, was dark and dirty. Factories burned coal, and most houses were heated by coal. The air was full of soot. In 1905, the term *smog* was created by combining the words *sm*oke and f*og* to describe this type of air pollution. Today, people in London burn much less coal. As a result, the air in London now is much cleaner than it was 100 years ago.

Air Pollution

As you are reading this, you are breathing without even thinking about it. Breathing brings air into your lungs, where the oxygen you need is taken into your body. You may also breathe in tiny particles or even a small amount of harmful gases. In fact, these particles and gases are a concern to people everywhere.

If you live in a large city, you probably already know what air pollution is. You may have noticed a brown haze or an unpleasant smell in the air. Even if you live far from a city, the air around you may be polluted. Harmful substances in the air, water, or soil are known as **pollutants**. Figure 5 shows some of the effects of air pollution on human health.

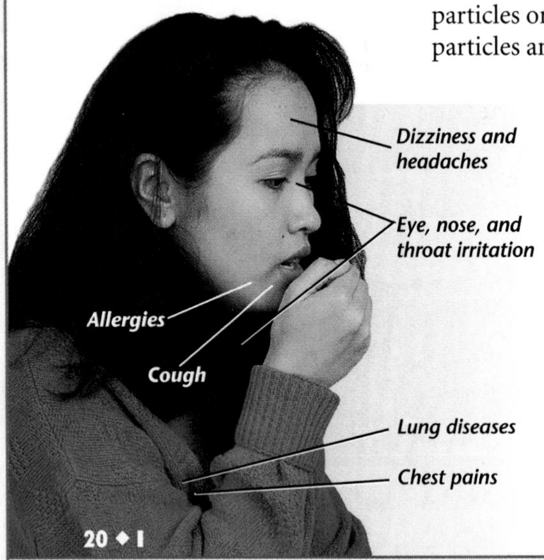

Figure 5 Air pollution can cause many different problems. Some air pollutants are natural, but most are caused by human activities. ***Interpreting Photographs*** *What parts of the body are most affected by air pollution?*

Reading Strategies

Reading Tip Evidence supporting the statement that air pollution is caused by human activities includes the fact that most air pollution is the result of burning fossil fuels. Evidence contradicting the statement includes the fact that many natural processes add particles to the air. Some particles from natural sources are ocean salt, molds, plant pollen, soil, and ashes from forest fires and volcanoes.

Program Resources

- ◆ **Teaching Resources** 1-2 Lesson Plan, p. 17; 1-2 Section Summary, p. 18
- ◆ **Interdisciplinary Exploration Series** "Metropolis," pp. 35–36
- ◆ **Integrated Science Laboratory Manual** I-1, "Examining Acid Rain"

Science Explorer Series *Environmental Science,* Chapter 5, gives more information on the causes of air pollution.

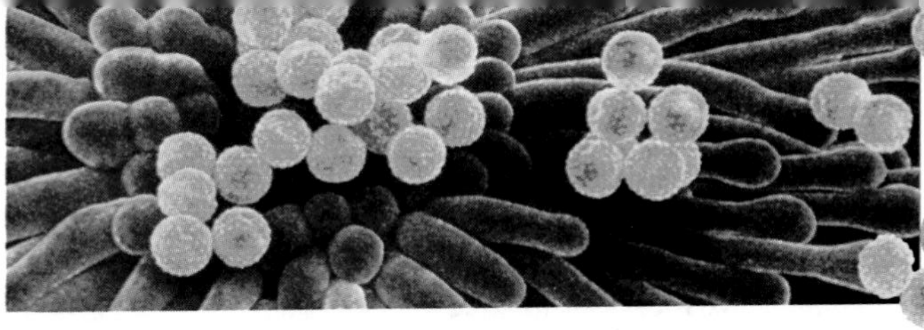

Figure 6 These pollen grains from a ragweed flower have been greatly magnified to show detail. Pollen can cause people who are allergic to it to sneeze.

Some air pollution occurs naturally, but much of it is caused by human activities. **Most air pollution is the result of burning fossil fuels such as coal, oil, gasoline, and diesel fuel.** Almost half of the air pollution from human activities comes from cars and other motor vehicles. A little more than one fourth comes from factories and power plants that burn coal and oil. Burning fossil fuels produces a number of air pollutants, including particles and gases that can form smog and acid rain.

☑ *Checkpoint* *What are two sources of air pollution that you see every day?*

Particles

As you know, air contains particles along with gases. When you draw these particles deep into your lungs, the particles can be harmful. Particles in the air come from both natural sources and human activities.

Natural Sources Many natural processes add particles to the atmosphere. When ocean waves splash salt water against rocks, some of the water sprays into the air and evaporates. Tiny salt particles stay in the air. The wind blows particles of molds and plant pollen. Forest fires, soil erosion, and dust storms add particles to the atmosphere. Erupting volcanoes spew out clouds of dust and ashes along with poisonous gases.

INTEGRATING HEALTH Even fairly clean air usually contains particles of dust and pollen. Figure 6 shows pollen, a fine, powdery material produced by many plants. The wind carries pollen not only to other plants, but also to people. One type of allergy, popularly called "hay fever," is caused by pollen from plants such as ragweed. Symptoms of hay fever include sneezing, a runny nose, red and itchy eyes, and headaches. Weather reports often include a "pollen count," which is the average number of pollen grains in a cubic meter of air.

Human Activities When people burn fuels such as wood and coal, particles made mostly of carbon enter the air. These particles of soot are what gives smoke its dark color. Farming and construction also release large amounts of soil particles into the air.

Figure 7 These people in Pontianak, Indonesia, are being given dust masks to protect them from smoke caused by widespread forest fires. *Inferring What effects do you think this smoke might have had on the people who live in this area?*

2 Facilitate

Air Pollution

Demonstration

Materials *cotton ball, fingernail polish remover, glass jar with lid, rayon cloth, tape*
Time 5 minutes one day; 5 minutes the next day

ACTIVITY

Point out that air pollution is bad for clothing and other materials as well as for people. To show students the effect of air pollution on cloth, saturate a cotton ball with fingernail polish remover, which contains acetone, and place it in the bottom of a glass jar. Tape a small piece of rayon to the inside of the jar lid and put the lid on tightly. Place another small piece of rayon beside the jar and leave both overnight. The next day, invite students to compare the two pieces of cloth. Ask: **Why did the cloth in the jar weaken?** *(The fingernail polish produced acetone vapors that attacked fibers in the cloth.)* Add that similar vapors pollute the air over cities. **learning modality: kinesthetic**

Particles

Integrating Health

Invite students to learn more about allergies such as hay fever by working in groups to conduct a survey. Each group member should ask family members, friends, and neighbors if they suffer from hay fever or other allergies. Then group members should pool their results and use the data to identify the frequency of such allergies. **cooperative learning**

Media and Technology

Audiotapes English-Spanish Summary 1-2

Transparencies "Effects of Air Pollutants on Humans," Transparency 2

Answers to Self-Assessment

Caption Questions

Figure 5 The respiratory system, including the nose, throat, and lungs
Figure 7 It might have caused respiratory and other health problems.

☑ *Checkpoint*

Motor vehicles and factories or power plants that burn coal or oil

Ongoing Assessment

Concept Mapping Have students make a concept map of particles found in the air, including sources and examples.

Smog

Integrating Chemistry

Materials *two small glass bottles, pan of hot water, bowl of ice, matches*
Time 10 minutes

ACTIVITY

Point out that smog is trapped near the ground when the air near the ground is cooler than the air above it. Demonstrate by placing a small glass bottle in a shallow pan of hot water and another in a bowl of ice. Then drop a smoking match into each bottle. Smoke will rise from the bottle of warm air but not from the bottle of cold air. Ask: **Why does smoke stay in the bottle of cold air?** *(Because cold air is denser than warm air and does not rise)* **learning modality: logical/mathematical**

Sharpen your Skills

Predicting

ACTIVITY

Time 10 minutes
Expected Outcome The amount of pollutants may vary by time of day and day of week. Cars and trucks produce the most pollution during morning and evening rush hours, and factories and plants produce pollutants throughout the workday. Thus, pollution levels are likely to be higher late in the day and on Fridays after pollutants have accumulated.
Extend Have students predict how pollutants in air might vary by season. **learning modality: logical/mathematical**

Acid Rain

Inquiry Challenge

ACTIVITY

Materials *two saucers, two pennies, tap water, vinegar*
Time 10 minutes one day; 5 minutes the next day

Challenge small groups to brainstorm a way to use the materials to show the effects of acid rain on metal. *(The most likely way is to place each penny on a saucer, cover one penny with vinegar and the other with water, and let them stand overnight.)* **cooperative learning**

Sharpen your Skills

Predicting

ACTIVITY

Are the amounts of pollutants in the air always at the same level, or do they change from time to time? At what time of the day do you think the major sources of air pollution— cars, trucks, power plants, and factories— might produce the most pollution? Overall, do you think there is more air pollution in the morning or in the evening? On Mondays or on Fridays? On what did you base your prediction?

Smog

London-type smog forms when particles in coal smoke combine with water droplets in humid air. Fortunately, London-type smog is no longer common in the United States. Today sunny cities like Los Angeles often have another type of smog. The brown haze that forms in cities is called **photochemical smog.** The *photo-* in photochemical means "light." Photochemical smog is caused by the action of sunlight on chemicals.

INTEGRATING CHEMISTRY Photochemical smog is formed by a complex process. All fossil fuels contain hydrocarbons, which are substances composed of carbon and hydrogen. When fossil fuels are burned, some hydrocarbons are not burned completely and escape into the air. At the same time, the high temperatures that accompany burning cause some of the nitrogen in the air to react with oxygen to form nitrogen oxides. **The nitrogen oxides, hydrocarbons, and other air pollutants then react with each other in the presence of sunlight to form a mix of ozone and other chemicals called photochemical smog.** The ozone in photochemical smog irritates breathing passages, harms plants, and damages rubber, paint, and some plastics.

☑ *Checkpoint* ***How do natural conditions combine with human activities to create photochemical smog?***

Acid Rain

One result of air pollution is acid rain. The burning of coal that contains a lot of sulfur produces substances composed of oxygen and sulfur called sulfur oxides. **Acid rain forms when nitrogen oxides and sulfur oxides combine with water in the air to form nitric acid and sulfuric acid.**

Figure 8 This scientist is studying trees damaged by acid rain. Acid rain is one of the results of air pollution.

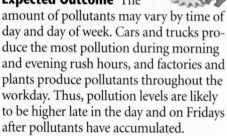

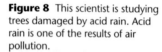

Background

Facts and Figures The 99.9% of the atmosphere that is made up of nitrogen, oxygen, and argon has remained relatively stable for the past 100 million years. Chemical interactions among fewer than 0.1% of molecules in the atmosphere are the cause of all the air quality problems facing us today, including smog and acid rain.

The average pH of rain water is about 4.2, which means that it is weakly acidic. Rain in remote areas little affected by pollution is less acidic and may have a pH as high as 4.8. Considerably more acidic water is found in the smog over Los Angeles. It may have a pH as low as 1.8. To put these values in perspective, consider that tomato juice has a pH of 4.3, vinegar a pH of 2.8, and battery acid a pH of 0.8.

Rain, sleet, snow, fog, and even dry particles carry these two acids from the air to trees, lakes, and buildings. Rain is naturally slightly acidic, but rain that contains more acid than normal is known as **acid rain.** Acid rain is sometimes strong enough to damage the surfaces of buildings and statues.

As Figure 8 shows, needle-leafed trees such as pines and spruce are especially sensitive to acid rain. Acid rain may make tree needles turn brown or fall off. It also harms lakes and ponds. Acid rain can make water so acidic that plants, amphibians, fish, and insects can no longer survive in it.

Improving Air Quality

The United States government and state governments have passed a number of laws and regulations to reduce air pollution. For example, pollution-control devices are required equipment on cars. Factories and power plants must install filters in smokestacks to remove pollutants from smoke before it is released into the atmosphere. These filters are called scrubbers.

Air quality in this country has generally improved over the past 30 years. The amounts of most major air pollutants have decreased. Newer cars cause less pollution than older models. Recently built power plants are less polluting than power plants that have been in operation for many years.

However, there are now more cars on the road and more power plants burning fossil fuels than in the past. Unfortunately, the air in many American cities is still polluted. Many people think that stricter regulations are needed to control air pollution. Others argue that reducing air pollution is very expensive and that the benefits of stricter regulations may not be worth the costs.

Section 2 Review

1. How is most air pollution produced?
2. Name two natural and two artificial sources of particles in the atmosphere.
3. How is photochemical smog formed? What kinds of harm does it cause?
4. What substances combine to form acid rain?
5. **Thinking Critically** **Inferring** Do you think that photochemical smog levels are higher during the winter or during the summer? Explain.

Science at Home

It's easy to see particles in the air. Gather your family members in a dark room. Open a window shade or blind slightly, or turn on a flashlight. Can they see tiny particles suspended in the beam of light? Discuss with your family where the particles came from. What might be some natural sources? What might be some human sources?

Media and Technology

Interactive Student Tutorial CD-ROM I-1

Exploring Earth Science Videodisc Unit 6, Side 2, "Caution: Breathing May Be Hazardous to Your Health"

Chapter 8

Answers to Self-Assessment

Checkpoint

Pollutants in the air produced by human activities react with each other in the presence of sunlight to form photochemical smog.

Program Resources

◆ **Teaching Resources** 1-2 Review and Reinforce, p. 19; 1-2 Enrich, p. 20

Improving Air Quality

Building Inquiry Skills: Inferring

Point out that nitrogen dioxide and sulfur dioxide emissions in the U.S. have decreased over the past 30 years. Ask: **How do you think the level of acid in rain has been affected by these trends in air pollutants?** *(Nitrogen dioxide and sulfur dioxide cause acid rain, so as they have decreased in the air, the amount of acid in rain probably has decreased as well.)* **learning modality: logical/mathematical**

3 Assess

Section 2 Review Answers

1. By the burning of fossil fuels
2. Natural: ocean salt, molds, plant pollen, forest fires, soil erosion, volcanoes; Artificial: burning of fossil fuels, farming, and construction
3. It forms when nitrogen oxides, hydrocarbons, and other pollutants react in the presence of sunlight. It can irritate breathing passages, harm plants, and damage rubber, paint, and some plastics.
4. Nitrogen oxides, sulfur oxides, and water in the air
5. During the summer, because the production of photochemical smog requires sunlight and the sun's rays are more direct then

ACTIVITY

Science at Home

Materials *flashlight*

Tips Students will see more particles if they stir up dust first. Point out that most particles in the air are too small to

Performance Assessment

Writing Challenge students to write letters to a newspaper to raise peoples' awareness of the causes and dangers of air pollution.

SCIENCE AND SOCIETY

Cars and Clean Air

Purpose

To help students learn ways that pollution from cars can be reduced and make a reasonable judgment about the best ways to do this.

Panel Discussion

Time one day to prepare; 30 minutes for panel discussion
After students have read the feature, ask for volunteers to form a panel to discuss the issues. Have each panel member assume one of the following roles: a car manufacturer, a person who commutes 50 miles a day to work, a person who lives near a busy intersection, a lawmaker, and a public health official. Students should take the point of view of the individual they represent and present relevant facts and opinions for that individual. Following the panel discussion, take a class vote on which methods of reducing pollution seem most effective and whether the methods should be voluntary or enforced.
Extend Challenge students to learn about alternative means of transportation in their community and report on the costs and availability of each.

You Decide

1. Even the least polluting cars cause some air pollution, and there are more cars on the road each year. More cars also mean more traffic jams, which produce more pollution than does driving on the open road. Automobiles pollute the air with particles such as soot and gases that contribute to smog and acid rain.
2. Driving cars that are more efficient and produce less pollution, and driving less
3. Students should illustrate more than one way to help reduce pollution from cars. Their captions should demonstrate that they understand how the solutions address the problem.

SCIENCE AND SOCIETY

Cars and Clean Air

New technology and strict laws have brought cleaner air to many American cities. But in some places the air is still polluted. Cars and trucks still cause about half the air pollution in cities. And there are more cars on the road every year!

Worldwide, there are about 500 million cars. More cars will mean more pollution and more traffic jams. Unfortunately, cars stuck in traffic produce three times as much pollution as cars on the open road. What can people do to reduce air pollution by cars?

The Issues

Can Cars Be Made To Pollute Less?
In the past 20 years, cars have become more fuel-efficient and pollution levels have been lowered. Now engineers are running out of ways to make cars run more efficiently and produce less pollution. But technology does offer other answers.

Some vehicles use fuels other than gasoline. For instance, natural gas can power cars and trucks. Burning natural gas produces less pollution than burning gasoline.

Battery-powered electric cars produce no air pollution. However, the electricity to charge the batteries often comes from power plants that burn oil or coal. So electric cars still produce some pollution indirectly. Car makers have produced a few electric cars, but they are expensive and can make only fairly short trips.

Should People Drive Less? Many car trips are shorter than a mile—an easy distance for most people to walk. For longer trips, people might consider riding a bicycle. Many cars on the road carry just one person. Some people might consider riding with others in car pools or taking buses or subways.

Are Stricter Standards or Taxes the Answer? Some state governments have led efforts to reduce pollution. The state of California, for example, has strict anti-pollution laws. These laws set standards for gradually reducing pollutants released by cars. Stricter laws might make some old cars illegal.

Another approach is to make driving more expensive so that people use their cars less. That might mean higher gasoline taxes or fees for using the roads at busy times.

You Decide

1. Identify the Problem
In your own words, explain why automobiles make it hard to improve air quality. What kinds of pollution are caused by automobiles?

2. Analyze the Options
What are some ways to reduce the pollution caused by cars? Should these actions be voluntary, or should governments require them?

3. Find a Solution
How would you encourage people to try to reduce the pollution from cars? Create a visual essay from newspaper and magazine clippings. Write captions to explain your solution.

Background

Young teens tend to see things in all-or-nothing terms. They may think that any method of reducing pollution from cars should be adopted and enforced. Help students appreciate that most methods of reducing pollution from cars have drawbacks by citing these two examples.

Catalytic converters convert unburned hydrocarbons in car exhaust into nonpoisonous gases. These devices have been required by law for many years on all new cars sold in the United States. However, catalytic converters also result in a higher production of sulfuric acid, which contributes to acid rain.

Cars that are more fuel-efficient burn less gas and produce fewer pollutants per mile driven. However, the number of cars on the road and the number of miles people drive every year are both increasing.

SECTION 3 Air Pressure

DISCOVER ACTIVITY

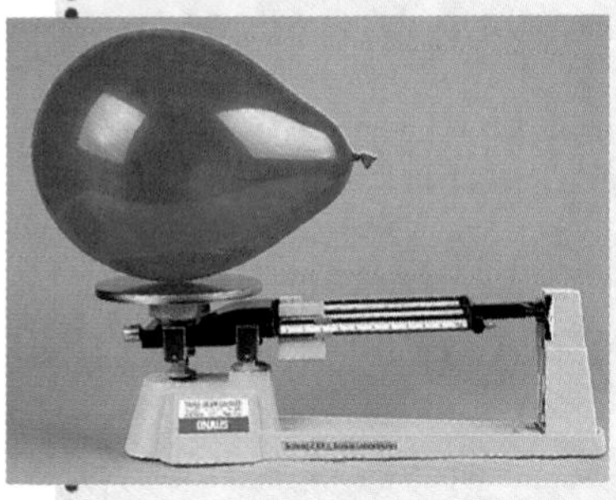

Does Air Have Mass?

1. Use a balance to find the mass of a deflated balloon.
2. Blow up the balloon and tie the neck closed. Do you think the mass of the inflated balloon will differ from the mass of the deflated balloon?
3. Find the mass of the inflated balloon. Compare this mass to the mass of the deflated balloon. Was your prediction correct?

Think It Over

Drawing Conclusions Did the mass of the balloon change after it was inflated? What can you conclude about whether air has mass?

One of the best parts of eating roasted peanuts is opening the jar. When a jar of peanuts is "vacuum packed," most of the air is pumped out, creating low pressure inside. When you break the seal, the "whoosh" you hear is air from the outside rushing into the jar. The "whoosh" is the result of a difference in pressure between the outside of the jar and the inside.

GUIDE FOR READING

- What are some of the properties of air?
- What instruments are used to measure air pressure?
- How does increasing altitude affect air pressure and density?

Reading Tip As you read this section, use the headings to make an outline about air pressure.

Properties of Air

It may seem to you that air has no mass. However, air consists of atoms and molecules, which have mass. So air must have mass. **Because air has mass, it also has other properties, including density and pressure.**

Density The amount of mass in a given volume of air is its **density**. You can calculate density by dividing mass by volume.

$$\text{Density} = \frac{\text{Mass}}{\text{Volume}}$$

If there are more molecules in a given volume of air, the density is greater. If there are fewer molecules, the density decreases.

Pressure The force pushing on an area or surface is known as **pressure**. A denser substance has more mass per unit volume than a less dense one. So denser air exerts more pressure than less dense air.

To understand pressure, think of carrying a heavy backpack. The weight presses the straps into your shoulders just as the pack does to the hiker in the photo.

READING STRATEGIES

Reading Tip Suggest to students that they summarize the main points under each heading in a few words and add these to their outline.
Vocabulary The terms *mass, volume, density,* and *pressure* are easily confused. To help students keep the terms straight, have them make a table that gives a concise definition and the correct units of measurement for each term.

Program Resources

- **Teaching Resources** 1-3 Lesson Plan, p. 21; 1-3 Section Summary, p. 22

Media and Technology

Audiotapes English-Spanish Summary 1-3

SECTION 3 Air Pressure

Objectives

After completing the lesson, students will be able to
- identify some of the properties of air;
- name instruments that are used to measure air pressure;
- explain how increasing altitude affects air pressure and density.

Key Terms density, pressure, air pressure, barometer, mercury barometer, aneroid barometer, altitude

1 Engage/Explore

Activating Prior Knowledge

Introduce students to the concept of air pressure by asking: **Did your ears ever "pop" when you rode in an elevator or airplane?** *(Many students probably have had this experience.)* Explain that as one goes higher, the pressure of the air outside the body decreases while the pressure of the air inside the body, including the ears, stays the same. The popping sensation is air escaping from inside the ears into the throat to even out the pressure. Tell students they will learn more about air pressure and other properties of air in this section.

DISCOVER ACTIVITY

Skills Focus drawing conclusions
Materials *balance, balloon*
Time 10 minutes
Tips You may want to review how to use the balance before students begin the activity. The larger the balloon, the greater the difference in mass will be. Inflatable balls may be substituted for balloons.
Expected Outcome The balloon should have a greater mass after it is inflated.
Think It Over Students should say that the mass of the balloon increased after it was inflated and conclude from this that air has mass.

2 Facilitate

Properties of Air

Including All Students

Materials *two sink plungers* ACTIVITY
Time 5 minutes

To help students appreciate how much pressure air exerts, give pairs of students two sink plungers and show them how to put the plungers together by matching the ends. Then have the students try to pull the plungers apart. Relate this to air pressure by asking: **Why are the plungers hard to pull apart?** *(Because air is pressing on the outside of the two plungers and holding them together)* **learning modality: kinesthetic**

Measuring Air Pressure

Building Inquiry Skills: Predicting

Reinforce students' understanding of how a mercury barometer works by asking: **Why must there be a vacuum in the tube of a mercury barometer?** *(So the mercury can rise inside the tube)* **What do you predict would happen if the tube was filled with air?** *(The column of mercury would not rise as high because of the pressure from the air in the tube. The barometer would give an incorrect reading.)* **learning modality: verbal**

Real-Life Learning

Materials *copies of newspaper weather reports* ACTIVITY
Time 15 minutes

Help students appreciate how barometer readings relate to weather. First, explain that the average air pressure worldwide is 29.9212 inches. A drop of less than an inch can be a sign of a major storm, and a rise of less than an inch a sign of fair weather. Then show students newspaper weather reports for several different days. Have them observe how changes in barometric pressure are related to weather conditions. **learning modality: logical/mathematical**

Figure 9 There is a column of air above you all the time. The weight of the air in the atmosphere causes air pressure.

When you take off a backpack, it feels as if all the pressure has been taken off your shoulders. But has it? The weight of the column of air above you remains, as shown in Figure 9.

Air pressure is the result of the weight of a column of air pushing down on an area. The weight of the column of air above your desk is about the same as the weight of a large school bus! So why doesn't air pressure crush your desk? The reason is that the molecules in air push in all directions—down, up, and sideways. So the air pushing down on the top of your desk is balanced by the air pushing up on the bottom of the desk.

Measuring Air Pressure

Have you ever heard a weather report say that the air pressure is falling? Falling air pressure usually indicates that a storm is approaching. Rising air pressure usually means that the weather is clearing. A **barometer** (buh RAHM uh tur) is an instrument that is used to measure changes in air pressure. **There are two kinds of barometers: mercury barometers and aneroid barometers.**

Mercury Barometers The first barometers invented were mercury barometers. Figure 10 shows how a mercury barometer works. A **mercury barometer** consists of a glass tube open at the bottom end and partially filled with mercury. The space in the tube above the mercury is almost a vacuum—it contains no air. The open end of the tube rests in a dish of mercury. The air pressure pushing down on the surface of the mercury in the dish is equal to the

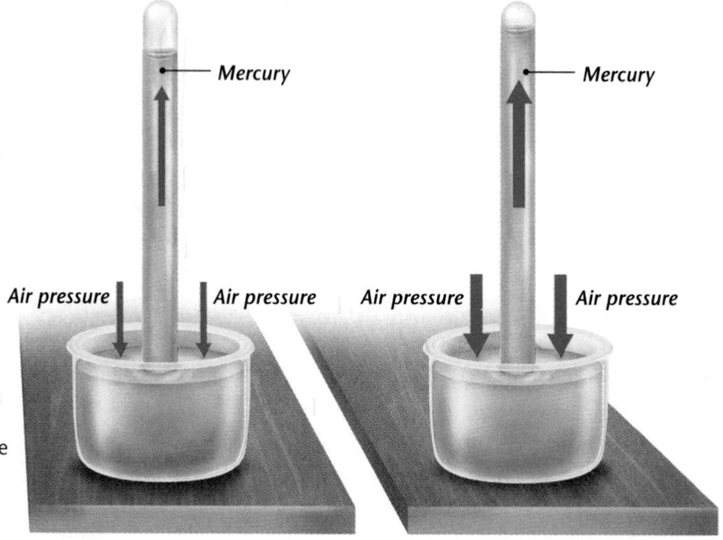

Figure 10 Air pressure pushes down on the surface of the mercury in the dish, causing the mercury in the tube to rise. *Predicting What happens when the air pressure increases?*

Background

History of Science The first mercury barometer was invented in 1643 by an Italian physicist named Evangelista Torricelli. Torricelli was studying why liquids rise only to a certain height in a column. Because mercury is so heavy, he thought it would rise to a lower height than water and be more convenient to study. He filled a long glass tube with mercury, blocked the open end with his finger, and turned the tube upside down in a container of mercury. The mercury in the glass tube went down to about 76 cm. Torricelli experimented with different-sized tubes, but the height of the mercury stayed the same. From this Torricelli concluded that the height of the mercury in the tube was directly related to the pressure of the air on the mercury in the container. Thus, he had invented a way to measure air pressure.

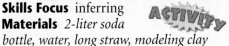

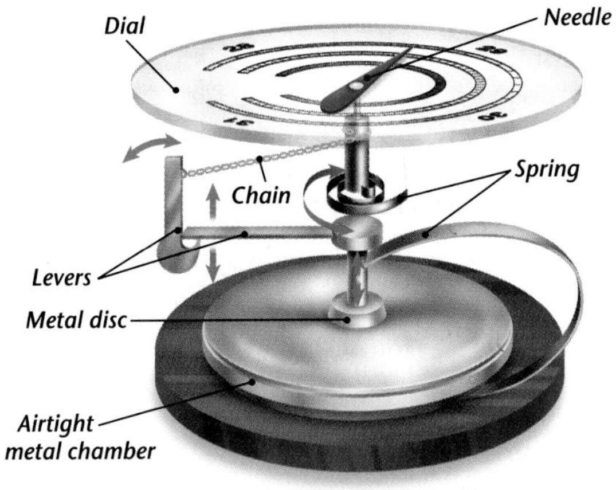

Figure 11 Changes in air pressure cause the walls of the airtight metal chamber to flex in and out. The needle on the dial indicates the air pressure.

weight of the column of mercury in the tube. At sea level the mercury column is about 76 centimeters high, on average.

When the air pressure increases, it presses down more on the surface of the mercury. Greater air pressure forces the column of mercury higher. What will happen to the column of mercury if the air pressure decreases? The column will fall.

Aneroid Barometers If you have a barometer on a desk or wall at home, it is probably an aneroid barometer. The word *aneroid* means "without liquid." An **aneroid barometer** (AN uh royd) has an airtight metal chamber, as shown in Figure 11. The metal chamber is sensitive to changes in air pressure. When air pressure increases, the thin walls of the chamber are pushed in. When the pressure drops, the walls bulge out. The chamber is connected to a dial by a series of springs and levers. As the shape of the chamber changes, the needle on the dial moves.

Aneroid barometers are smaller than mercury barometers and don't contain a liquid. Therefore, they are portable and often more practical for uses such as airplane instrument panels.

Units of Air Pressure Weather reports use several different units for air pressure. Most weather reports for the general public use inches of mercury. For example, if the column of mercury in a mercury barometer is 30 inches high, the air pressure is "30 inches of mercury" or just "30 inches."

National Weather Service maps indicate air pressure in millibars. One inch of mercury equals approximately 33.87 millibars, so 30 inches of mercury is approximately equal to 1,016 millibars.

Checkpoint *Name two common units used to measure air pressure.*

TRY THIS

Soda-Bottle Barometer

ACTIVITY

Here's how to build a device that shows changes in air pressure.

1. Fill a 2-liter soda bottle one-half full with water.
2. Lower a long straw into the bottle so that the end of the straw is in the water. Seal the mouth of the bottle around the straw with modeling clay.
3. Squeeze the sides of the bottle. What happens to the level of the water in the straw?
4. Let go of the sides of the bottle. Watch the level of the water in the straw.

Inferring Explain your results in terms of air pressure.

Including All Students

Materials *calculator*
Time 10 minutes

ACTIVITY

Invite students who need additional challenges to do this activity. It will give them a better appreciation of how air pressure is measured. First, tell students that if you laid a quarter on a table, it would exert a pressure of 0.00013 kg per cm^2. Then say that the pressure exerted by the atmosphere at sea level is 1.03 kg per cm^2. Ask: **How many quarters would you need to stack on top of each other for the quarters to exert the same pressure as the air at sea level?** *(1.03 kg ÷ 0.00013 kg = 7,923)* **If six quarters are about 1 cm thick, how high would the stack of quarters be?** *(7,923 ÷ 6 = 1,321 cm, or about 1.3 km)* **learning modality: logical/mathematical**

TRY THIS

ACTIVITY

Skills Focus inferring
Materials *2-liter soda bottle, water, long straw, modeling clay*
Time 15 minutes
Tips Before students seal the mouth of the bottle with clay, make sure the straw is in the water but not touching the bottom of the bottle.
Expected Outcome When students squeeze the sides of the bottle, the water level rises in the straw. When they let go of the sides, the water level falls in the straw. Students should infer that the water rises in the straw because air pressure increases in the bottle when the sides of the bottle are squeezed.
Extend Ask: **What do you think would happen if you heated the air in the bottle?** *(The air would expand and make the water rise in the straw.)* **learning modality: logical/mathematical**

Program Resources

- **Product Testing Activities by *Consumer Reports*** "Testing Food Wraps," pp. 1–8
- **Science Explorer Series** *Chemical Building Blocks*, Chapter 2, provides more information on the behavior of gases.

Answers to Self-Assessment

Caption Question

Figure 10 When the air pressure increases, the column of mercury in the tube of a mercury barometer goes up.

Checkpoint

Two common units used to measure air pressure are inches and millibars.

Ongoing Assessment

Skills Check Challenge students to make a table comparing and contrasting mercury barometers and aneroid barometers.

Skills Lab

Measuring

Working Under Pressure

Preparing for Inquiry

Key Concept A flexible wall of a sealed container will expand and contract with changes in the pressure of the outside air.

Skills Objectives Students will be able to
- measure air pressure with a simple barometer that they construct;
- observe daily weather conditions;
- infer from their data the kinds of weather conditions that are associated with high and low air pressure.

Time 40 minutes the first day; 10 minutes each day for the next two days

Advance Planning You may wish to have students work in pairs for this activity, because it is easier for two people to assemble the barometer. If possible, bring a commercial aneroid barometer to class to familiarize students with air pressure readings before they begin the activity. You may want to leave the barometer so students can compare their readings with the readings on the commercial barometer. When students record weather conditions during the lab, at a minimum they should record whether the sky is cloudy or fair. You may want them to record additional factors, including temperature. If so, place an outdoor thermometer where students can see it from the classroom.

Alternative Materials Students can use beakers instead of wide-mouthed glass jars, rubber dental dams instead of balloons, and rulers instead of cardboard strips.

Guiding Inquiry

Invitation Show students a commercial aneroid barometer and then ask: **How does the aneroid barometer work?** *(Changes in air pressure cause slight movements in or out of the walls of a box, and these movements are measured on a scale.)* Tell students that they will make a barometer that works the same way as a commercial aneroid barometer. However, their barometer will be less accurate.

Increasing Altitude

The air pressure at the top of Alaska's Mount McKinley—more than 6 kilometers above sea level—is less than half the air pressure at sea level. **Altitude,** or elevation, is the distance above sea level, the average level of the surface of the oceans. **Air pressure decreases as altitude increases. As air pressure decreases, so does density.**

Altitude Affects Air Pressure Imagine a stack of ten books. Which book has more weight on it, the second book from the top or the book at the bottom? The second book from the top has only the weight of one book on top of it. The book at the bottom

Skills Lab — **Measuring**

Working Under Pressure

Air pressure changes are related to changing weather conditions. In this lab, you will build and use your own barometer to measure air pressure.

Problem

How can a barometer detect changes in air pressure?

Materials

modeling clay	scissors
white glue	tape
pencil	wide-mouthed glass jar
metric ruler	rubber band

large rubber balloon
drinking straw, 12–15 cm long
cardboard strip, 10 cm x 25 cm

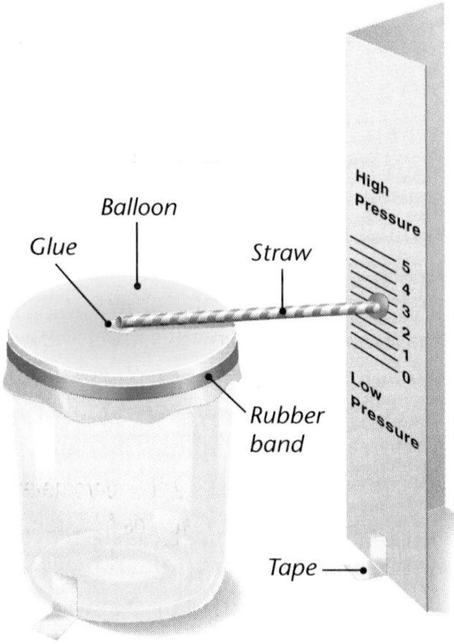

Procedure

1. Cut off the narrow opening of the balloon.
2. Fold the edges of the balloon outward. Carefully stretch the balloon over the open end of the glass jar. Use a rubber band to hold the balloon on the rim of the glass jar.
3. Place a small amount of glue on the center of the balloon top. Attach one end of the straw to the glue. Allow the other end to extend several centimeters beyond the edge of the glass jar. This is your pointer. Add a pea-sized piece of modeling clay to the end of the pointer.

28 ◆ I

Introducing the Procedure

Have students read the entire procedure. Then ask: **What part of your barometer is like the flexible sides of the metal box in a commercial aneroid barometer?** *(The balloon stretched across the jar)* Point out that the balloon will expand when the air pressure falls. Ask: **Why does the expanding balloon make the pointer in your barometer fall?** *(Students may think that the pointer should rise, not fall, as the balloon expands.)* Explain that the pointer resting on the jar is like a seesaw. The rim of the jar acts like a fulcrum, and the clay weights down the free end of the straw. The free end falls when the expanding balloon causes the other end of the straw to rise.

Troubleshooting the Experiment
- Before students cut their balloon, suggest they inflate it to stretch the rubber.
- Caution students to avoid making holes in the balloon when they cut it. Once the balloon is in place, they should make sure it does not leak air.

of the stack has the weight of all the other books pressing on it.

Air at sea level is like the bottom book. Recall that air pressure is the weight of the column of air pushing down on an area. Sea-level air has the weight of the whole atmosphere pressing on it. So air pressure is greatest at sea level. Air near the top of the atmosphere is like the second book from the top. There, the air has less weight pressing on it, and thus has lower air pressure.

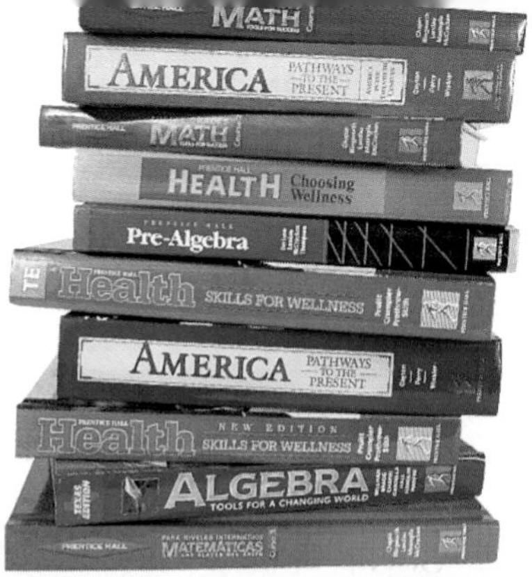

DATA TABLE

Date and Time	Air Pressure	Weather Conditions

4. While the glue dries, fold the cardboard strip lengthwise and draw a scale along the edge with marks 0.5 cm apart. Write "High pressure" at the top of your scale and "Low pressure" at the bottom.
5. After the glue dries, place your barometer and its scale in a location that is as free from temperature changes as possible. Arrange the scale and the barometer as shown in the diagram. Note that the pointer of the straw must just reach the cardboard strip.
6. Tape both the scale and the barometer to a surface so they do not move during your experiment.
7. In your notebook, make a data table like the one at the left. Record the date and time. Note the level of the straw on the cardboard strip.
8. Check the barometer twice a day. Record your observations in your data table.
9. Record the weather conditions for each day.

Analyze and Conclude

1. What change in atmospheric conditions must occur to cause the free end of the straw to rise? What change must occur for it to fall?
2. According to your observations, what kind of weather is usually associated with high air pressure? With low air pressure?
3. If the balloon had a tiny hole in it, what would happen to the accuracy of your barometer?
4. **Think About It** What effect, if any, would a great temperature change have on the accuracy of your barometer?

More to Explore

Compare changes in air pressure shown by your barometer with high and low air pressure readings shown on newspaper weather maps during the same time period. How do your readings compare with the readings in the newspapers?

Sample Data Table

Date and Time	Air Pressure	Weather Conditions
April 2, 10:00 A.M.	1	rainy, 24°C
April 2, 2:00 P.M.	2	cloudy, 23°C
April 4, 10:00 A.M.	4	sunny, 18°C
April 4, 2:00 P.M.	5	sunny, 19°C

Program Resources

- **Teaching Resources** Skills Lab blackline masters, pp. 32–33

Safety

In Step 2, to reduce chances of the jar breaking, suggest that one student hold the jar while the other stretches the balloon and rubber band over it. Review the safety guidelines in Appendix A.

Expected Outcome
When the air pressure outside is low, the higher air pressure inside the jar pushes up on the balloon, causing the pointer to fall. When the air pressure outside is high, it pushes down on the balloon, causing the pointer to rise. Low air pressure is likely to be followed by cloudy or even stormy weather conditions. High air pressure is likely to be followed by fair weather conditions.

Analyze and Conclude
1. Air pressure must rise for the free end of the straw to rise. Air pressure must fall for the free end of the straw to fall.
2. Clear, dry weather usually is associated with high air pressure. Cloudy, wet, or stormy weather usually is associated with low air pressure.
3. A tiny hole in the balloon would cause the barometer not to work because air would leak in or out to equalize the air pressure inside and outside the jar.
4. **Think About It** A great increase in temperature would cause the air inside the barometer to expand and a large decrease in temperature would cause it to contract, affecting the readings.

Extending the Inquiry

More to Explore Students' air pressure readings should agree in general with high and low air pressure readings given in the newspaper. If the readings do not agree, it may be because students' barometers are faulty. Balloons may leak air or not be stretchy enough, or the lumps of clay may be too large. Also, students' barometers are not likely to be accurate enough to reflect minor fluctuations in air pressure. In addition, the readings reported in the newspaper may have been taken at a different time of day when air pressure was lower or higher.

Increasing Altitude

Integrating Life Science

People who live at high altitudes have developed adaptations to the low pressure and density of oxygen in the air around them. Ask: **What kinds of adaptations would allow people to live successfully at high altitudes?** *(A larger chest and lungs would allow a person to take in more air.)* **learning modality: logical/mathematical**

3 Assess

Section 3 Review Answers

1. It increases its pressure.
2. Air presses down on the mercury in the bottom of the barometer, and this forces the mercury up into the sealed tube. The greater the air pressure, the higher the mercury rises and the higher the air pressure reading.
3. Because it has low pressure and density, there are fewer oxygen molecules in each lungful of air.
4. You would expect to see the air pressure increase above the value for sea level, because the column of air pressing down on the barometer would be taller.

Science at Home

ACTIVITY

Materials *glass, tap water, piece of heavy cardboard*

Tips Students should fill the glass until the level of water bulges over the rim and then slide the cardboard *completely* over the rim, being careful not to let any air bubbles under the cardboard. Some water may overflow the glass, so students should do this over a sink.

Performance Assessment

Skills Check Call on volunteers to infer why an inflated balloon flies around the room when it is released. *(The force of the air escaping the balloon propels the balloon.)*

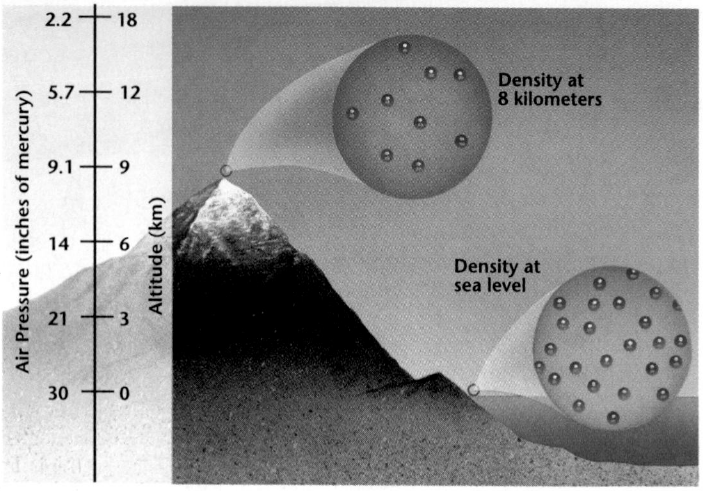

Figure 12 The density of air decreases as altitude increases. Air at sea level has more gas molecules in each cubic meter than air at the top of a mountain.

Altitude Also Affects Density *Integrating Life Science* If you were near the top of Mount McKinley and tried to run, you would get out of breath quickly. Why would you have difficulty breathing at high altitudes?

As you go up through the atmosphere, the air pressure decreases. As air pressure decreases, the density of the air decreases. So density decreases as altitude increases, as shown in Figure 12.

Whether air is at sea level or at 6 kilometers above sea level, the air still contains 21 percent oxygen. However, since the air is less dense at a high altitude, there are fewer oxygen molecules to breathe in each cubic meter of air than there are at sea level. You are taking in less oxygen with each breath. That is why you get out of breath quickly.

Section 3 Review

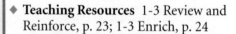

1. How does increasing the density of a gas affect its pressure?
2. Describe how a mercury barometer measures air pressure.
3. Why is the air at the top of a mountain hard to breathe?
4. **Thinking Critically Predicting** What changes in air pressure would you expect to see if you carried a barometer down a mine shaft? Explain.

Science at Home

Here's how you can show your family that air has pressure. Fill a glass with water. Place a piece of heavy cardboard over the top of the glass. Hold the cardboard in place with one hand as you turn the glass upside down. **CAUTION:** *Be sure the cardboard does not bend.* Now remove your hand from the cardboard. What happens? Explain to your family that the cardboard doesn't fall because the air pressure pushing up on it is greater than the weight of the water pushing down.

Media and Technology

Transparencies "Density of Air at Two Altitudes," Transparency 3

Exploring Physical Science Videodisc Unit 1, Side 1, "Racing Hot Air Balloons"

Chapter 3

Program Resources

- **Teaching Resources** 1-3 Review and Reinforce, p. 23; 1-3 Enrich, p. 24

Media and Technology

Interactive Student Tutorial CD-ROM I-1

SECTION 4 Layers of the Atmosphere

DISCOVER ACTIVITY

Is Air There?

1. Use a heavy rubber band to tightly secure a plastic bag over the top of a wide-mouthed jar.
2. Gently try to push the bag into the jar. What happens? Is the air pressure higher inside or outside of the bag?
3. Remove the rubber band and line the inside of the jar with the plastic bag. Use the rubber band to tightly secure the edges of the bag over the rim of the jar.
4. Gently try to pull the bag out of the jar with your fingertips. What happens? Is the air pressure higher inside or outside of the bag?

Think It Over

Predicting Explain your observations in terms of air pressure. How do you think differences in air pressure would affect a weather balloon as it traveled up through the atmosphere?

GUIDE FOR READING

◆ **What are the characteristics of the main layers of the atmosphere?**

Reading Tip **Before you read, preview *Exploring Layers of the Atmosphere.* Make a list of unfamiliar words. Look for the meanings of these words as you read.**

Imagine taking a trip upward into the atmosphere in a hot-air balloon. You begin on a warm beach near the ocean, at an altitude of 0 kilometers.

You hear a roar as the balloon's pilot turns up the burner to heat the air in the balloon. The balloon begins to rise, and Earth's surface gets farther and farther away. As the balloon rises to an altitude of 3 kilometers, you realize that the air is getting colder. As you continue to rise, the air gets colder and colder. At 6 kilometers you begin to have trouble breathing. The air is becoming less dense. It's time to go back down.

What if you could have continued your balloon ride up through the atmosphere? As you rose farther up through the atmosphere, the air pressure and temperature would change dramatically. **The four main layers of the atmosphere are classified according to changes in temperature. These layers are the troposphere, the stratosphere, the mesosphere, and the thermosphere.**

The Troposphere

You live in the inner, or lowest, layer of Earth's atmosphere, the **troposphere** (TROH puh sfeer). *Tropo-* means "turning" or "changing"; conditions in the troposphere are more variable than in the other layers. The troposphere is where Earth's weather occurs.

READING STRATEGIES

Vocabulary Help students remember the term *aurora borealis* by explaining that Aurora was the Roman goddess of dawn, or first light, and *borealis* is the Latin word for "northern." Thus, *aurora borealis* means "Northern Lights." It refers to lights in the night sky that are visible only in the Northern Hemisphere. There are also *aurora australis,* or "Southern Lights," visible only in the Southern Hemisphere.

Program Resources

◆ **Teaching Resources** 1-4 Lesson Plan, p. 25; 1-4 Section Summary, p. 26

Media and Technology

Audiotapes English-Spanish Summary 1-4

Transparencies "Layers of the Atmosphere," Transparency 4

SECTION 4 Layers of the Atmosphere

Objectives

After completing this lesson, students will be able to

◆ describe the characteristics of the main layers of the atmosphere.

Key Terms troposphere, stratosphere, mesosphere, thermosphere, ionosphere, aurora borealis, exosphere

1 Engage/Explore

Activating Prior Knowledge

Ask: **Did you ever see a shooting star?** *(Most students probably will say yes.)* **What is a shooting star?** *(A meteor burning up because of friction as it falls through Earth's atmosphere)* Point out that most shooting stars are visible from about 50 to 80 km above Earth in a layer of the atmosphere called the mesosphere. This layer protects us from being bombarded by shooting stars and other space debris. The mesosphere is just one of four major layers of the atmosphere students will read about in this section.

DISCOVER ACTIVITY

Skills Focus predicting
Materials *heavy rubber band, plastic bag, wide-mouthed glass jar*
Time 10 minutes
Tips Make sure the rubber band is tight and the plastic bag does not have holes in it. Caution students to push gently on the bag to avoid breaking the bag or the jar.
Expected Outcome Students should find it difficult to push the bag into or pull it out of the jar.
Think It Over Trying to push the bag into the jar decreases the volume and increases the air pressure inside the jar. Trying to pull the bag out of the jar increases the volume and decreases the air pressure inside the jar. As a weather balloon traveled up, it would expand until it burst as the air pressure outside the balloon became lower than the air pressure inside.

2 Facilitate

The Troposphere

Building Inquiry Skills: Graphing

Challenge students to calculate the temperature for every 1,000 m above Earth's surface in the troposphere, starting at sea level and ending at 10,000 m. They should assume that the temperature is 15.0°C at sea level and decreases 6.5 Celsius degrees for each 1,000-m increase in altitude. Then have students draw a graph that shows the relationship between altitude and temperature in the troposphere. **learning modality: logical/mathematical**

The Stratosphere

Addressing Naive Conceptions

In Section 2, students read that ozone is a harmful chemical in smog. In this section, they read that ozone is a natural component of the atmosphere that protects Earth from solar radiation. Students may wonder if ozone is harmful or not. Explain that the ozone in the stratosphere absorbs, and thus protects us from, too much sunlight. Ozone in this layer occurs naturally. However, ozone in the troposphere harms our health and contributes to photochemical smog. Ozone in this layer is caused by pollution. **limited English proficiency**

The Mesosphere

Building Inquiry Skills: Inferring

Challenge students to explain why there is a temperature reversal between the stratosphere and mesosphere. Ask: **Why is the mesosphere colder than the stratosphere?** *(Because it contains no ozone molecules to absorb solar radiation and convert the radiation into heat)* **learning modality: logical/mathematical**

Figure 13 This weather balloon will carry a package of instruments to measure weather conditions high in the atmosphere. *Applying Concepts Which is the first layer of the atmosphere the balloon passes through on its way up?*

Although hot-air balloons cannot travel very high into the troposphere, other types of balloons can. To measure weather conditions, scientists launch weather balloons that carry instruments up into the atmosphere. The balloons are not fully inflated before they are launched. Recall that air pressure decreases as you rise through the atmosphere. Leaving the balloon only partly inflated gives the gas inside the balloon room to expand as the air pressure outside the balloon decreases.

The depth of the troposphere varies from more than 16 kilometers above the equator to less than 9 kilometers above the North and South Poles. Even though it is the shallowest layer of the atmosphere, the troposphere contains almost all of the mass of the atmosphere.

As altitude increases in the troposphere, the temperature decreases. On average, for every 1-kilometer increase in altitude the air gets about 6.5 Celsius degrees cooler. At the top of the troposphere, the temperature stops decreasing and stays constant at about –60°C. Water here forms thin, feathery clouds of ice.

☑ *Checkpoint* *Why are clouds at the top of the troposphere made of ice crystals instead of drops of water?*

The Stratosphere

The **stratosphere** extends from the top of the troposphere to about 50 kilometers above Earth's surface. *Strato-* is similar to *stratum,* which means "layer" or "spreading out."

The lower stratosphere is cold, about −60°C. You might be surprised to find out that the upper stratosphere is warmer than the lower stratosphere. Why is this? The upper stratosphere contains a layer of ozone, the three-atom form of oxygen. When the ozone in the stratosphere absorbs energy from the sun, the energy is converted into heat, warming the air.

As a weather balloon rises through the stratosphere, the air pressure outside the balloon continues to decrease. The volume of the balloon increases. Finally, the balloon bursts, and the instrument package falls back to Earth's surface.

The Mesosphere

Above the stratosphere, a drop in temperature marks the beginning of the next layer, the **mesosphere.** *Meso-* means "middle," so the mesosphere is the middle layer of the atmosphere. The mesosphere begins 50 kilometers above Earth's surface and ends at 80 kilometers. The outer mesosphere is the coldest part of the atmosphere, with temperatures near −90°C.

Background

Facts and Figures You may wish to share the following facts and figures about the mesosphere with students.

- The mesosphere is the coldest part of the atmosphere. Temperatures there reach lows that are as cold as the lowest temperatures ever recorded anywhere on Earth.
- Oddly, air temperatures in the mesosphere are colder in summer than in winter. Temperatures there also are colder over the equator than over the North and South poles.
- The clouds that form in the mesosphere are unlike any other clouds in the atmosphere. They are formed of ice crystals and are called noctilucent clouds because they are visible only at night.

EXPLORING *Layers of the Atmosphere*

The atmosphere is divided into four layers: the troposphere, the stratosphere, the mesosphere, and the thermosphere. The thermosphere is further divided into the ionosphere and the exosphere.

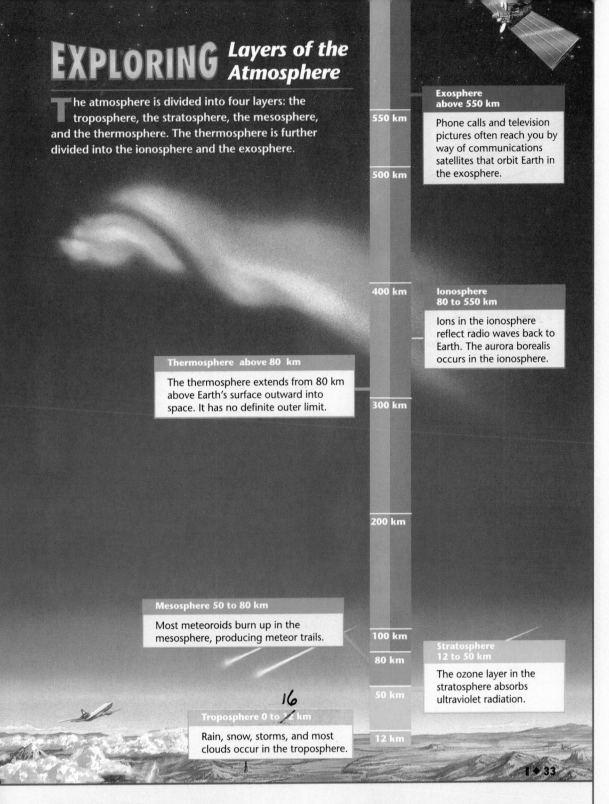

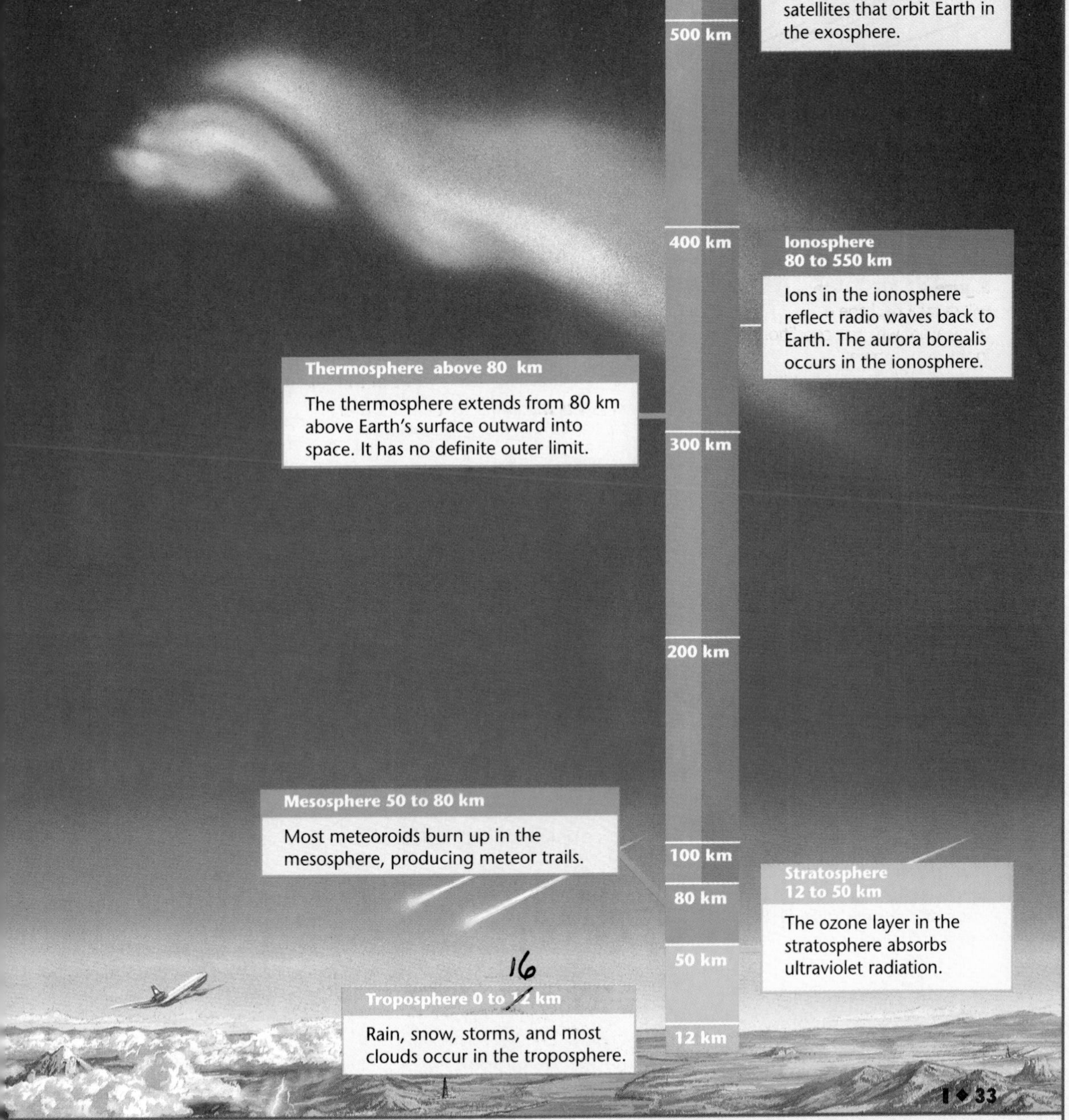

Exosphere above 550 km
Phone calls and television pictures often reach you by way of communications satellites that orbit Earth in the exosphere.
Ionosphere 80 to 550 km
Ions in the ionosphere reflect radio waves back to Earth. The aurora borealis occurs in the ionosphere.
Thermosphere above 80 km
The thermosphere extends from 80 km above Earth's surface outward into space. It has no definite outer limit.
Mesosphere 50 to 80 km
Most meteoroids burn up in the mesosphere, producing meteor trails.
Stratosphere 12 to 50 km
The ozone layer in the stratosphere absorbs ultraviolet radiation.
Troposphere 0 to 12 km
Rain, snow, storms, and most clouds occur in the troposphere.
550 km
500 km
400 km
300 km
200 km
100 km
80 km
50 km
12 km
16
I ◆ 33

EXPLORING

Layers of the Atmosphere

ACTIVITY

Materials *posterboard, colored markers, index cards, buttons and other small objects for game pieces*
Time 30 minutes

Divide the class into groups and have each group use the information presented in the feature to create a board game. The object of the game should be to get from the ground to the top of the atmosphere. Reaching the objective might involve overcoming various obstacles in the different layers of the atmosphere, such as clouds and storms in the troposphere, very high temperatures in the stratosphere, meteoroids in the mesosphere, electrically charged ions in the ionosphere, and orbiting satellites in the exosphere. To advance through the layers of the atmosphere, players might be required to correctly answer questions about each layer, such as the layer's temperature or height above Earth's surface. Group members should work together to brainstorm the objectives and rules of the game. The actual work of constructing the game board and other parts of the game should be divided up among individual group members. Suggest that the groups exchange games and try them out. **cooperative learning**

Media and Technology

Exploring Earth Science Videodisc
Unit 2, Side 2, "A Trip Through the Earth"

Chapter 1

Answers to Self-Assessment

Caption Question

Figure 13 The first layer is the troposphere.

Checkpoint

Because the temperature at that altitude is always below the freezing point of water

Ongoing Assessment

Writing Challenge students to write a short story describing their imaginary ascent up through the troposphere and stratosphere in a hydrogen balloon. They should describe the conditions they pass through in each layer.

Portfolio Students can save their stories in their portfolios.

The Mesosphere, continued

Integrating Space Science

Stress that the mesosphere protects Earth from meteoroids that are pulled toward the planet by gravity. Tell students that the moon has gravity, too, but no atmosphere to protect it from meteoroids. As a result, meteoroids crash on the moon's surface, forming large depressions called craters. Challenge students to draw labeled diagrams showing what happens to meteoroids that fall toward the moon as compared with those that fall toward Earth. **limited English proficiency**

SCIENCE & History

Point out that exploring the atmosphere is difficult because it requires scientists or their instruments to reach high altitudes. Ask: **What are some ways explorers of the atmosphere have made scientific observations at high altitudes?** *(By climbing to the tops of mountains, ascending in hydrogen balloons, flying kites, and attaching instruments to balloons and satellites)* **What have these explorers learned through these means?** *(That air pressure decreases with altitude, that lightning is a form of electricity, how the sun influences the atmosphere, and the temperature, air pressure, and humidity at various altitudes)*

In Your Journal Ask volunteers to read their paragraphs aloud to the class. The items students would take with them should show they understand how the atmosphere changes with altitude. For example, warm clothing would be necessary above an altitude of just a few kilometers because temperature declines steadily with increasing altitude. Also, a supply of oxygen would be needed above about 7 km. Instruments should include at least a thermometer for measuring changes in temperature and a barometer for measuring changes in air pressure. **learning modality: verbal**

INTEGRATING SPACE SCIENCE If you watch a shooting star streak across the night sky, you are seeing a meteoroid burn up as it enters the mesosphere. The mesosphere protects Earth's surface from being hit by most meteoroids, which are chunks of stone and metal from space. What you see as a shooting star, or meteor, is the trail of hot, glowing gases the burning meteoroid leaves behind.

☑ *Checkpoint* ***What is the depth of the mesosphere?***

The Thermosphere

Near the top of the atmosphere, the air is very thin. The air 80 kilometers above Earth's surface is only about 0.001 percent as dense as the air at sea level. It's as though you took a cubic

SCIENCE & History

Explorers of the Atmosphere

The atmosphere has been explored from the ground and from space.

1746

Franklin's Experiment with Electricity

American statesman and inventor Benjamin Franklin and some friends in Philadelphia experimented with electricity in the atmosphere. To demonstrate that lightning is a form of electricity, Franklin flew a kite in a thunderstorm. However, Franklin did not hold the kite string in his hand, as this historical print shows.

1600 — 1700 — 1800

1643

Torricelli Invents the Barometer

Italian physicist and mathematician Evangelista Torricelli improved existing scientific instruments and invented some new ones. In 1643 he invented the barometer, using a column of mercury 1.2 meters high.

1804

Gay-Lussac Studies the Upper Troposphere

French chemist Joseph-Louis Gay-Lussac ascended to a height of about 7 kilometers in a hydrogen balloon to study the upper troposphere. Gay-Lussac studied pressure, temperature, and humidity.

Background

Facts and Figures At sea level, an air molecule can travel just a fraction of a centimeter before colliding with another, whereas in the upper thermosphere it can travel as far as 10 km before colliding with another. Because of their very high temperatures, air molecules in the upper thermosphere move at speeds of up to 40,000 km per hour, allowing many to escape into outer space. Therefore, where the thermosphere ends and outer space begins is arbitrary. Air molecules become farther and farther apart as you travel higher above Earth's surface until, somewhere thousands of kilometers above the surface, there are no more air molecules.

meter of air at sea level and expanded it into 100,000 cubic meters at the top of the mesosphere. The outermost layer of the atmosphere, the **thermosphere**, extends from 80 kilometers above Earth's surface outward into space. It has no definite outer limit. The atmosphere does not end suddenly at the outer edge of the thermosphere. Gas atoms and molecules there are so far apart that the air blends gradually with outer space.

The *thermo-* in thermosphere means "heat." Even though the air in the thermosphere is thin, it is very hot, up to 1,800°C. The temperature in the thermosphere is actually higher than the temperature in a furnace used to make steel! But why is the thermosphere so hot? Energy coming from the sun strikes the thermosphere first. Nitrogen and oxygen molecules convert energy from the sun into heat.

In Your Journal

Imagine you were one of the first people to go up into the atmosphere in a balloon. What would you need to take? Find out what the early explorers took with them in their balloons. Write at least two paragraphs about what you would take, and why.

1931

Piccard Explores the Stratosphere

Swiss-Belgian physicist Auguste Piccard made the first ascent into the stratosphere. He reached a height of about 16 kilometers in an airtight cabin attached to a huge hydrogen balloon. Piccard is shown here with the cabin.

1900 **2000**

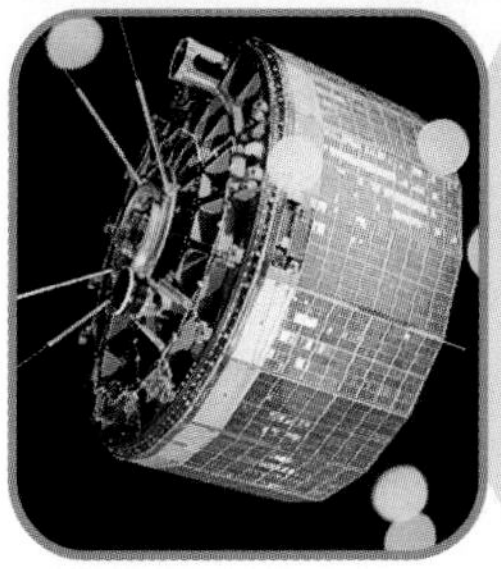

1960

First Weather Satellite Launched

TIROS-1, the first weather satellite equipped with a camera to send data back to Earth, was put into orbit by the United States. As later weather satellites circled Earth, they observed cloud cover and recorded temperatures and air pressures in the atmosphere.

1994

Space Shuttle Investigates the Atmosphere

The NASA space shuttle *Atlantis* traveled to a height of 300 kilometers in the thermosphere. *Atlantis* carried the ATLAS–3 research program, which observed the sun's influence on the atmosphere.

The Thermosphere

Building Inquiry Skills: Modeling

Time 5 minutes

ACTIVITY

Challenge a group of student volunteers to pretend they are atoms and molecules and to demonstrate the density and speed of atoms and molecules in the atmosphere, first at sea level, then in the thermosphere. *(For sea level, students should stand close together and move very slowly. For the thermosphere, they should stand as far apart as possible and move very quickly.)* Point out that the classroom would have to be much larger for them to be as far apart as atoms and molecules really are in the thermosphere. Ask: **How much larger would the classroom have to be?** *(Almost 100,000 times larger)* **learning modality: kinesthetic**

Including All Students

To help students whose native language is not English remember that the defining characteristic of the thermosphere is its high temperature, stress that the prefix *thermo-* means "heat." Ask: **What are some other words that start with this prefix?** *(thermometer, thermostat, thermal, thermos)* Have students explain how each of the terms is related to heat. **limited English proficiency**

Program Resources

Interdisciplinary Exploration Series "Wagons West," p. 41

Answers to Self-Assessment

Checkpoint

The mesosphere extends from 50 to 80 km above Earth's surface, so it has a depth of 30 km.

Ongoing Assessment

Oral Presentation Call on students to describe density, temperature, and pressure of air in the thermosphere as compared with the troposphere. Call on other students to explain why the thermosphere has these characteristics.

The Thermosphere, continued

Integrating Technology

Help students understand why satellites orbit Earth at such high altitudes. First point out that molecules in air create resistance that can slow down objects orbiting Earth. Then ask: **What happens to the density of molecules in air as you go higher above Earth's surface?** *(It decreases.)* **Why do you think satellites orbit Earth at such high altitudes?** *(The lower density of air molecules creates less resistance to slow down orbiting satellites.)* **learning modality: logical/mathematical**

3 Assess

Section 4 Review Answers

1. Answers may vary. The troposphere is where weather occurs. The stratosphere contains the ozone layer. The mesosphere is where most meteoroids burn up. The thermosphere is very hot.
2. A shooting star, or meteor, is a trail of hot, glowing gas left by a meteoroid as it burns up in the atmosphere. You would see it in the mesosphere.
3. A glowing light display caused when energy from the sun causes gas molecules to become electrically charged; it occurs in the lower layer of the thermosphere.
4. Because it does not absorb much energy from the sun

Check Your Progress (Chapter Project 1)

Students may observe such trends in their observations as cooler temperatures after a storm and fair weather after an increase in air pressure. Which weather conditions changed most will depend partly on how precisely the variables were measured. Also, some weather variables, such as temperature and wind speed, have a greater range than others, including air pressure.

Figure 14 The aurora borealis, seen from Fairbanks, Alaska, creates a spectacular display in the night sky.

Despite the high temperature, however, you would not feel warm in the thermosphere. An ordinary thermometer would show a temperature well below 0°C. Why is that? Temperature is the average amount of energy of motion of each molecule of a substance. The gas molecules in the thermosphere move very rapidly, so the temperature is very high. However, the molecules are spaced far apart in the thin air. And there are not enough of them to collide with a thermometer and warm it very much. So an ordinary thermometer would not detect the molecules' energy.

The Ionosphere The thermosphere is divided into two layers. The lower layer of the thermosphere, called the **ionosphere** (eye AHN uh sfeer), begins 80 kilometers above the surface and ends at 550 kilometers. Energy from the sun causes gas molecules in the ionosphere to become electrically charged particles called ions. Radio waves bounce off ions in the ionosphere and then bounce back to Earth's surface.

The brilliant light displays of the **aurora borealis**—the Northern Lights—also occur in the ionosphere. The aurora borealis is caused by particles from the sun that enter the ionosphere near the North Pole. These particles strike oxygen and nitrogen atoms in the ionosphere, causing them to glow.

The Exosphere *Exo-* means "outer," so the **exosphere** is the outer layer of the thermosphere. *INTEGRATING TECHNOLOGY* The exosphere extends from 550 kilometers outward for thousands of kilometers. When you make a long-distance phone call or watch television, the signal may have traveled up to a satellite orbiting in the exosphere and then back down to your home. Satellites are also used for watching the world's weather and carrying telescopes that look deep into space.

Section 4 Review

1. Describe one characteristic of each of the four main layers of the atmosphere.
2. What is a shooting star? In which layer of the atmosphere would you see it?
3. What is the aurora borealis? In which layer of the atmosphere does it occur?
4. **Thinking Critically** **Drawing Conclusions** Why is the mesosphere the coldest part of the atmosphere?

Check Your Progress (Chapter Project 1)

At this point, review your weather log. What do you notice about the weather on one day that might allow you to predict the next day's weather? What weather conditions changed the most from day to day? Continue to record your observations and start thinking about how you will present them.

Background

Facts and Figures Another sphere around Earth, called the magnetosphere, extends above the atmosphere to more than 65,000 km above Earth's surface. It is a magnetic field that traps charged particles from the sun. The trapped particles follow the lines of magnetic force and bounce back and forth from one pole to the other, sometimes breaking through into the ionosphere to produce auroras.

Program Resources

- **Teaching Resources** 1-4 Review and Reinforce, p. 27; 1-4 Enrich, p. 28

Media and Technology

Interactive Student Tutorial CD-ROM I-1

STUDY GUIDE

CHAPTER 1 REVIEW

SECTION 1 The Air Around You

Key Ideas
- Earth's atmosphere makes conditions on Earth suitable for living things.
- Earth's atmosphere is made up of molecules of nitrogen, oxygen, carbon dioxide, and water vapor, as well as some other gases and particles of liquids and solids.

Key Terms

weather
atmosphere
ozone
water vapor

SECTION 2 Air Quality

INTEGRATING ENVIRONMENTAL SCIENCE

Key Ideas
- Most air pollution results from the burning of fossil fuels such as coal, oil, gasoline, and diesel fuel.
- Nitrogen oxides, hydrocarbons, and other air pollutants react with each other in the presence of sunlight to form a mix of ozone and other chemicals called photochemical smog.
- Acid rain forms when nitrogen oxides and sulfur oxides combine with water in the air to form nitric acid and sulfuric acid.

Key Terms

pollutant
photochemical smog
acid rain

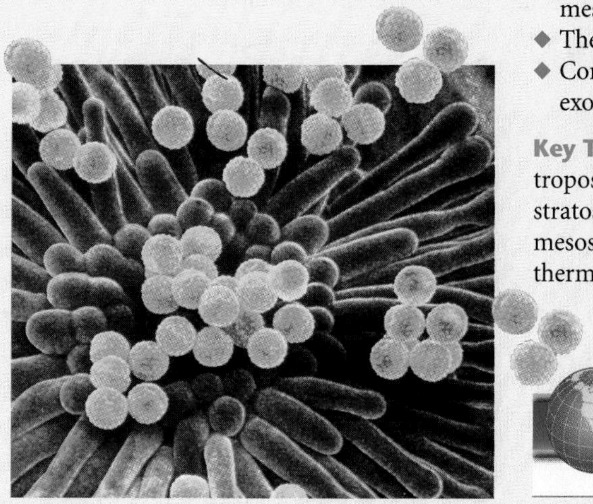

SECTION 3 Air Pressure

Key Ideas
- Properties of air include mass, density, and pressure.
- Air pressure is the result of the weight of a column of air pushing down on an area.
- Air pressure is measured with mercury barometers and aneroid barometers.
- Air pressure decreases as altitude increases. As air pressure decreases, so does density.

Key Terms

density
pressure
air pressure
barometer
mercury barometer
aneroid barometer
altitude

SECTION 4 Layers of the Atmosphere

Key Ideas
- The four main layers of the atmosphere are classified according to changes in temperature. These layers are the troposphere, the stratosphere, the mesosphere, and the thermosphere.
- Rain, snow, storms, and most clouds occur in the troposphere.
- Ozone in the stratosphere absorbs energy from the sun.
- Most meteoroids burn up in the mesosphere, producing meteor trails.
- The aurora borealis occurs in the ionosphere.
- Communications satellites orbit Earth in the exosphere.

Key Terms

troposphere
stratosphere
mesosphere
thermosphere
ionosphere
aurora borealis
exosphere

ACTIVITY
USING THE INTERNET
www.science-explorer.phschool.com

Program Resources

- **Teaching Resources** Chapter 1 Project Scoring Rubric, p. 12; Chapter 1 Performance Assessment, pp. 134–136; Chapter 1 Test, pp. 137–140

Media and Technology

Interactive Student Tutorial CD-ROM I-1

Computer Test Bank Chapter 1 Test

Performance Assessment

Writing Challenge students to write crossword puzzles using all the boldfaced terms in the section. Then have students exchange crossword puzzles with a partner and try to solve their partner's puzzle.

CHAPTER 1 REVIEW

Reviewing Content: Multiple Choice

1. d **2.** d **3.** c **4.** b **5.** b

True or False

6. true **7.** carbon dioxide (Other possible answers: nitrogen oxides, sulfur oxides, soot) **8.** acid rain **9.** more **10.** decreases

Checking Concepts

11. Carbon dioxide is added to the atmosphere through the respiration of animals and the burning of fossil fuels.
12. It is difficult to include water vapor in a graph that shows the percentages of different gases in the atmosphere because the percentage of water vapor varies greatly.
13. Photochemical-type smog is caused by the action of sunlight on chemicals in the air. It forms over sunny cities like Los Angeles today. London-type smog was caused by particles in coal smoke combining with water droplets in humid air. It once blanketed industrial cities like London but is no longer common.
14. Moving upward from Earth's surface, the layers are troposphere, stratosphere, mesosphere, thermosphere.
15. As you move upward through the troposphere, the temperature decreases by about 6.5°C for each 1,000-meter increase in altitude.
16. Students' letters should demonstrate a thorough understanding of their chosen layer of the atmosphere.

Thinking Visually

17. a. Density **b.** Altitude **c.** Barometers **d.** Mercury

Applying Skills

18. Students' graphs should show a line with a negative slope, that is, a line that slopes downward to the right. See sample graph below.
19. The temperature was -15°C at about 4 kilometers above the ground.
20. At 2.4 kilometers over Omaha, the approximate temperature was -6.5°C.
21. The approximate temperature at 6.8 kilometers above Omaha was -36°C, which was about 36° colder than the temperature at ground level.

CHAPTER 1 REVIEW

Reviewing Content

For more review of key concepts, see the Interactive Student Tutorial CD-ROM.

Multiple Choice

Choose the letter of the answer that best completes each statement.

1. The most abundant gas in the atmosphere is
   a. ozone. b. carbon dioxide.
   c. oxygen. d. nitrogen.
2. Most air pollution is caused by
   a. dust and pollen.
   b. acid rain.
   c. erupting volcanoes.
   d. the burning of fossil fuels.
3. A barometer is used to measure
   a. temperature. b. smog.
   c. air pressure d. density.
4. The layers of the atmosphere are classified according to changes in
   a. altitude.
   b. temperature.
   c. pressure.
   d. density.
5. The inner layer, or "weather layer," of the atmosphere is called the
   a. mesosphere.
   b. troposphere.
   c. thermosphere.
   d. stratosphere.

True or False

If the statement is true, write true. If it is false, change the underlined word or words to make the statement true.

6. Plants need carbon dioxide from the atmosphere to make food.
7. Burning fuels add nitrogen to the atmosphere.
8. When sulfur and nitrogen oxides mix with water in the air, they form smog.
9. If the mass of a fixed volume of air increases, it becomes less dense.
10. Air pressure increases as you climb from land at sea level to the top of a mountain.

Checking Concepts

11. Name two ways in which carbon dioxide is added to the atmosphere.
12. Explain why it is difficult to include water vapor in a graph that shows the percentages of various gases in the atmosphere.
13. What is the difference between photochemical smog and London-type smog?
14. List the following layers of the atmosphere in order moving up from Earth's surface: thermosphere, stratosphere, troposphere, mesosphere.
15. Describe the temperature changes that occur as you move upward through the troposphere.
16. **Writing to Learn** You are a scientist who has a chance to join a research mission to explore the atmosphere. To win a place on this mission, you must write a persuasive letter telling which layer of the atmosphere you want to research and why you chose it.

Thinking Visually

17. **Concept Map** Copy the air pressure concept map onto a separate sheet of paper. Then complete it and add a title. (For more on concept maps, see the Skills Handbook.)

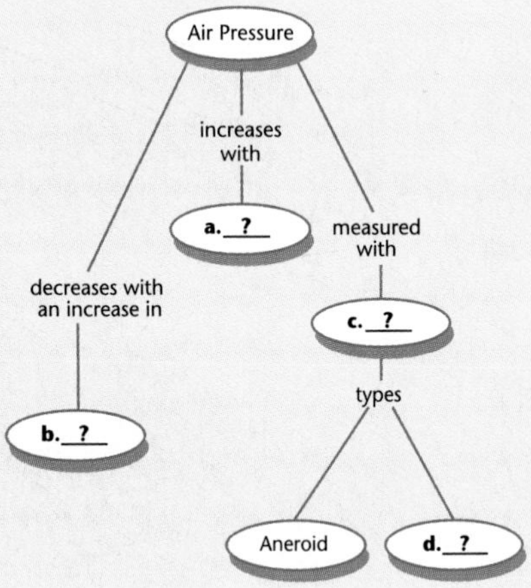

Thinking Critically

22. You would experience a decrease in temperature and also in the pressure and density of the air. You would feel cold unless you dressed appropriately. You would also feel the effects of low oxygen pressure and density. For example, you might be short of breath and tire easily.
23. Air pressure decreases as elevation or altitude increases. An aneroid barometer can be calibrated to show the change in air pressure as a change in altitude.
24. Burning high-sulfur coal can produce sulfur oxides and other air pollutants that may lead to the formation of acid rain hundreds of kilometers away, where it might harm a forest.
25. Natural sources of air pollution include molds, dust, pollen, salt from ocean spray, and particles from forest fires, soil erosion, dust storms, and volcanoes. Human sources of air pollution include soot and carbon dioxide and other gases from the burning of fuels, such as wood, coal, oil, and gas, and dust particles from farming and construction.

Applying Skills

The table below shows temperature at various altitudes above Omaha, Nebraska, on a day in January. Use the table to answer the questions that follow.

Altitude (kilometers)	0	1.6	3.2	4.8	6.4	7.2
Temperature (°C)	0	–4	–9	–21	–32	–40

18. Graphing Make a line graph of the data in the table. Put temperature on the horizontal axis and altitude on the vertical axis. Label your graph.

19. Interpreting Graphs At about what height above the ground was the temperature –15°C?

20. Interpreting Graphs What was the approximate temperature 2.4 kilometers over Omaha?

21. Calculating Suppose an airplane was about 6.8 kilometers above Omaha on this day. What was the approximate temperature at 6.8 kilometers? How much colder was the temperature at 6.8 kilometers above the ground than at ground level?

Thinking Critically

22. Predicting Describe the changes in the atmosphere that you would experience while climbing a mountain four or more kilometers high. How might these changes affect you physically?

23. Applying Concepts Why can an aneroid barometer be used to measure elevation as well as air pressure?

24. Relating Cause and Effect How can burning high-sulfur coal in a power-generating plant harm a forest hundreds of kilometers away?

25. Classifying Which sources of air pollution occur naturally, and which are caused by humans?

CHAPTER 1 REVIEW

Performance Assessment

CHAPTER PROJECT 1

Wrap Up

Presenting Your Project For your class presentation, prepare a display of your weather observations. Include drawings, graphs, and tables that summarize the weather you observed. Practice presenting your project to your group. Do you need to make any improvements? If so, make them now.

Reflect and Record In your journal, write how you might improve your weather log. What weather conditions would you like to know more about? What factors could you have measured more accurately using instruments?

Getting Involved

In Your Community With some classmates, investigate air quality in and around your school or neighborhood. Listen to weather reports or check newspapers for the pollen count and for levels of other pollutants. With the approval of your teacher, design experiments using filters, dust masks, or other devices to examine air particles. Then write a report summarizing your findings and identifying sources where pollution could be reduced.

Sample Graph for Question 18

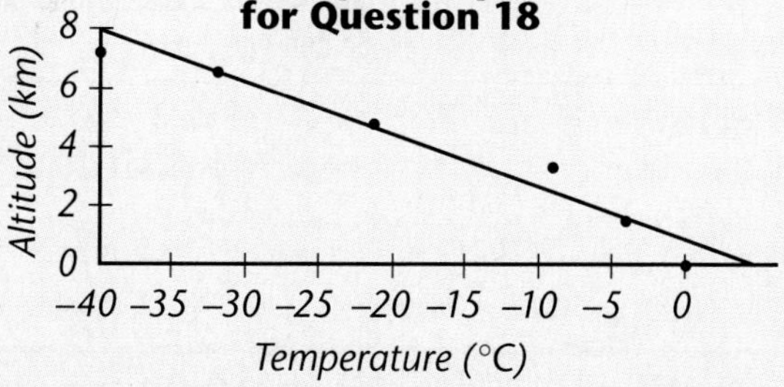

Program Resources

- **Inquiry Skills Activity Book** Provides teaching and review of all inquiry skills

Performance Assessment

CHAPTER PROJECT 1

Wrap Up

Presenting Your Project Displays should show how, where, and when observations were made and what scale was used to categorize each weather variable. Encourage students to present their observations in creative ways, such as weather centers, bulletin boards, or newspaper or television weather reports. Students should be prepared to discuss any trends they have identified in their observations.

Reflect and Record Students may be able to improve their weather logs by observing more weather variables or making more frequent or detailed observations. Encourage students to look at other students' logs for additional ideas. Weather factors that are not directly observable, such as temperature and air pressure, could be measured more accurately using instruments.

Getting Involved

In Your Community Other pollutants in air are reported in the newspaper as the air quality index, or AQI, which ranges from 0 to 500, with a value over 100 reflecting an unhealthy level of air pollution. Students can get a rough estimate of the particulate matter in the air around their school or neighborhood by wearing a dust mask when they are active outside or by leaving a white index card smeared with petroleum jelly on an outside windowsill. Students should try to observe specific sources of pollution that might be reduced, such as factories, plants, and heavy traffic. They should look for dark smoke because it contains the most pollutants.

CHAPTER 2

Weather Factors

Sections	Time	Student Edition Activities	ACTIVITY Other Activities
CHAPTER PROJECT 2 **Your Own Weather Station** p. 41	Ongoing (2-3 weeks)	Check Your Progress, p. 51 Check Your Progress, p. 60 Check Your Progress, p. 70 Wrap Up, p. 73	
1 Energy in the Atmosphere pp. 42–47 ◆ State in what form energy travels from the sun to Earth. ◆ Explain what happens to energy from the sun when it reaches Earth.	3-4 periods/ $1\frac{1}{2}$–2 blocks	**Discover** Does a Plastic Bag Trap Heat?, p. 42 **Science at Home,** p. 45 **Skills Lab: Developing Hypotheses** Heating Earth's Surface, pp. 46–47	**TE** Integrating Physics, p. 43 **TE** Exploring Energy in the Atmosphere, p. 44
2 *Integrating Physics* **Heat Transfer** pp. 48–51 ◆ Describe how temperature is measured. ◆ Name the three ways heat is transferred.	1–2 periods/ $\frac{1}{2}$–1 block	**Discover** What Happens When Air Is Heated?, p. 48 **Try This** Temperatures at Two Heights, p. 50	**TE** Demonstration, p. 49 **TE** Building Inquiry Skills: Calculating, p. 49 **TE** Inquiry Challenge, p. 50 **IES** "Wagons West," pp. 31–32 **PTA** "Testing Disposable Cups," pp. 1–8
3 Winds pp. 52–60 ◆ Explain what causes winds. ◆ Distinguish between local winds and global winds. ◆ Identify where the major global wind belts are located.	3–4 periods/ $1\frac{1}{2}$–2 blocks	**Discover** Which Way Does the Wind Turn?, p. 52 **Try This** Build a Wind Vane, p. 53 **Real-World Lab: You and Your Community** Where's the Wind?, pp. 54–55	**TE** Demonstration, p. 53 **TE** Including All Students, p. 56 **TE** Demonstration, p. 57 **TE** Including All Students, p. 58
4 Water in the Atmosphere pp. 61–66 ◆ Describe how relative humidity is measured. ◆ Explain how clouds form. ◆ Name the three main types of clouds.	2–3 periods/ 1–$1\frac{1}{2}$ blocks	**Discover** How Does Fog Form?, p. 61 **Sharpen Your Skills** Interpreting Data, p. 63 **Science at Home,** p. 66	**TE** Inquiry Challenge, p. 62 **TE** Building Inquiry Skills: Measuring, p. 63 **TE** Building Inquiry Skills: Inferring, p. 64 **ISLM** I-2, "Using a Psychrometer to Determine Relative Humidity"
5 Precipitation pp. 67–70 ◆ Identify the main types of precipitation. ◆ Describe how precipitation is measured and ways that it might be controlled.	1–2 periods/ $\frac{1}{2}$–1 block	**Discover** How Can You Make Hail?, p. 67 **Sharpen Your Skills** Calculating, p. 69	**TE** Building Inquiry Skills: Observing, p. 68 **TE** Building Inquiry Skills: Measuring, p. 69 **IES** "Where River Meets Sea," pp. 24–25; "India Beyond the Golden Age," p. 33
Study Guide/Chapter Review pp. 71–73	1 period/ $\frac{1}{2}$ block		

For Standard or Block Schedule The Resource Pro® CD-ROM gives you maximum flexibility for planning your instruction for any type of schedule. Resource Pro® contains Planning Express®, an advanced scheduling program, as well as the entire contents of the Teaching Resources and the Computer Test Bank.

CHAPTER PLANNING GUIDE

Program Resources	Assessment Strategies	Media and Technology
TR Chapter 2 Project Teacher Notes, pp. 34–35 **TR** Chapter 2 Project Student materials, pp. 36–39 **TR** Chapter 2 Project Scoring Rubric, p. 40	**SE** Performance Assessment: Chapter 2 Project Wrap Up, p. 73 **TE** Check Your Progress, pp. 51, 60, 70 **TR** Chapter 2 Project Scoring Rubric, p. 40	Science Explorer Internet Site
TR 2-1 Lesson Plan, p. 41 **TR** 2-1 Section Summary, p. 42 **TR** 2-1 Review and Reinforce, p. 43 **TR** 2-1 Enrich, p. 44 **TR** Skills Lab blackline masters, pp. 61–63 **SES** Book O, *Sound and Light,* Chapters 3 and 4	**SE** Section 1 Review, p. 45 **SE** Analyze and Conclude, p. 47 **TE** Ongoing Assessment, p. 43 **TE** Performance Assessment, p. 45 **TR** 2-1 Review and Reinforce, p. 43	Exploring Earth Science Videodisc, Unit 4 Side 2, "Heating the Earth" Audiotapes, English-Spanish Summary 2-1 Transparency 5, "Energy in the Atmosphere" Interactive Student Tutorial CD-ROM, I-2
TR 2-2 Lesson Plan, p. 45 **TR** 2-2 Section Summary, p. 46 **TR** 2-2 Review and Reinforce, p. 47 **TR** 2-2 Enrich, p. 48 **SES** Book M, *Motion, Forces, and Energy,* Chapter 6	**SE** Section 2 Review, p. 51 **TE** Ongoing Assessment, p. 49 **TE** Performance Assessment, p. 51 **TR** 2-2 Review and Reinforce, p. 47	Audiotapes, English-Spanish Summary 2-2 Transparency 6, "Types of Heat Transfer" Interactive Student Tutorial CD-ROM, I-2
TR 2-3 Lesson Plan, p. 49 **TR** 2-3 Section Summary, p. 50 **TR** 2-3 Review and Reinforce, p. 51 **TR** 2-3 Enrich, p. 52 **TR** Real-World Lab blackline masters, pp. 64–65	**SE** Analyze and Conclude, p. 55 **SE** Section 3 Review, p. 60 **TE** Ongoing Assessment, pp. 53, 57, 59 **TE** Performance Assessment, p. 60 **TR** 2-3 Review and Reinforce, p. 51	Exploring Earth Science Videodisc, Unit 2 Side 2, "The Power of Heat" Audiotapes, English-Spanish Summary 2-3 Transparency 7, "Global Winds" Interactive Student Tutorial CD-ROM, I-2
TR 2-4 Lesson Plan, p. 53 **TR** 2-4 Section Summary, p. 54 **TR** 2-4 Review and Reinforce, p. 55 **TR** 2-4 Enrich, p. 56 **SES** Book H, *Earth's Water,* Chapter 1	**SE** Section 4 Review, p. 66 **TE** Ongoing Assessment, pp. 63, 65 **TE** Performance Assessment, p. 66 **TR** 2-4 Review and Reinforce, p. 55	Audiotapes, English-Spanish Summary 2-4 Transparency 8, "The Water Cycle"; Transparency 9, "Clouds" Interactive Student Tutorial CD-ROM, I-2
TR 2-5 Lesson Plan, p. 57 **TR** 2-5 Section Summary, p. 58 **TR** 2-5 Review and Reinforce, p. 59 **TR** 2-5 Enrich, p. 60	**SE** Section 5 Review, p. 70 **TE** Ongoing Assessment, p. 69 **TE** Performance Assessment, p. 70 **TR** 2-5 Review and Reinforce, p. 59	Exploring Earth Science Videodisc, Unit 6 Side 2, "What's in Our Tap?" Audiotapes, English-Spanish Summary 2-5 Interactive Student Tutorial CD-ROM, I-2
TR Chapter 2 Performance Assessment, pp. 141–143 **TR** Chapter 2 Test, pp. 144–147	**SE** Chapter 2 Review, pp. 71–73 **TR** Chapter 2 Performance Assessment, pp. 141–143 **TR** Chapter 2 Test, pp. 144–147 **CTB** Chapter 2 Test	Interactive Student Tutorial CD-ROM, I-2 Computer Test Bank, Chapter 2 Test

Key: **SE** Student Edition
CTB Computer Test Bank
ISAB Inquiry Skills Activity Book
TE Teacher's Edition
SES Science Explorer Series Text
PTA Product Testing Activities by *Consumer Reports*
TR Teaching Resources
ISLM Integrated Science Laboratory Manual
IES Interdisciplinary Explorations Series

Meeting the National Science Education Standards and AAAS Benchmarks

National Science Education Standards

Science As Inquiry (Content Standard A)

◆ **Use appropriate tools and techniques to gather, analyze, and interpret data** Students create a weather station. Students investigate wind patterns. *(Chapter Project; Real-World Lab)*

◆ **Think critically and logically to make the relationships between evidence and explanations** Students compare heating and cooling rates of sand and water. *(Skills Lab)*

Physical Science (Content Standard B)

◆ **Transfer of energy** Energy travels to Earth from the sun as electromagnetic waves. Different materials absorb radiation at different rates. Heat is transferred by radiation, conduction, and convection. *(Sections 1, 2; Skills Lab)*

Earth and Space Science (Content Standard D)

◆ **Structure of the Earth system** The movement of air between the equator and the poles produces global winds. Water moves between the atmosphere and Earth's surface in the water cycle. Precipitation is any form of water that falls to Earth. *(Sections 3, 4, 5)*

◆ **Earth in the solar system** Nearly all the energy in Earth's atmosphere comes from the sun. Winds are caused by unequal heating of the atmosphere by the sun. As the sun heats Earth's surface, the amount of water in the atmosphere changes. *(Sections 1, 3, 4)*

Benchmarks for Science Literacy

1B Scientific Inquiry Students create a weather station. Students investigate heating and cooling rates of sand and water. Students investigate wind patterns. *(Chapter Project; Skills Lab; Real-World Lab)*

3A Technology and Science Students use instruments to measure weather conditions. Students measure wind to determine the best location for a door on a building. *(Chapter Project; Real-World Lab)*

4B The Earth Nearly all the energy in Earth's atmosphere comes from the sun. The movement of air between the equator and the poles produces global winds. Water moves between the atmosphere and Earth's surface in the water cycle. Precipitation is any form of water that falls from clouds to Earth's surface. *(Sections 1, 3, 4, 5)*

4E Energy Transformation The direct transfer of energy by electromagnetic waves is called radiation. Different materials absorb radiation at different rates. Heat is transferred by radiation, conduction, and convection. Winds are caused by unequal heating of the atmosphere. *(Sections 1, 2, 3; Skills Lab)*

4F Motion Visible light is a mixture of all the colors of the rainbow. *(Section 1)*

12C Manipulation and Observation Students measure weather conditions using various instruments. *(Chapter Project)*

Unifying Themes

◆ **Energy** Nearly all the energy in Earth's atmosphere comes from the sun. Different materials absorb radiation at different rates. The energy transferred from a hotter object to a cooler one is referred to as heat. Wind is the movement of air. *(Sections 1, 2, 3; Skills Lab)*

◆ **Modeling** Students create a weather station. Students make a simple anemometer. *(Chapter Project; Real-World Lab)*

◆ **Patterns of Change** Students look for patterns in their weather data. Monsoons change direction with the seasons. Students investigate wind patterns around a building. *(Chapter Project; Section 3; Real-World Lab)*

◆ **Systems and Interactions** When Earth's surface is heated, it radiates some of the heat back into the atmosphere. Winds are caused by the unequal heating of Earth and its atmosphere. Water moves between the atmosphere and Earth's surface in the water cycle. *(Sections 1, 3, 4)*

◆ **Unity and Diversity** Most light reaches Earth in the form of visible light, infrared radiation, and ultraviolet radiation. Heat is transferred by radiation, conduction, and convection. Both local winds and global winds are caused by differences in air pressure. The three main types of clouds are cumulus, stratus, and cirrus. Rain, sleet, freezing rain, hail, and snow are types of precipitation. *(Sections 1, 2, 3, 4, 5)*

Media and Technology

Exploring Earth Science Videodiscs

◆ **Section 1** "Heating the Earth" defines heat as kinetic energy and provides examples of conduction, convection, and radiation.

◆ **Section 3** "The Power of Heat" illustrates how convection transfers heat in the atmosphere, oceans, and Earth's mantle.

◆ **Section 5** "What's in Our Tap?" gives a tour of a wastewater treatment plant.

Interactive Student Tutorial CD-ROM

◆ **Chapter Review** Interactive questions help students self-assess their mastery of key chapter concepts.

Student Edition Connection Strategies

◆ **Section 1** **Integrating Physics,** p. 42

◆ **Section 2** **Integrating Physics,** pp. 48–51

◆ **Section 3** **Social Studies Connection,** p. 58

◆ **Section 4** **Integrating Life Science,** p. 62

◆ **Section 5** **Integrating Technology,** p. 70

ACTIVITY

USING THE INTERNET

www.science-explorer.phschool.com

Visit the Science Explorer Internet site to find an up-to-date activity for Chapter 2 of *Weather and Climate.*

ACTIVITY	Time (minutes)	Materials *Quantities for one work group*	Skills
Section 1			
Discover, p. 42	10	**Consumable** plastic bag, 2 small pieces of paper, tape **Nonconsumable** 2 thermometers	Measuring
Science at Home, p. 45	home	No special materials required.	Observing
Skills Lab, pp. 46–47	40	**Consumable** 300 mL water, string, 300 mL sand, graph paper **Nonconsumable** 2 thermometers, 2 400-mL beakers, metric ruler, ring stand and ring clamp, lamp with 100-W bulb, clock or stopwatch	Developing Hypotheses, Measuring, Creating Data Tables, Drawing Conclusions
Section 2			
Discover, p. 48	10	**Consumable** aluminum pie plate, thread, candle **Nonconsumable** heavy scissors, hot plate or incandescent light	Inferring
Try This, p. 50	10, 10, 10, 20	**Consumable** graph paper **Nonconsumable** 2 thermometers, metric tape measure, watch or clock	Interpreting Data
Section 3			
Discover, p. 52	10	**Consumable** heavy-duty tape **Nonconsumable** pencil, large smooth ball, marker	Making Models
Try This, p. 53	15	**Consumable** construction paper, soda straw, tape, straight pin **Nonconsumable** scissors, metric ruler, pencil with eraser	Observing
Real-World Lab, pp. 54–55	40	**Consumable** 15 cm x 20 cm corrugated cardboard sheet, round toothpick, 2 wooden coffee stirrers, narrow masking tape **Nonconsumable** pen, wind vane, meter stick	Measuring, Interpreting Data, Drawing Conclusions
Section 4			
Discover, p. 61	10	**Consumable** hot tap water, 2 ice cubes, cold tap water **Nonconsumable** narrow-necked plastic bottle	Developing Hypotheses
Sharpen Your Skills, p. 63	10	No special materials required.	Interpreting Data
Science at Home, p. 66	home	**Consumable** cold water, ice cubes **Nonconsumable** large glass	Communicating
Section 5			
Discover, p. 67	15	**Consumable** 15 g salt, 50 mL water, 15 mL cold water, crushed ice **Nonconsumable** beaker, stirrer, clean test tube, watch or clock	Inferring
Sharpen Your Skills, p. 69	15	**Nonconsumable** funnel, narrow straight-sided glass jar, metric ruler, calculator	Calculating

A list of all materials required for the Student Edition activities can be found beginning on page T14. You can order Materials Kits by calling 1-800-828-7777 or by accessing the Science Explorer Internet site at **www.science-explorer.phschool.com.**

CHAPTER PROJECT 2

Your Own Weather Station

In this chapter, students will learn more about specific weather factors, how they are related, and how they can be measured with instruments. The Chapter 2 Project gives students an opportunity to use instruments to take measurements of each of the weather factors.

Purpose In this project, students will set up a weather station and use instruments to measure weather factors over a two-week period. At the end of the project, students will look for patterns in their data and use them to try to predict the weather. Doing the project will give students a better understanding of weather factors and how they can be used to predict the weather.

Skills Focus After completing this project, students will be able to

- ◆ plan and create a model weather station;
- ◆ use their weather station to measure weather factors;
- ◆ record the data in a weather log;
- ◆ graph their data and analyze it for trends;
- ◆ use the trends to try to predict the weather;
- ◆ compare their predictions with actual weather conditions;
- ◆ communicate their findings to the rest of the class.

Project Time Line The entire project will take about three weeks. On the first day, introduce the project and hand out the Chapter 2 Project Overview, pages 36–37 in Teaching Resources. Allow time for class discussion of the project rules and for students to brainstorm weather factors, how they can be measured, and ways to record the measurements. At this time, you may wish to divide the class into small groups to carry out the project.

Distribute the Chapter Project 2 Worksheet 1, page 38 in Teaching Resources, to help students plan their weather station, and Worksheet 2, page 39 in Teaching Resources, to show students a way to measure cloud cover. You also may wish to distribute the Chapter 2 Project Scoring Rubric, page 40 in the Teaching Resources, so students will be clear about what is expected of them.

Give students a day or two to plan their weather station and assemble the instruments and other materials they will need. Allow one class period for students to set up their weather station and practice using the instruments. You may wish to give students enough class time each day over the next two weeks to measure and record weather data. At the end of two weeks, give students a day or two to graph and analyze their data. Finally, set aside a class period at the end of the project for students to make their presentations and discuss the results.

For more detailed information on supervising the chapter project, see Chapter 2 Project Teacher Notes, pages 34–35 in Teaching Resources.

Suggested Shortcuts You can streamline the project by having students make and share a single weather station. If you assemble the instruments and materials for the shared weather station yourself, you will save another day or two. You can streamline the project even

CHAPTER 2

Weather Factors

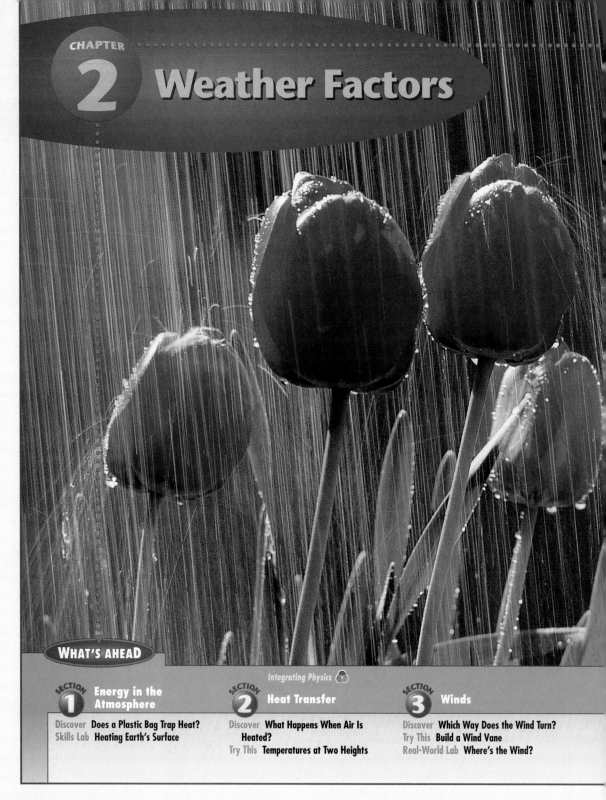

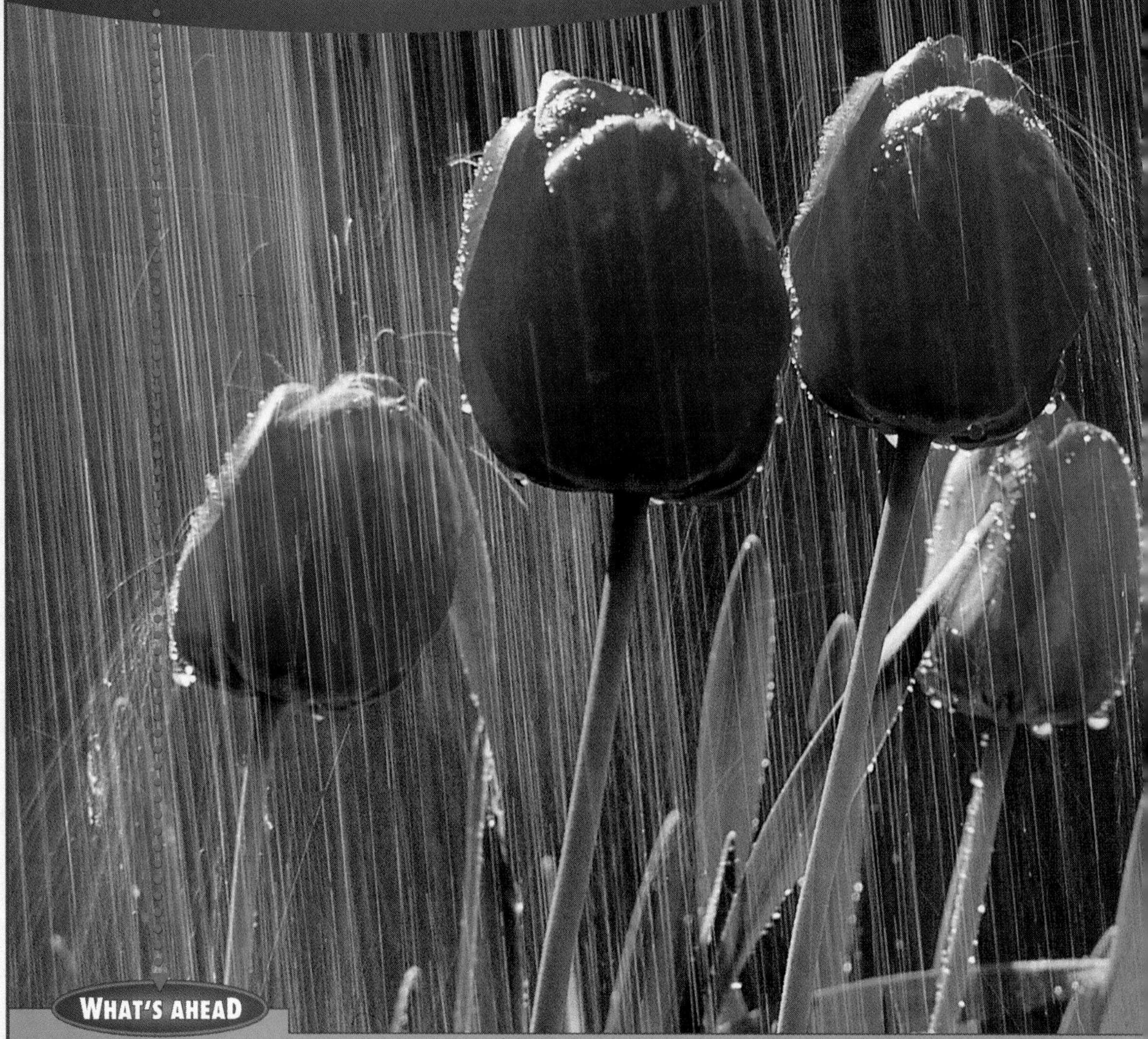

WHAT'S AHEAD

SECTION 1 **Energy in the Atmosphere**
Discover **Does a Plastic Bag Trap Heat?**
Skills Lab **Heating Earth's Surface**

Integrating Physics
SECTION 2 **Heat Transfer**
Discover **What Happens When Air Is Heated?**
Try This **Temperatures at Two Heights**

SECTION 3 **Winds**
Discover **Which Way Does the Wind Turn?**
Try This **Build a Wind Vane**
Real-World Lab **Where's the Wind?**

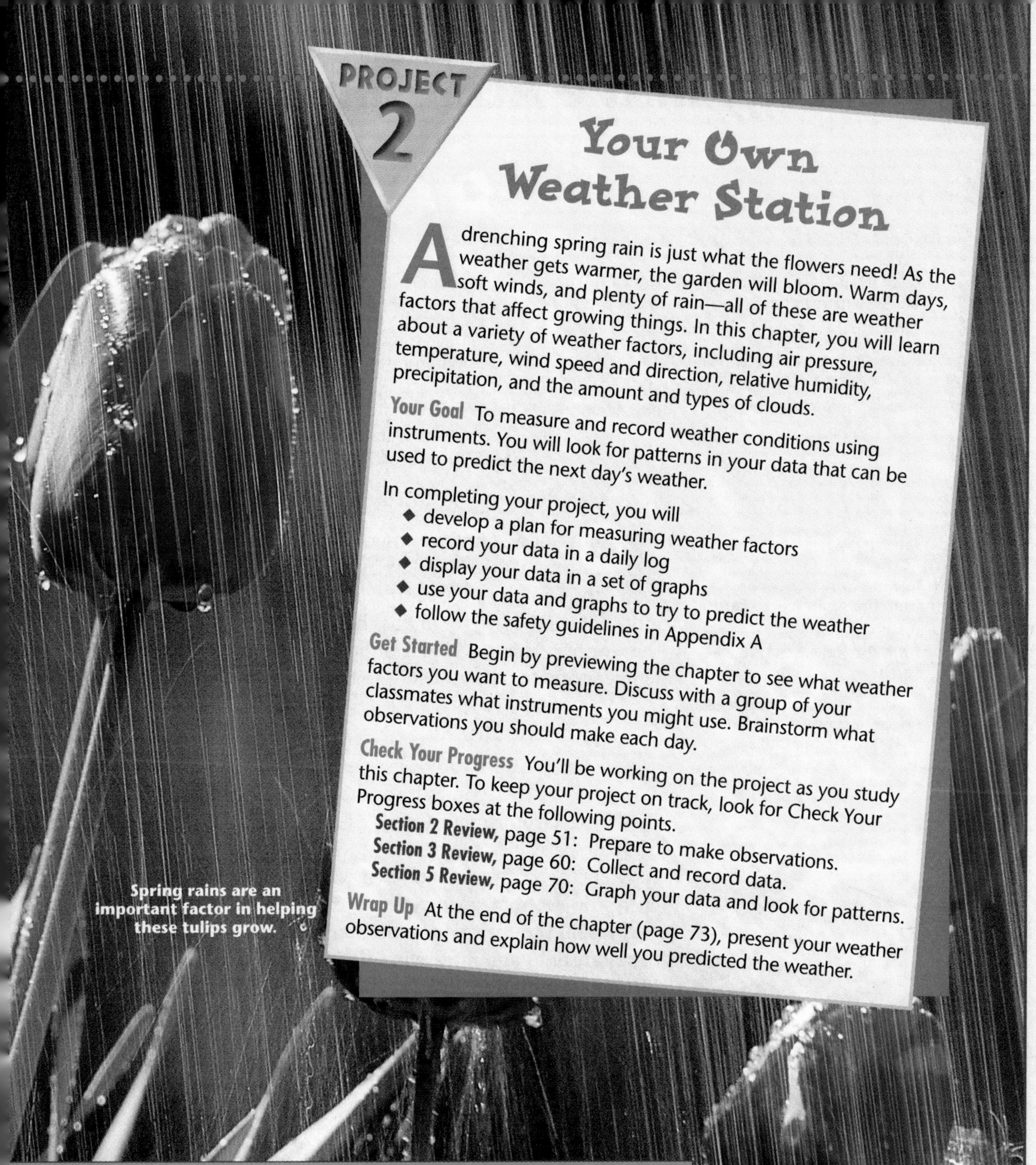

PROJECT 2

Your Own Weather Station

A drenching spring rain is just what the flowers need! As the weather gets warmer, the garden will bloom. Warm days, soft winds, and plenty of rain—all of these are weather factors that affect growing things. In this chapter, you will learn about a variety of weather factors, including air pressure, temperature, wind speed and direction, relative humidity, precipitation, and the amount and types of clouds.

Your Goal To measure and record weather conditions using instruments. You will look for patterns in your data that can be used to predict the next day's weather.

In completing your project, you will
- ◆ develop a plan for measuring weather factors
- ◆ record your data in a daily log
- ◆ display your data in a set of graphs
- ◆ use your data and graphs to try to predict the weather
- ◆ follow the safety guidelines in Appendix A

Get Started Begin by previewing the chapter to see what weather factors you want to measure. Discuss with a group of your classmates what instruments you might use. Brainstorm what observations you should make each day.

Check Your Progress You'll be working on the project as you study this chapter. To keep your project on track, look for Check Your Progress boxes at the following points.

Section 2 Review, page 51: Prepare to make observations.
Section 3 Review, page 60: Collect and record data.
Section 5 Review, page 70: Graph your data and look for patterns.

Wrap Up At the end of the chapter (page 73), present your weather observations and explain how well you predicted the weather.

Spring rains are an important factor in helping these tulips grow.

SECTION 4 **Water in the Atmosphere**
Discover **How Does Fog Form?**
Sharpen Your Skills **Interpreting Data**

SECTION 5 **Precipitation**
Discover **How Can You Make Hail?**
Sharpen Your Skills **Calculating**

more by doing the project as a class project. Assign different students to make the weather observation each day and have them record the observations on a large weather log posted in the classroom.

Possible Materials A weather station requires a sheltered place outdoors, such as the slatted wooden box described in Worksheet 1. Several different instruments are needed, including a thermometer, psychrometer, barometer, wind vane, anemometer, and rain gauge. Useful additions to the weather station are a device for measuring cloud cover (see Worksheet 2 for materials) and a chart showing cloud types (or use Exploring Clouds, page 65 in the text).

Students will need commercial thermometers and psychrometers. They can use the barometer they made in the Skills Lab in Chapter 1, pages 28–29 in the text. They also can make their own wind vane (Try This, page 53 in the text), anemometer (Real-World Lab, pages 54–55 in the text), and rain gauge (Sharpen Your Skills, page 69 in the text). However, commercial versions of these instruments will give more accurate readings and should be used if possible.

Launching the Project Introduce the project by discussing weather stations. Ask: **If you were going to visit another city, what would you want to know about the weather so you would be prepared?** *(Students may say they would want to know how hot or cold it was and if it was raining or snowing.)* **How could you find out what the weather conditions in the city were?** *(Students may say they would watch a national weather report on television or look at a national weather map in a newspaper.)* Point out that weather information for specific locations is collected and recorded by weather stations. The information is shown on weather maps with symbols and numbers. Tell students that in this project they will make their own weather station and observe and record weather factors for a location near their school.

Program Resources

- ◆ **Teaching Resources** Chapter 2 Project Teacher Notes, pp. 34–35; Chapter 2 Project Student Materials, pp. 36–39; Chapter 2 Project Scoring Rubric, p. 40

Performance Assessment

To assess students' performance in this project, use the Chapter 2 Project Scoring Rubric on page 40 in Teaching Resources. Students will be assessed on their
- ◆ weather observations and weather log;
- ◆ graphical presentation and interpretation of weather data;
- ◆ presentation of the results to the class;
- ◆ group participation, if they worked in groups.

Section 1 Energy in the Atmosphere

Objectives

After completing the lesson, students will be able to
- ◆ state in what form energy travels from the sun to Earth;
- ◆ explain what happens to energy from the sun when it reaches Earth.

Key Terms electromagnetic waves, radiation, infrared radiation, ultraviolet radiation, scattering, greenhouse effect

1 Engage/Explore

Activating Prior Knowledge

Encourage students to think about the way the sun heats Earth's surface by asking: **Which is cooler on a hot, sunny day, a lawn or a parking lot?** *(a lawn)* Point out that even without trees, a grass-covered surface stays cooler than a surface covered by blacktop. Ask: **Why doesn't the lawn get as hot as the parking lot?** *(Students may not know.)* Tell students that grass absorbs less light than pavement even when both surfaces receive the same amount of sun. As a result, the grass does not get as hot. Add that such differences in the heating of Earth's surface, on a large scale, are the major cause of Earth's weather.

Discover Activity

Skills Focus measuring
Materials
2 thermometers, plastic bag, 2 small pieces of paper, tape
Time 10 minutes
Tips Make sure the bulbs of both thermometers are shaded by the pieces of paper from direct rays of light or both may show equally high temperatures.
Expected Outcome The thermometer in the bag should show a higher temperature.
Think It Over The plastic bag trapped the heat inside it from the sun, and this caused the thermometer in the bag to show a higher temperature.

Section 1 Energy in the Atmosphere

Discover Activity

Does a Plastic Bag Trap Heat?

1. Record the initial temperatures on two thermometers. (You should get the same readings.)
2. Place one of the thermometers in a plastic bag. Put a small piece of paper in the bag so that it shades the bulb of the thermometer. Seal the bag.
3. Place both thermometers on a sunny window ledge or near a light bulb. Cover the bulb of the second thermometer with a small piece of paper. Predict what you think will happen.
4. Wait five minutes. Then record the temperatures on the two thermometers.

Think It Over
Measuring Were the two temperatures the same? How could you explain any difference?

Guide for Reading
- ◆ In what form does energy from the sun travel to Earth?
- ◆ What happens to energy from the sun when it reaches Earth?

Reading Tip Before you read, skim the section for boldfaced words that are unfamiliar to you. As you read, find their meanings.

Think of a sunny summer day. When you get up in the morning, the sun is low in the sky and the air is cool. As the sun rises, the temperature increases. By noon it is quite hot. As you will see in this chapter, heat is a major factor in the weather. The movement of heat in the atmosphere causes temperatures to change, winds to blow, and rain to fall.

Energy from the Sun

INTEGRATING PHYSICS Nearly all the energy in Earth's atmosphere comes from the sun. This energy travels to Earth as **electromagnetic waves,** a form of energy that can travel through space. Electromagnetic waves are classified according to wavelength, or distance between waves. The direct transfer of energy by electromagnetic waves is called **radiation.**

Most of the energy from the sun reaches Earth in the form of visible light and infrared radiation, and a small amount of ultraviolet radiation. Visible light is a mixture of all of the colors that you see in a rainbow: red, orange, yellow, green, blue, and violet. The different colors are the result of different wavelengths

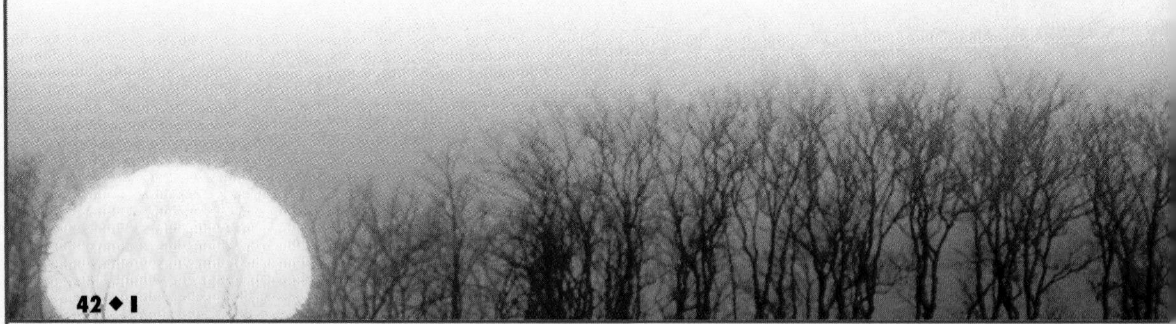

Reading Strategies

Study and Comprehension Suggest that students they use one of the following ways to remember the order of colors in the spectrum of visible light, going from longer to shorter wavelengths: ROY G. BV or "*R*ichard *o*f *Y*ork *g*ained *b*attles in *v*ain." In both cases, the colors represented by the letters are red, orange, yellow, green, blue, indigo, and violet. Challenge students to think of other ways to remember the order.

Media and Technology

Audiotapes English-Spanish Summary 2-1

Exploring Earth Science Videodisc Unit 4, Side 2, "Heating the Earth"

Chapter 1

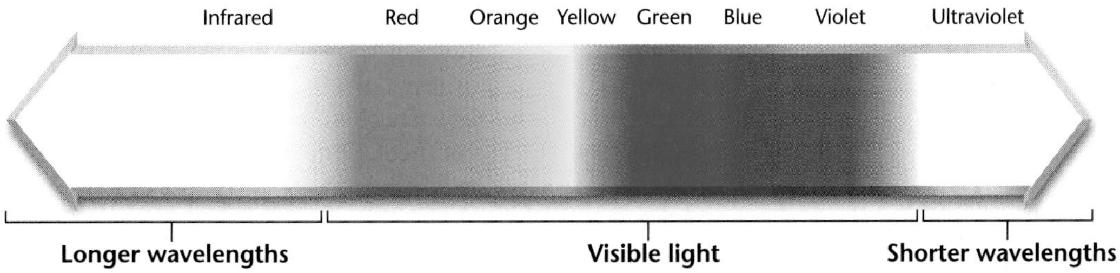

Figure 1 Electromagnetic waves include infrared radiation, visible light, and ultraviolet radiation. *Interpreting Diagrams What type of radiation has wavelengths that are shorter than visible light? What type has wavelengths that are longer?*

of visible light. Red and orange light have the longest wavelengths, while blue and violet light have the shortest wavelengths.

Infrared radiation is a form of energy with wavelengths that are longer than red light. Infrared radiation is not visible, but can be felt as heat. Heat lamps used to keep food warm in restaurants give off both visible red light and invisible infrared radiation. The sun also gives off **ultraviolet radiation,** which has wavelengths that are shorter than violet light. Sunburns are caused by ultraviolet radiation. This radiation can also cause skin cancer and eye damage.

☑ *Checkpoint* *Which color of visible light has the longest wavelengths?*

Energy in the Atmosphere

Before the sun's rays can reach Earth's surface, they must pass through the atmosphere. The path of the sun's rays is shown in *Exploring Energy in the Atmosphere* on the following page.

Some of the energy from the sun is absorbed within the atmosphere. Water vapor and carbon dioxide absorb some infrared radiation. The ozone layer in the stratosphere absorbs most of the ultraviolet radiation. Clouds, dust, and other gases also absorb energy from the sun.

Some of the sun's rays are reflected. Clouds in the atmosphere act like mirrors, reflecting some solar energy back into space. In addition, dust particles and molecules of gases in the atmosphere reflect light from the sun in all directions.

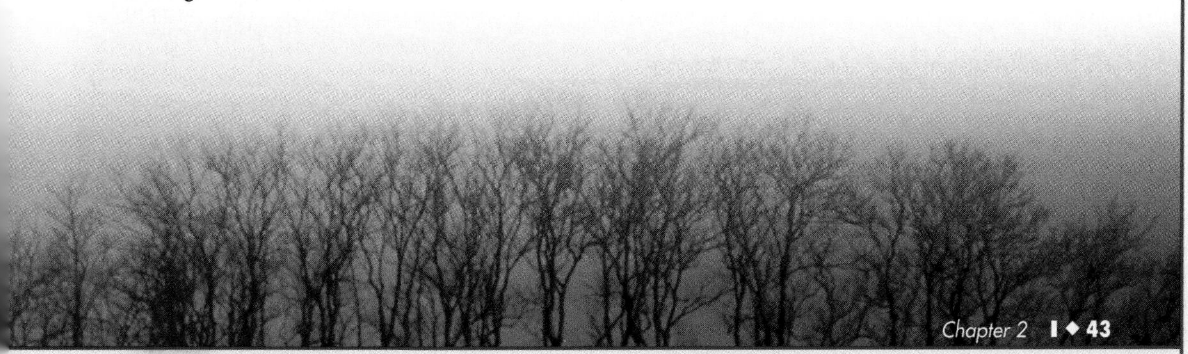

2 Facilitate

Energy from the Sun

Integrating Physics

Materials *prism*
Time 5 minutes

ACTIVITY

Show students a prism and explain that its angled sides bend the different colors in sunlight by different amounts, splitting the light into a rainbow. Demonstrate by placing the prism in sunlight. Then ask: **Where does light have the shortest wavelength and where does light have the longest wavelength?** *(The end with violet light is the shortest, and the end with red light is the longest.)* **learning modality: visual**

Energy in the Atmosphere

Building Inquiry Skills: Inferring

Describe the following hypothetical situation to the class. City A is located where the ozone layer of the stratosphere has become very thin. City B is located where the ozone layer is still relatively thick. Ask: **How do you think the two cities compare in terms of the ultraviolet radiation they receive?** *(City A would get more ultraviolet radiation than City B because less of the ultraviolet radiation would be absorbed by ozone in the stratosphere.)* **learning modality: logical/mathematical**

Program Resources

◆ **Teaching Resources** 2-1 Lesson Plan, p. 41; 2-1 Section Summary, p. 42

Media and Technology

Transparencies "Energy in the Atmosphere," Transparency 5

Interactive Student Tutorial CD-ROM I-2

Answers to Self-Assessment

Caption Question

Figure 1 Ultraviolet radiation has wavelengths that are shorter than visible light. Infrared radiation has wavelengths that are longer than visible light.

☑ *Checkpoint*

Red light has the longest wavelengths.

Ongoing Assessment

Drawing Have students draw a representation of the visible spectrum, showing the different colors of visible light in order by wavelength.

Energy in the Atmosphere, continued

Including All Students

Remind students that the moon, unlike Earth, has no atmosphere. Then ask: **If you were standing on the moon during the day, what color would the sky appear to be?** *(Students may know from photographs that the sky would appear to be black.)* **Why wouldn't the sky appear to be blue?** *(Because without an atmosphere on the moon there are no gas molecules to scatter the light and make it look blue)* **learning modality: logical/mathematical**

EXPLORING

Energy in the Atmosphere

ACTIVITY

Materials *several sheets of light- and dark-colored construction paper, bandanas or other material for blindfolds*
Time 10 minutes

Point out to students that all parts of Earth's surface are not heated equally by energy from the sun. Demonstrate this point by placing several pieces of construction paper in direct sunlight. Use white, black, and at least one or two other light and dark colors. After the papers have been in the sun for at least five minutes, ask volunteers to put on blindfolds. Then rearrange the order of the papers and have the volunteers try to tell which papers are light colored and which are dark colored based on how warm or cool they feel to the touch. Ask: **Why do the dark-colored papers feel warmer than the light-colored papers?** *(Dark-colored surfaces absorb more of the light that strikes them, whereas light-colored surfaces reflect more of the light that strikes them.)* **Which surfaces on Earth do you think reflect more of the sun's light back into space?** *(Light-colored surfaces such as sand or snow)* **Which surfaces absorb more of the sun's light?** *(Dark-colored surfaces such as bare soil or blacktop pavement)* **learning modality: kinesthetic**

Reflection of light in all directions is called **scattering.** When you look at the sky, the light you see has been scattered by gas molecules in the atmosphere. Gas molecules scatter short wavelengths of visible light (blue and violet) more than long wavelengths (red and orange). Scattered light is therefore bluer than ordinary sunlight, which is why the daytime sky looks blue.

When the sun is rising or setting, light from the sun passes through a greater thickness of the atmosphere than when the sun is higher in the sky. More light from the blue end of the spectrum is removed by scattering before it reaches your eyes. The remaining light from the sun contains mostly red and orange light. The sun looks red, and clouds around it become very colorful.

☑ *Checkpoint* ***Why would particles from volcanic eruptions make sunsets and sunrises more red?***

EXPLORING *Energy in the Atmosphere*

Most of the energy that keeps Earth warm comes from the sun. Some of this energy is reflected or absorbed in the atmosphere. The rest of the energy reaches Earth's surface, where it is reflected or absorbed.

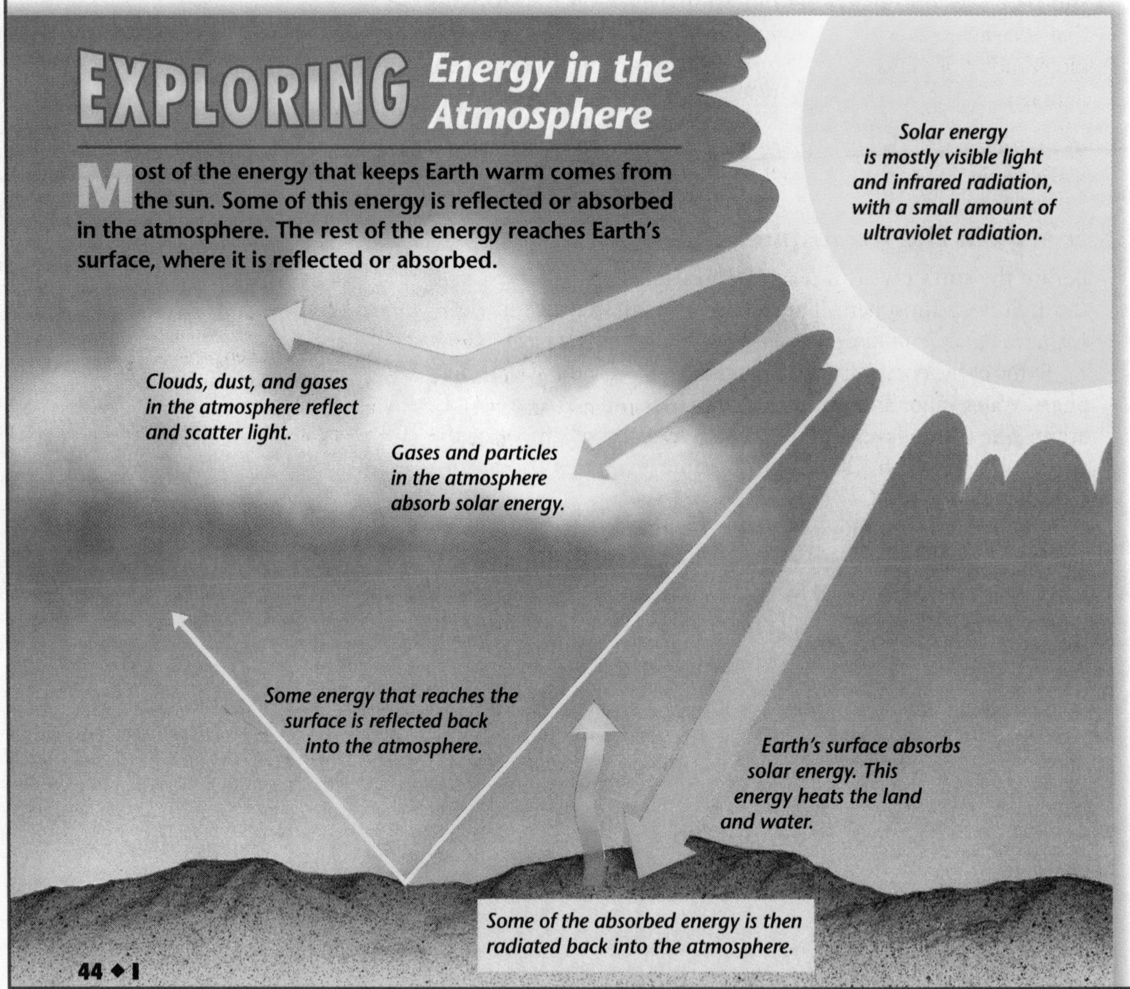

Solar energy is mostly visible light and infrared radiation, with a small amount of ultraviolet radiation.
Clouds, dust, and gases in the atmosphere reflect and scatter light.
Gases and particles in the atmosphere absorb solar energy.
Some energy that reaches the surface is reflected back into the atmosphere.
Earth's surface absorbs solar energy. This energy heats the land and water.
Some of the absorbed energy is then radiated back into the atmosphere.
44 ♦ I

Background

Facts and Figures The amount of energy produced by the sun is amazing. An area of the sun's surface the size of a postage stamp gives off enough energy to power 500 60-watt light bulbs. Although only one part in two billion of the total amount of solar energy reaches Earth, this is still a huge amount. If the amount of solar energy reaching Earth in just one hour could be used, it would meet the world's total energy needs for a year. If the amount of solar energy reaching Earth in a day could be used, it would take 700 billion tons of coal to match it.

A tiny fraction of the sun's energy actually is trapped and used for power. Solar energy plants collect sunlight with mirrors and focus it with lenses on tubes filled with fluid. The fluid heats up, and the heat is used to boil water into steam that powers electric generators.

Energy at Earth's Surface

Some of the sun's energy reaches Earth's surface and is reflected back into the atmosphere. Some of the energy, however, is absorbed by the land and water and changed into heat.

When Earth's surface is heated, it radiates some of the energy back into the atmosphere as infrared radiation. This infrared radiation cannot travel all the way through the atmosphere back into space. Instead, much of it is absorbed by water vapor, carbon dioxide, methane, and other gases in the air. The energy from the absorbed radiation heats the gases in the air. These gases form a "blanket" around Earth that holds heat in the atmosphere. The process by which gases hold heat in the air is called the **greenhouse effect.**

Have you ever been inside a greenhouse during the winter? Even on a cold day, a greenhouse is warm. Greenhouses trap heat in two ways. First, infrared radiation given off in the interior cannot easily pass through glass and is trapped inside. Second, warm air inside the greenhouse cannot rise because the glass blocks the movement of air. What happens in Earth's atmosphere is similar to the first way that greenhouses trap heat.

The greenhouse effect is a natural process that keeps Earth's atmosphere at a temperature that is comfortable for most living things. Human activities over the last 200 years, however, have increased the amount of carbon dioxide in the atmosphere, which may be warming the atmosphere. You will learn more about the greenhouse effect in Chapter 4.

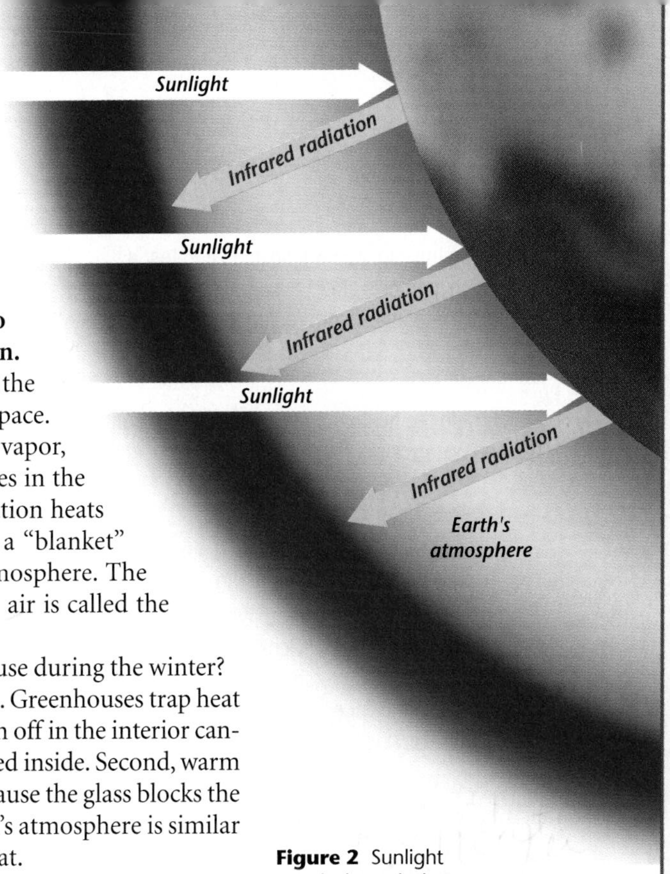

Figure 2 Sunlight travels through the atmosphere to Earth's surface. Earth's surface then gives off infrared radiation. Much of this energy is held by the atmosphere, warming it.

Section 1 Review

1. List three forms of radiation from the sun. How are these alike? How are they different?
2. What happens to the energy from the sun that is absorbed by Earth's surface?
3. Why is the sky blue? Why are sunsets often red?
4. **Thinking Critically Applying Concepts** What might conditions on Earth be like without the greenhouse effect?

Science at Home

With an adult family member, explore the role radiation plays in heating your home. Are some rooms warmer and sunnier in the morning? Are other rooms warmer and sunnier in the afternoon? How does opening and closing curtains or blinds affect the temperature of a room? Explain your observations to your family.

3 Assess

Section 1 Review Answers

1. Visible light, infrared radiation, and ultraviolet radiation; they differ in their wavelengths.
2. It is changed into heat.
3. The sky is blue because short-wavelength blue light is scattered more by gas molecules in the atmosphere. Sunsets are often red because the light from the setting sun passes through a greater thickness of the atmosphere than when the sun is higher in the sky, and more blue light is removed by scattering, leaving mostly red light to reach your eyes.
4. Without the greenhouse effect, more infrared radiation reflected back from Earth's surface would escape into space instead of being held in the atmosphere, so Earth's surface would be much colder.

Science at Home

ACTIVITY

Tips Suggest to students that they try to do this activity on a sunny day, preferably when the furnace or other source of artificial heat is not operating.

Program Resources

Science Explorer Series *Sound and Light,* Chapters 3 and 4, have more information on the electromagnetic spectrum and visible light.
◆ **Teaching Resources** 2-1 Review and Reinforce, p. 43; 2-1 Enrich, p. 44

Answers to Self-Assessment

Checkpoint

The particles would scatter more light from the sun. This would remove more light from the blue end of the spectrum, causing the remaining light to look mostly red.

Performance Assessment

Oral Presentation Call on students to explain in their own words one of the various things that can happen to sunlight that reaches Earth's atmosphere.

Skills Lab

Developing Hypotheses

Heating Earth's Surface

In this lab, you will develop and test a hypothesis about how quickly different materials absorb radiation.

Problem

How do the heating and cooling rates of sand and water compare?

Materials

2 thermometers	ring stand and ring clamp
2 beakers, 400 mL	sand, 300 mL
water, 300 mL	lamp with 100-W bulb
metric ruler	clock or stopwatch
string	graph paper

Procedure

1. Do you think sand or water will heat up faster? Record your hypothesis in the form of an "If . . . then. . . ." statement. Explain what information you used to form your hypothesis. Then follow these steps to test your hypothesis.
2. Copy the data table into your notebook. Add enough rows to record data for 15 minutes.
3. Fill one beaker with 300 mL of dry sand.
4. Fill the second beaker with 300 mL of water at room temperature.
5. Arrange the beakers beneath the ring stand.
6. Place one thermometer in each beaker.
7. Suspend the thermometers from the ring stand with string. This will hold the thermometers in place so they do not fall.
8. Adjust the height of the clamp so that the bulb of each thermometer is covered by about 0.5 cm of sand or water in a beaker.
9. Position the lamp so that it is about 20 cm above the sand and water. There should be no more than 8 cm between the beakers. **CAUTION:** *Be careful not to splash water onto the hot light bulb.*
10. Record the temperature of the sand and water in your data table.
11. Turn on the lamp. Read the temperature of the sand and water every minute for 15 minutes. Record the temperatures in the Light On column in the data table.
12. Which material do you think will cool off more quickly? Record your hypothesis. Again, give reasons why you think your hypothesis is correct.
13. Turn the light off. Read the temperature of the sand and water every minute for another 15 minutes. Record the temperatures in the Light Off column (16–30 minutes).

DATA TABLE

Temperature with Light On (°C)			Temperature with Light Off (°C)		
Time (min)	Sand	Water	Time (min)	Sand	Water
Start			16		
1			17		
2			18		
3			19		
4			20		
5			21		

Skills Lab

Developing Hypotheses

Heating Earth's Surface

Preparing for Inquiry

Key Concept Sand heats and cools more quickly than water.
Skills Objectives Students will be able to
- develop hypotheses about how quickly sand and water heat and cool;
- measure the temperature of sand and water while they are heating and cooling;
- create a data table to record their measurements;
- conclude from their data whether sand or water heats and cools more quickly.

Time 40 minutes
Advance Planning To be sure students have enough class time to record temperatures for a full 30 minutes, you may wish to set up the equipment and measure out the sand and water ahead of time. Make sure the sand is dry. Both sand and water should be at room temperature when the lab begins.
Alternative Materials Students can use small wide-mouthed glass jars instead of beakers, as long as both jars are the same size and shape. They also can substitute sugar for sand. If ring stands and clamps are not available, you can substitute two 2-L soda bottles placed about 30 cm apart and connected by a ruler placed across the tops. The thermometers can be suspended from the ruler.

Guiding Inquiry

Invitation To help students formulate hypotheses about the heating and cooling of sand and water, have them recall walking barefoot on a beach. Ask: **Did you ever walk barefoot on the beach on a sunny day? What was the temperature of the sand like?** *(The sand was probably hot.)* **When you reached the water, how did it feel by comparison to the hot sand?** *(much cooler)* **If you ever walked barefoot on the beach after dark, which felt warmer, the sand or the water?** *(the water)* Challenge students to think of other past observations that might help them formulate their hypotheses.

Introducing the Procedure
Have students read through the steps of the procedure. Clarify any steps they do not understand. Emphasize the importance of following each step of the procedure precisely. For example, students should use exactly the same amount of sand as water and place both beakers exactly the same distance from the lamp. Explain that by making these factors the same for both the sand and water they will be controlling other variables that might affect the outcome of the experiment.

Troubleshooting the Experiment
- To reduce the number of setups needed, divide the class into groups and have each group use one setup.
- Make sure that each lamp is positioned so it shines evenly on the two beakers. If one beaker receives more direct rays than the other, it may bias the results. Also check that both thermometers are positioned the same

Analyze and Conclude

1. Draw two line graphs to show the data for the temperature change in sand and water over time. Label the horizontal axis from 0 to 30 minutes and the vertical axis in degrees Celsius. Draw both graphs on the same piece of graph paper. Use a dashed line to show the temperature change in water and a solid line to show the temperature change in sand.
2. Calculate the total change in temperature for each material.
3. Based on your data, which material had the greater increase in temperature?
4. What can you conclude about which material absorbed heat faster? How do your results compare with your hypothesis?
5. Review your data again. In 15 minutes, which material cooled faster?
6. How do these results compare to your second hypothesis?
7. **Think About It** If your results did not support either of your hypotheses, why do you think the results differed from what you expected?
8. **Apply** Based on your results, which do you think will heat up more quickly on a sunny day: the water in a lake or the sand surrounding it? Which will cool off more quickly after dark?

More to Explore

Do you think all solid materials heat up as fast as sand? For example, consider gravel, crushed stone, or different types of soil. Write a hypothesis about their heating rates as an "If . . . then. . . ." statement. With the approval and supervision of your teacher, develop a procedure to test your hypothesis. Was your hypothesis correct?

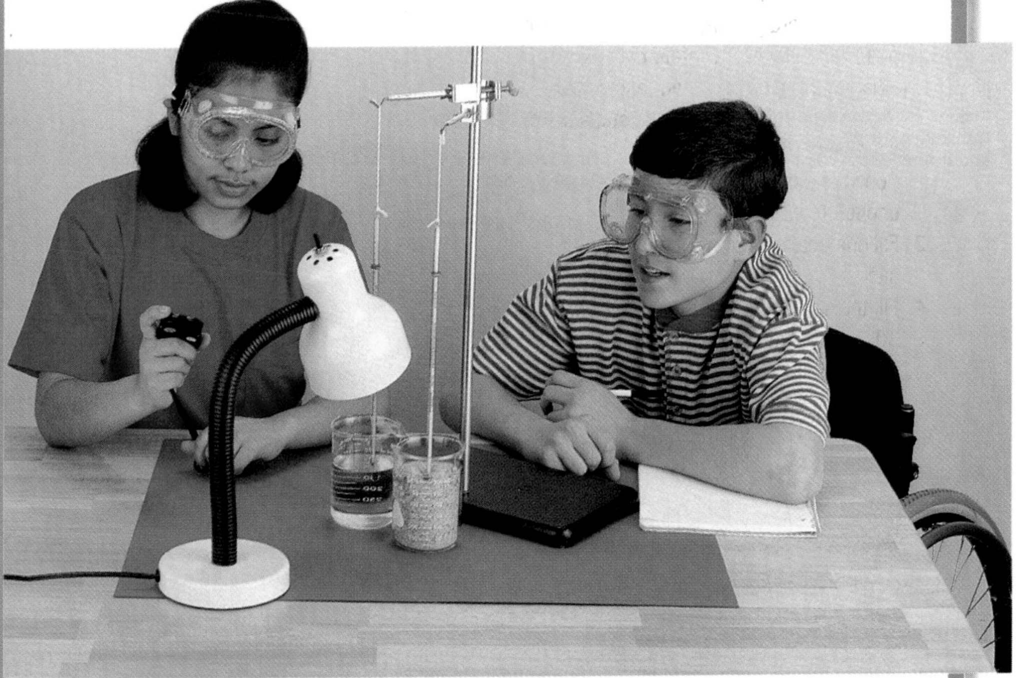

distance below the surface and held in an upright position by the string.

Expected Outcome
Students should find that the sand heats and cools more quickly than the water.

Analyze and Conclude
1. Both graphs should rise steadily during the first 15 minutes and then decline steadily during the second 15 minutes. The line for sand temperature should rise and fall more steeply than the line for water temperature, indicating a greater rate of change in temperature for sand than water.
2. Exact answers will vary depending on the specific temperatures recorded. However, the sand should show a greater total change in temperature than the water.
3. The data should show that the sand had a greater increase in temperature.
4. Students should conclude that the sand absorbed heat faster than the water. These results may or may not agree with their hypothesis.
5. The data should show that the sand cooled faster.
6. These results may or may not agree with their second hypothesis.
7. Answers may vary. One possible answer is that they expected both the sand and water to heat and cool at the same rate because there were equal amounts of the two substances.
8. Based on their results, students should say that the sand surrounding a lake will heat up more quickly on a sunny day and cool off more quickly after dark than the water in the lake.

Extending the Inquiry

More to Explore Students may think that solids with a different texture, made of different materials, or having different colors might heat up at different rates than sand. For example, students may think that rock would heat up faster than sand because it is more solid. Students may hypothesize that soil will heat up faster than sand because it is darker in color. They can test their hypothesis by repeating the skills lab and substituting soil or other materials for water.

Program Resources

◆ **Teaching Resources** Skills Lab blackline masters, pp. 61–63

Safety

Caution students to be careful not to touch the light bulb or splash water on it. Review the safety guidelines in Appendix A.

INTEGRATING PHYSICS

SECTION 2 Heat Transfer

Objectives

After completing the lesson, students will be able to

- ◆ describe how temperature is measured;
- ◆ name the three ways heat is transferred.

Key Terms thermal energy, temperature, thermometer, heat, conduction, convection

1 Engage/Explore

Activating Prior Knowledge

Introduce students to the concept of heat transfer by helping them recall the shimmery effect produced by heated air rising from hot pavement. Ask: **On a hot sunny day, did you ever see cars, buildings, or other objects appear to shimmer or waver on the other side of a street or parking lot?** *(Most students probably will say yes.)* **What causes this effect?** *(Hot air rising from the pavement)* Explain that the sun heats up the ground more quickly than the air, especially if the surface of the ground is dark colored. The heated air then rises and bends light waves as they pass through it, making objects on the other side shimmer.

DISCOVER ACTIVITY

Skills Focus inferring
Materials *aluminum pie plate, heavy scissors, thread, candle or hot plate or incandescent light*
Time 10 minutes
Tips You may want to poke the holes in the flat parts yourself.
Expected Outcome The spiral will spin.
Think It Over The spiral spun because warm air rose from the heat source and pushed against the spiral.

INTEGRATING PHYSICS

SECTION 2 Heat Transfer

DISCOVER ACTIVITY

What Happens When Air Is Heated?

1. Use heavy scissors to cut the flat part out of an aluminum pie plate. Use the tip of the scissors to poke a small hole in the middle of the flat part.
2. Cut the part into a spiral shape, as shown in the photo. Tie a 30-centimeter piece of thread to the middle of the spiral.
3. Hold the spiral over a source of heat, such as a candle, hot plate, or incandescent light bulb.

Think It Over
Inferring What happened to the spiral? Why do you think this happened?

GUIDE FOR READING

- ◆ **How is temperature measured?**
- ◆ **In what three ways is heat transferred?**

Reading Tip **As you read, make a list of the types of heat transfer. Write a sentence about how each type occurs.**

You know that energy from the sun is absorbed by Earth's surface. Some energy is then transferred from the surface to the atmosphere in the form of heat. The heat then moves from place to place within the atmosphere. But how does heat move in the atmosphere?

Energy and Temperature

Gases are made up of small particles, called molecules, that are constantly moving. The faster the molecules are moving, the more energy they have. Figure 3 shows how the motion of

Figure 3 The lemonade is cold, so the molecules move slowly. The herbal tea is hot, so the molecules move faster than the molecules in the lemonade. *Inferring Which liquid has a higher temperature?*

48 ◆ I

READING STRATEGIES

Vocabulary The terms *thermal energy* and *temperature* are very similar. Make sure students understand how the two terms are different by pointing out that temperature is the *average* thermal energy of a substance. Students may have heard of temperatures measured on the centigrade scale. Explain to them that the centigrade scale is the same as the Celsius scale, which is named after the scientist who developed it.

Program Resources

- ◆ **Teaching Resources** 2-2 Lesson Plan, p. 45; 2-2 Section Summary, p. 46
- ◆ **Product Testing Activities by *Consumer Reports*** "Testing Disposable Cups," pp. 1–8
- ◆ **Interdisciplinary Explorations Series** "Wagons West," pp. 31–33

molecules is related to the amount of energy they hold. The total energy of motion in the molecules of a substance is called **thermal energy.** On the other hand, **temperature** is the *average* amount of energy of motion of each molecule of a substance. That means that temperature is a measure of how hot or cold a substance is.

Measuring Temperature

Ask someone what the weather is like. The answer will probably include the temperature. Temperature is one of the most important elements of weather. **Air temperature is usually measured with a thermometer.** A **thermometer** is a thin glass tube with a bulb on one end that contains a liquid, usually mercury or colored alcohol.

Thermometers work because liquids expand when they are heated and contract when they are cooled. When the air temperature increases, the liquid in the bulb expands and rises up the column. What happens when the temperature decreases? The liquid in the bulb contracts and moves down the tube.

Temperature is measured in units called degrees. The two most common scales are shown in Figure 4. Scientists use the Celsius scale. On the Celsius scale, the freezing point of pure water is 0°C (read "zero degrees Celsius"). The boiling point of pure water is 100°C. Weather reports in the United States use the Fahrenheit scale. On the Fahrenheit scale, the freezing point of water is 32°F and the boiling point is 212°F.

☑ *Checkpoint* ***How many degrees Celsius are there between the freezing point of water and the boiling point of water?***

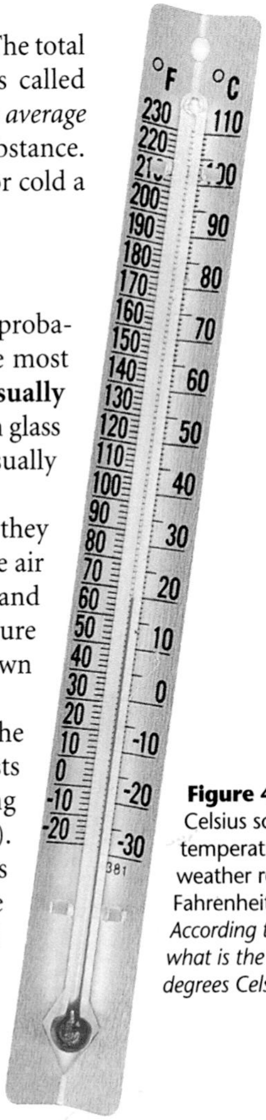

Figure 4 Scientists use the Celsius scale to measure temperature. However, weather reports use the Fahrenheit scale. *Measuring According to this thermometer, what is the air temperature in degrees Celsius?*

How Heat Is Transferred

The energy transferred from a hotter object to a cooler one is referred to as **heat**. The types of heat transfer are shown in Figure 5 on the next page. **Heat is transferred in three ways: radiation, conduction, and convection.**

Radiation Have you ever felt the warmth of the sun's rays on your face? You were feeling energy coming directly from the sun as radiation. Recall that radiation is the direct transfer of energy by electromagnetic waves. The heat you feel from the sun or a campfire travels directly to you as infrared radiation. You cannot see infrared radiation, but you can feel it as heat.

2 Facilitate

Energy and Temperature

Demonstration

ACTIVITY

Materials *glass jar with lid, black and white sheets of construction paper, toothpick, thread, glue, tape, scissors*
Time 15 minutes

Make a radiometer to show students that heat increases the movement of air molecules. Cut four 2-cm squares from white construction paper and four from black construction paper. Glue each black square to a white square. Holding a toothpick vertically, glue one edge of each square to the shaft of the toothpick, like feathers sticking out from the shaft of an arrow. Arrange the squares so that colors alternate between black and white. Tape the end of a piece of thread to one end of the toothpick. Tape the other end of the thread to the inside of a jar lid. Put the lid on the jar, making sure the toothpick dangles freely, and place the jar in sunlight. Soon the toothpick will start to spin. When it does, ask: **What causes the toothpick to spin?** *(The black squares heat up faster than the white squares, and this heats the air molecules close to them. The heated air molecules bounce off the black squares, pushing the toothpick around in a circle.)* **learning modality: visual**

Measuring Temperature

Building Inquiry Skills: Calculating

ACTIVITY

Materials *calculator*
Time 10 minutes

Help students become more familiar with the Celsius scale by having them convert several Fahrenheit temperatures to their Celsius equivalents, using the formula °C = (°F - 32) x 5/9. **learning modality: logical/mathematical**

Ongoing Assessment

Skills Check Have students compare and contrast the terms *thermal energy, temperature,* and *heat.*

Media and Technology

Audiotapes English-Spanish Summary 2-2

Transparencies "Types of Heat Transfer," Transparency 6

Answers to Self-Assessment

Caption Questions

Figure 3 The herbal tea has a higher temperature.

Figure 4 The air temperature is about 20 degrees Celsius.

☑ *Checkpoint*

Between the freezing point of water and the boiling point of water there are 100 Celsius degrees.

How Heat Is Transferred

Inquiry Challenge

Materials *ball*
Time 5 minutes

ACTIVITY

Challenge students to model the three different types of heat transfer by using a ball to represent heat and students to represent air molecules. Then have students move the ball around the classroom in different ways to model radiation, conduction, and convection. Ask: **How would you move the ball to represent radiation?** *(Toss or roll it.)* **How would you move the ball to represent conduction?** *(Pass it from one student to another.)* **How would you move the ball to represent convection?** *(Have one student walk with it.)* **learning modality: kinesthetic**

Heat Transfer in the Troposphere

TRY THIS

ACTIVITY

Skills Focus interpreting data
Materials *2 thermometers, metric tape measure, watch or clock, graph paper*
Time 10 minutes per day for 3 days; 20 minutes to graph and analyze data
Tips Doing this activity on sunny days will lead to greater differences in temperatures at the two heights.
Expected Outcome Students should find that the temperature 1 cm above the ground varies more than the temperature 1.25 m above the ground. The ground heats up during the day as it absorbs sunlight. It cools quickly at night as it radiates the heat back into the air. Heat is not effectively transferred through air, so air close to the ground will be more affected by these variations in ground temperature than air farther above the ground.
Extend Have students repeat the activity in a shady location and then compare the data obtained from the two locations. They should find less variation in the shady-location readings. Challenge students to explain why. **learning modality: logical/mathematical**

TRY THIS

Temperatures at Two Heights

ACTIVITY

How much difference do you think there is between air temperatures near the ground and air temperatures higher up? Give reasons for your prediction.

1. Take all of your measurements at a location that is sunny all day.
2. Early in the morning, measure the air temperature 1 cm and 1.25 m above the ground. Record the time of day and the temperature for both locations. Repeat your measurements late in the afternoon.
3. Record these measurements in the morning and afternoon for two more days.
4. Graph your data for each height with temperature on the vertical axis and time on the horizontal axis. Draw both lines on the same piece of graph paper using the same axes. Label both lines.

Interpreting Data At which height did the temperature vary the most? How can you explain the difference?

Conduction Have you ever walked barefoot on hot sand? Your feet felt hot because heat moved directly from the sand into your feet. When a fast-moving molecule bumps into a nearby slower-moving molecule, it transfers some of its energy. The direct transfer of heat from one substance to another substance that it is touching is called **conduction.** The molecules that gain energy can in turn pass the energy along to other nearby molecules. When you walk on hot sand, the fast-moving molecules in the sand transfer heat into the slower-moving molecules in your feet.

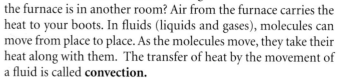

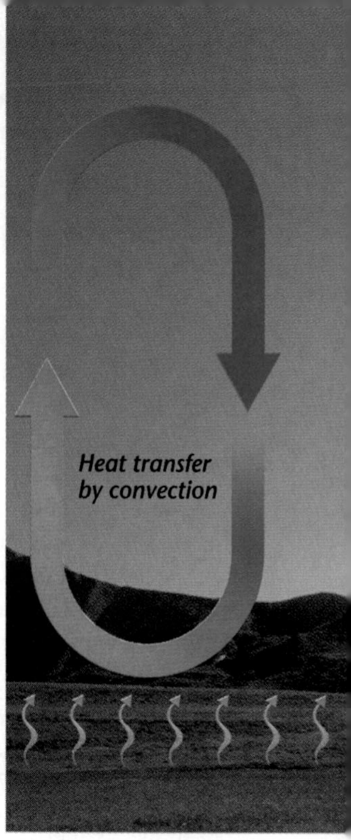

The closer together the molecules in a substance are, the more effectively they can conduct heat. Conduction works well in some solids, such as metals, but not as well in liquids and gases. Air and water do not conduct heat very well.

Convection How can you dry your boots over a hot-air vent, even though the furnace is in another room? Air from the furnace carries the heat to your boots. In fluids (liquids and gases), molecules can move from place to place. As the molecules move, they take their heat along with them. The transfer of heat by the movement of a fluid is called **convection.**

☑ *Checkpoint* ***Give at least one example each of radiation, conduction, and convection in your daily life.***

Heat Transfer in the Troposphere

Radiation, conduction, and convection work together to heat the troposphere. When Earth's surface absorbs solar energy during the day, the surface of the land becomes warmer than the air. Air near Earth's surface is warmed by radiation and conduction of heat from the surface to the air. However, heat is not easily conducted from one air molecule to another. Only the first few meters of the troposphere are heated by conduction. Thus, the air close to the ground is usually warmer than the air a few meters up.

Convection causes most of the heating of the troposphere. When the air near the ground is heated, the molecules have more energy. Because they have more energy, the molecules move

Background

Facts and Figures The highest air temperature ever recorded near Earth's surface is 58°C (136°F), which was recorded in Libya in northern Africa. The highest average annual air temperature ever recorded is 34°C (94°F), which is the average daytime temperature in Ethiopia in eastern Africa. The highest air temperature ever recorded in the Western Hemisphere is 57°C (134°F), at Death Valley, California.

Program Resources

- **Teaching Resources** 2-2 Review and Reinforce, p. 47; 2-2 Enrich, p. 48
- **Science Explorer Series** *Motion, Forces, and Energy,* Chapter 6, has more information about heat energy, temperature, and heat transfer.

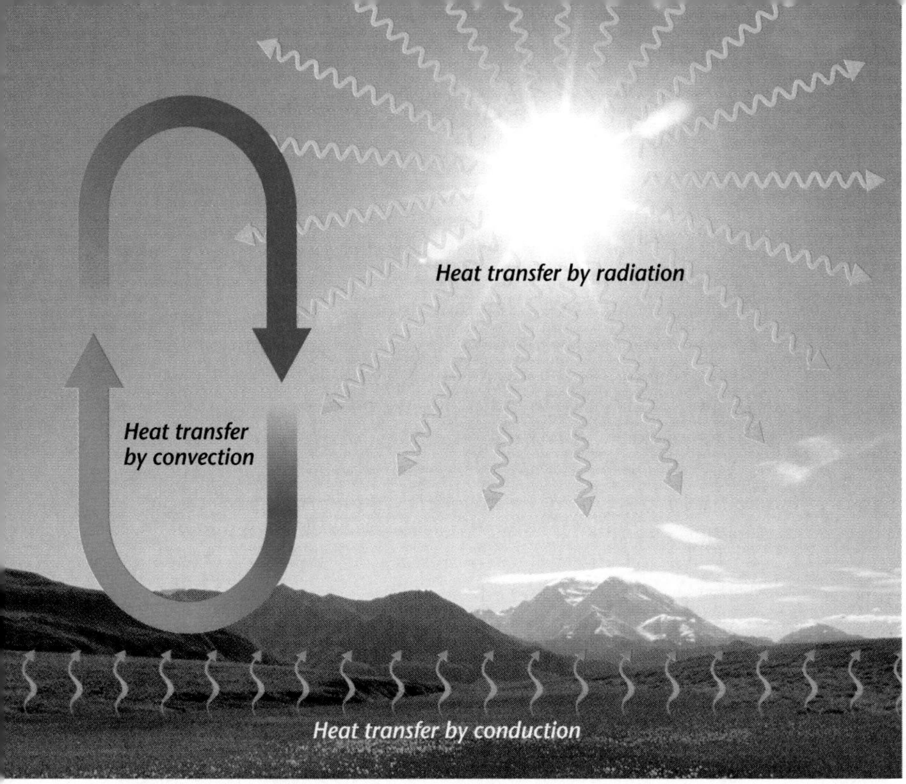

faster. As the molecules in the heated air move, they bump into each other and move farther apart. The air becomes less dense. Cooler, denser air sinks, forcing the warmer, less dense air to rise.

The upward movement of warm air and the downward movement of cool air form convection currents. Convection currents move heat throughout the troposphere.

Figure 5 All three types of heat transfer—radiation, convection, and conduction—occur near Earth's surface.

Section 2 Review

1. What is temperature?
2. Describe how a thermometer works.
3. Name three ways that heat can be transferred. Briefly explain how the three work together to heat the troposphere.
4. **Thinking Critically Applying Concepts** When you light a fire in a fireplace, warm air rises by convection and goes up the chimney. How, then, does a fireplace heat a room? Why do only the people directly in front of the fireplace feel the warmth of the fire?

Check Your Progress CHAPTER PROJECT 2

Gather the instruments you will need to measure the weather factors. (*Hint:* Make sure you know how to take accurate measurements.) Plan when and where to measure weather factors. Be sure to take your measurements at the same location and at the same time of day.

Media and Technology

Interactive Student Tutorial CD-ROM I-2

Answers to Self-Assessment

Checkpoint

Possible examples might include heat radiating from a campfire, heat being conducted through the bottom of a metal pot on a stove, and heat flowing in convection currents through a house heated by a furnace.

Using the Visuals: Figure 5

Call students' attention to the illustration and have them locate the arrows showing each of the three types of heat transfer. Point out that radiation occurs from Earth's surface as well as from the sun. Ask: **How would you represent radiation from Earth's surface in the illustration?** *(With arrows pointing upward from Earth's surface for a long distance, indicating that radiation travels back up through the atmosphere)* **learning modality: visual**

3 Assess

Section 2 Review Answers

1. The average amount of energy of motion in the molecules of a substance
2. When the air temperature increases, the liquid in the bulb of a thermometer expands and rises up the column. When the air temperature decreases, the liquid contracts and moves down the column.
3. Heat can be transferred by radiation, conduction, and convection. Air near Earth's surface is warmed by radiation and by conduction of heat from the surface to the air. When the air near the ground is heated, it becomes less dense and rises in convection currents.
4. A fireplace heats a room by radiation. Only people sitting directly in front of the fire feel its warmth because radiation is the direct transfer of energy and does not effectively heat areas of the room out of the direct line of the fireplace.

Check Your Progress CHAPTER PROJECT 2

Check that students have all the instruments they need and know how to use them. Make sure that the place they plan to take their measurements is suitable. Remind students to take their measurements in the same place and at the same time each day.

Performance Assessment

Drawing Have students draw a diagram to show how heat is transferred from Earth's surface to the atmosphere.

Section 3 Winds

Objectives

After completing the lesson, students will be able to
- explain what causes winds;
- distinguish between local winds and global winds;
- identify where the major global wind belts are located.

Key Terms wind, anemometer, wind-chill factor, local winds, sea breeze, land breeze, monsoons, global winds, Coriolis effect, latitude, jet streams

1 Engage/Explore

Activating Prior Knowledge

Introduce students to winds by helping them recall a time when they flew a kite. Ask: **What made the kite fly in the air?** *(the wind)* **What is wind?** *(the movement of air)*. Then remind students how hard it can be to hold on to a kite against the force of a strong wind. Stress that even though air is an invisible gas, it still consists of molecules, and their movement, especially at high speeds, can exert a lot of force. Tell students they will learn more about wind in this section.

Discover Activity

Skills Focus making models
Materials *heavy-duty tape, pencil, large smooth ball, marker*
Time 10 minutes
Tips Make sure students spin the ball in a counterclockwise direction before their partner draws on it with the marker. You might want to have students also draw a line from the "South Pole" to the "Equator" to see what direction winds blow in the Southern Hemisphere due to Earth's rotation.
Expected Outcome The lines students draw should veer to the west as the marker goes from the "North Pole" to the "Equator" of the ball.
Think It Over The movement of cold air from Canada to the United States would turn toward the west.

Section 3 Winds

Discover Activity

Which Way Does the Wind Turn?

Do this activity with a partner. Think of the ball as a model of Earth and the marker as representing wind.

1. Using heavy-duty tape, attach a pencil to a large smooth ball so that you can spin the ball from the top without touching it.
2. One partner should hold the pencil. Slowly turn the ball counterclockwise when seen from above.
3. While the ball is turning, the second partner should use a marker to try to draw a straight line from the "North Pole" to the "equator" of the ball. What shape does the line form?

Think It Over
Making Models If cold air were moving south from Canada into the United States, how would its movement be affected by Earth's rotation?

Guide for Reading
- What causes winds?
- What are local winds and global winds?
- Where are the major global wind belts located?

Reading Tip **Before you read, preview the illustrations and read their captions. Write down any questions you have about winds. As you read, look for answers to your questions.**

The highest point in the northeastern United States, at 1,917 meters above sea level, is Mount Washington in New Hampshire. Sometimes winds near the top of this mountain are so strong that hikers cannot safely reach the summit! The greatest wind speed ever measured at Earth's surface—370 kilometers per hour—was measured on April 12, 1934, at the top of Mount Washington. What causes this incredible force?

What Causes Winds?

Because air is a fluid, it can move easily from place to place. The force that makes air move is caused by a difference of air pressure. Fluids tend to move from areas of high pressure to areas of low pressure. A **wind** is the horizontal movement of air from an area of high pressure to an area of lower pressure. **All winds are caused by differences in air pressure.**

Reading Strategies

Vocabulary Urge students to look up the word *doldrums* in a dictionary. In addition to being the name for the equatorial zone of calm winds, students will find that it also means "a period of inactivity or stagnation." Call students' attention to the explanation given in the text for the name *horse latitudes.* Knowing the rather memorable story behind it will help them remember that the *horse latitudes* also are zones of calm.

Study and Comprehension Because this is a long section, students may benefit from making a section outline using the headings and subheadings. Suggest that, as they read the section, they annotate their outline with a brief list of main points under each head and subhead. Urge students to use their annotated outlines for study guides.

Most differences in air pressure are caused by unequal heating of the atmosphere. As you learned in the previous section, convection currents form when an area of Earth's surface is heated by the sun's rays. Air over the heated surface expands and becomes less dense. As the air becomes less dense, its air pressure decreases. If a nearby area is not heated as much, the air above the less-heated area will be cooler and denser. The cool, dense air has a higher air pressure so it flows underneath the warm, less dense air. This process forces the warm air to rise.

Measuring Wind

Winds are described by their direction and speed. Wind direction is determined with a wind vane. The wind swings the wind vane so that one end points into the wind. The name of a wind tells you where the wind is coming from. For example, a south wind blows from the south toward the north. A north wind blows to the south.

Wind speed is measured with an **anemometer** (an uh MAHM uh tur). An anemometer has three or four cups mounted at the ends of spokes that spin on an axle. The force of the wind against the cups turns the axle. A speedometer attached to the axle shows the wind speed.

A cool breeze can be very refreshing on a warm day. However, during the winter, a similar breeze can make you feel uncomfortably cold. The wind blowing over your skin removes body heat. The stronger the wind, the colder you feel. The increased cooling that a wind can cause is called the **wind-chill factor.** Thus a weather report may say, "The temperature is 20 degrees Fahrenheit. But with a wind speed of 30 miles per hour, the wind-chill factor makes it feel like 18 degrees below zero."

☑ *Checkpoint* *Toward what direction does a west wind blow?*

TRY THIS

Build a Wind Vane

Here's how to build your own wind vane. ACTIVITY

1. Use scissors to cut out a pointer and a slightly larger tail fin from construction paper.
2. Make a slit 1 cm deep in each end of a soda straw.
3. Slide the pointer and tail fin into place on the straw, securing them with small pieces of tape.

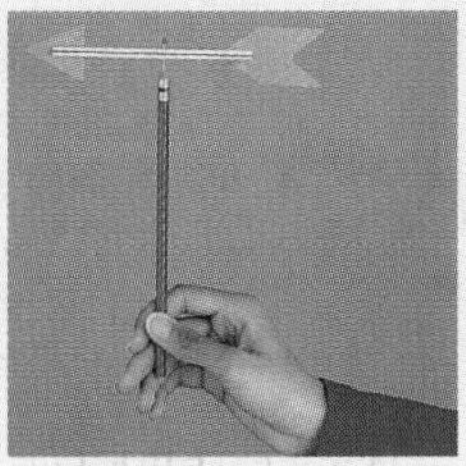

4. Hold the straw on your finger to find the point at which it balances.
5. Carefully push a pin through the balance point and into the eraser of a pencil. Move the wind vane back and forth to make sure it can spin freely.

Observing How can you use your wind vane to tell the direction of the wind?

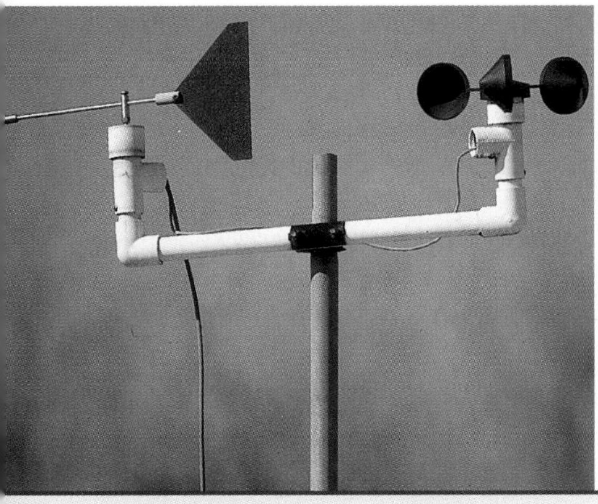

Figure 6 The wind vane on the left points in the direction the wind is blowing from. The anemometer on the right measures wind speed. The cups catch the wind, turning faster when the wind blows faster.

2 Facilitate

What Causes Winds?

Demonstration

Materials *pinwheel, lamp with incandescent light bulb* ACTIVITY
Time 10 minutes

Show students how differences in temperature cause air movement by holding a pinwheel over a lamp. First hold the pinwheel over the lamp with the light bulb turned off. The pinwheel will remain stationary. Then hold the pinwheel over the lamp with the light bulb turned on. Once the light bulb gets hot, the pinwheel will start to spin. Ask: **Why did the pinwheel start spinning after the lightbulb was turned on?** *(The hot light bulb heated the air around it, which rose and turned the pinwheel.)* **learning modality: visual**

Measuring Wind

TRY THIS

Skills Focus observing ACTIVITY
Materials *scissors, construction paper, metric ruler, soda straw, tape, straight pin, pencil with eraser*
Time 15 minutes
Expected Outcome Students should find when they take their wind vane outside in the wind or blow on it that the wind vane points in the direction from which the wind is coming.
Extend If students set their wind vane in the center of a compass, it will show them whether it is an east, west, north, or south wind. Remind students that winds are named for the direction from which they blow. **learning modality: kinesthetic**

Ongoing Assessment

Drawing Have students make a simple drawing with arrows and labels to show how differences in air temperature cause wind.

Portfolio Students can keep their drawings in their portfolios.

Media and Technology

Audiotapes English-Spanish Summary 2-3

Exploring Earth Science Videodisc Unit 2, Side 2, "The Power of Heat"

Chapter 3

Answers to Self-Assessment

☑ *Checkpoint*

A west wind blows toward the east.

Program Resources

◆ **Teaching Resources** 2-3 Lesson Plan, p. 49; 2-3 Section Summary, p. 50

Real-World Lab

You and Your Community

Where's the Wind?

Preparing for Inquiry

Key Concept Obstacles such as buildings can change the speed and direction of the wind.

Skills Objectives Students will be able to

- measure the direction and speed of the wind on all sides of the school building;
- interpret their data to determine which side of the building is less windy than the other sides;
- conclude from the data which side of the building provides the best location for a door.

Time 40 minutes

Advance Planning Follow weather reports when scheduling the lab so students take their measurements on a day when the wind is blowing steadily, not in gusts, and from its usual direction (west in most of the United States). Students can make the anemometers one day and measure wind speed and direction another day. You may want to have a fan or hair dryer for students to use to test their anemometers.

Alternative Materials If you do not have a wind vane, students can measure wind direction by observing the direction that flags are flying or smoke is drifting. Instead of using a corrugated cardboard sheet to make the anemometer, students may use a piece of plastic foam cut from the bottom of a plastic foam plate. Also, wooden craft sticks may be used in place of wooden stirrers. Other types of tape, such as adhesive or electrical tape, will work as well as masking tape.

Guiding Inquiry

Invitation Help students focus on the problem in the lab by asking: **Which two factors do you need to know to determine wind patterns?** *(Wind direction and wind speed)* **How can you measure wind direction?** *(With a wind vane or by observing the direction in which objects are blowing in the wind)* **How can you measure wind speed?** *(With an anemometer)* Point out to students that in this lab they will make a simple anemometer. Then they will use a wind vane to measure wind direction and their anemometer to measure wind speed. Making the measurements on all sides of their school building will let them determine wind patterns around it and from this decide on the best location for a door.

Introducing the Procedure
Have students read through the entire procedure. Explain that the second coffee stirrer added to the anemometer provides a balance for the stirrer that measures wind speed. Point out that the numbers on the dial do not represent actual units, such as kilometers per hour. However, they do allow wind speeds to be quantified for comparison. Stress the importance of taking all measurements the same distance from the building. Suggest that they select a spot near

Local Winds

Have you ever flown a kite at the beach on a hot summer day? Even if there is no wind inland, there may be a cool breeze blowing in from the water toward the beach. This breeze is an example of a local wind. **Local winds** are winds that blow over short distances. **Local winds are caused by unequal heating of Earth's surface within a small area.** Local winds form only when no winds are blowing from farther away.

Real-World Lab

You and Your Community

WHERE'S THE WIND?

Your city is planning to build a new community center. You and your classmates want to be sure that the doors will not be hard to open or close on windy days. You need to know which side of the building will be sheltered from the wind. You decide to measure wind speeds around a similar building.

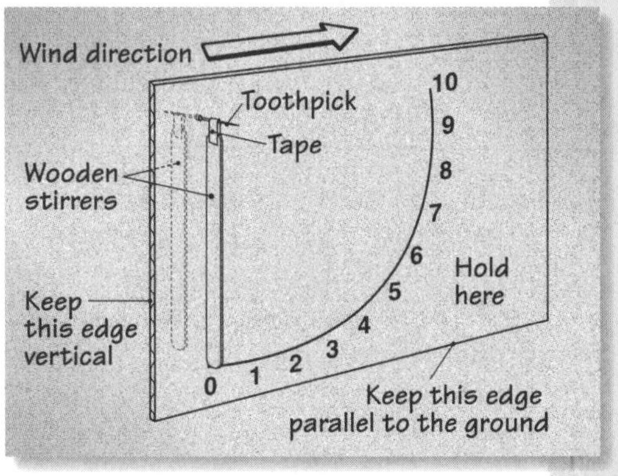

Problem

How can you determine wind patterns around a building?

Skills Focus

measuring, interpreting data, drawing conclusions

Materials

pen	round toothpick
wind vane	2 wooden coffee stirrers
meter stick	narrow masking tape
corrugated cardboard sheet, 15 cm x 20 cm	

Procedure

1. You'll begin by making a simple anemometer that uses wooden coffee stirrers to indicate wind speed. On your piece of cardboard, draw a curved scale like the one shown in the diagram. Mark it in equal intervals from 0 to 10.
2. Carefully use the pen to make a small hole where the toothpick will go. Insert the toothpick through the hole.
3. Tape the wooden coffee stirrers to the toothpick as shown in the diagram, one on each side of the cardboard.
4. Copy the data table into your notebook.
5. Take your anemometer outside the school. Stand about 2–3 m away from the building and away from any corners or large plants.

54 ◆ I

Unequal heating often occurs on land that is next to a large body of water. It takes more energy to warm up a body of water than it does to warm up an equal area of land. This means that as the sun heats Earth's surface during the day, the land warms up faster than the water. The air over the land becomes warmer than the air over the water. The warm air expands and rises, creating a low-pressure area. Cool air blows inland from the water and moves underneath the warm air. A wind that blows

DATA TABLE

Location	Wind Direction	Wind Speed

Analyze and Conclude

1. Was the wind stronger on one side of the school building than the other sides? How can you explain your observation?
2. Do your classmates' results agree with yours? What might account for any differences?
3. **Apply** Based on your data, which side of the building provides the best location for a door?

6. Use the wind vane to find out what direction the wind is coming from. Hold your anemometer so that the card is straight, vertical, and parallel to the wind direction. Observe which number the wooden stirrer is closest to. Record your data.
7. Repeat your measurements on all the other sides of the building. Record your data.

More to Explore

What effect do plants have on the wind speed in an area? Could bushes and trees be planted so that they reduce the wind speed near the doors? What measurements could you make to find out?

Sample Data Table

Location	Wind Direction	Wind Speed
East side of building	W	1
South side of building	NW	4
West side of building	W	3
North side of building	SW	6

Program Resources

- **Teaching Resources** Real-World Lab blackline masters, pp. 64–65

Safety

Do not do this lab on a day when there is danger of lightning or high winds. Review the safety guidelines in Appendix A.

the middle of each side about 2 to 3 m from the building.

Troubleshooting the Experiment

- Have students test their anemometers before they take them outside to measure wind speed. They can use a fan or hair dryer set on low or simply blow on them. They should make sure the coffee stirrers blow freely in the wind and adjust them if necessary.
- Check that students are holding their anemometers parallel to wind direction. Otherwise, the wind will be less effective at moving the coffee stirrer and the anemometer will give a reading that is too low.

Expected Outcome

Students will probably find that one side of the building had winds blowing at a lower speed than the other sides. If a west wind was blowing, then the east side of the building probably was the least windy. Students also may find that wind direction is different from one side of the building to another.

Analyze and Conclude

1. Students probably will find that the wind was stronger on the side of the building that the wind was coming from. Students should explain their observations by saying that the building blocked and slowed the wind on the other sides of the building.
2. Classmates' results may or may not agree. Differences could be due to students measuring the wind at somewhat different locations around the building, wind gusts, or slight differences in how the anemometers were made or used.
3. Students should conclude that the best location is the side of the building that has winds with the lowest speed.

Extending the Inquiry

More to Explore Students may say that bushes and trees can block the wind and reduce its speed near the doors. They could find out by determining wind patterns around bushes and trees, as they did around the school building, to see how these obstacles affect wind direction and speed.

Local Winds

Using the Visuals: Figure 7

Help students analyze the figure's details by asking: **How do the two pictures differ?** *(One shows daytime, the other shows nighttime; warm air is shown rising over the land in the daytime picture and over the water in the nighttime picture.)* **What do the differences tell you about the heating and cooling of land compared with water?** *(Land warms up and cools off more quickly than water.)* **learning modality: visual**

Including All Students

ACTIVITY

Materials *bubble-blowing kit*
Time 10 minutes

Point out to students that, on a local scale, wind direction can be affected by such features as hills, trees, and buildings. Even bushes and cars can cause the wind to change direction. Help students appreciate this by having them blow soap bubbles outside on a breezy day and observe the bubbles as they go around or over obstacles. Ask: **How did the obstacles affect the direction of the bubbles?** *(Answers will vary depending on local winds and obstacles. One possible answer is that a parked car caused the bubbles to rise over the top of it.)* **learning modality: kinesthetic**

Monsoons

Cultural Diversity

Point out to students that the word *monsoon* comes from an Arabic word meaning "season." It used to mean a wind in South and Southeast Asia that changed direction with the seasons, although now it means *any* wind that changes direction with the seasons. Add that many other local winds also have special names. Have students who need an extra challenge look up the following names for local winds in other parts of the world: *chinook, levanter, mistral, sirocco,* and *Santa Ana.* They should find out what each name means and what type of wind it refers to. Then give the students a chance to share what they learn with the rest of the class. **learning modality: verbal**

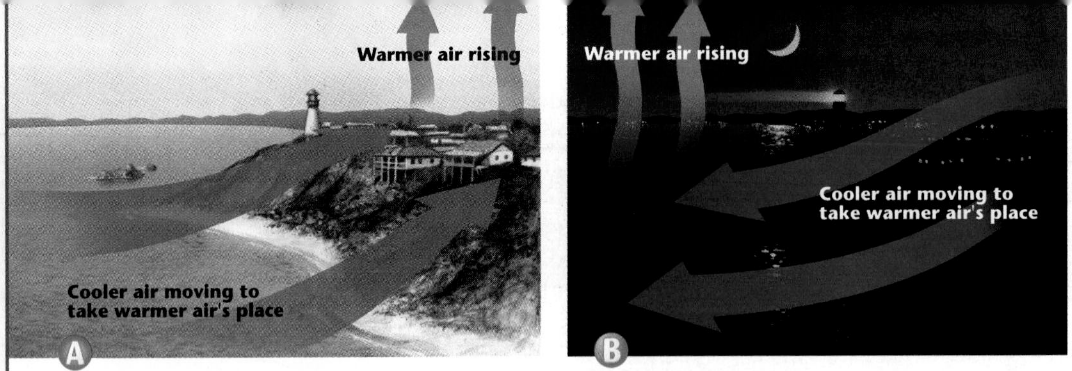

Figure 7 **A.** During the day, cool air moves from the sea to the land, creating a sea breeze. **B.** At night, cooler air moves from the land to the sea. *Forming Operational Definitions What type of breeze occurs at night?*

from an ocean or lake onto land is known as a **sea breeze** or a lake breeze. Figure 7A shows a sea breeze.

At night, the situation is reversed. Land cools more quickly than water, so the air over the land becomes cooler than the air over the water. As the warmer air over the water rises, cooler air moves from the land to take its place. The flow of air from land to a body of water is called a **land breeze.**

Monsoons

A process similar to land and sea breezes can occur over wider areas. In the summer in South and Southeast Asia, the land gradually gets warmer than the ocean. A large "sea breeze" blows steadily inland from the ocean all summer, even at night. In the winter, the land cools and becomes colder than the ocean. A "land breeze" blows steadily from the land to the ocean.

Sea and land breezes over a large region that change direction with the seasons are called **monsoons.** The summer monsoon in South Asia and Southeast Asia is very important for the crops grown there. The air blowing from the ocean during the rainy season is very warm and humid. As the humid air rises over the land, the air cools, producing heavy rains that supply the water needed by rice and other crops.

Figure 8 This heavy rain in Nepal is part of the summer monsoon, which blows from the ocean to the land. In the winter, the monsoon reverses and blows from the land to the ocean.

Summer Monsoon **Winter Monsoon**

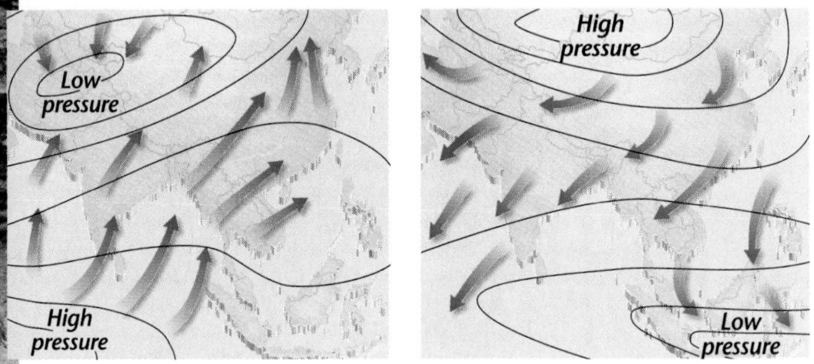

Background

Facts and Figures Mount Washington, New Hampshire, not only has the highest wind speed ever recorded, as stated in the text. It also has the highest average wind speed in the United States, at 56 kilometers per hour. The overall windiest state is not New Hampshire, however, but Alaska, because it holds the most local records for highest average wind speed. Other especially windy places include Amarillo, Texas; Boston, Massachusetts; Wichita, Kansas; Buffalo, New York; and Honolulu, Hawaii.

High wind speeds can make you feel much colder because of wind-chill. For example, if the actual air temperature is 4°C (40°F), a 10-mph wind makes it feel like it's -2°C (28°F). Increase wind speed to 30 mph, and the same 4°C temperature feels like -11°C (13°F). Winds greater than 30 mph cause very little additional chilling.

Global Winds

Winds that blow steadily from specific directions over long distances are called **global winds.** Like local winds, global winds are created by unequal heating of Earth's surface. Refer to Figure 9 to see how sunlight strikes Earth's surface. In the middle of the day near the equator, the sun is almost directly overhead. The direct rays from the sun heat Earth's surface intensely. Near the North Pole or South Pole, the sun's rays strike Earth's surface at a lower angle, even at noon. The sun's energy is spread out over a larger area, so it heats the surface less. As a result, temperatures near the poles are much lower than they are near the equator.

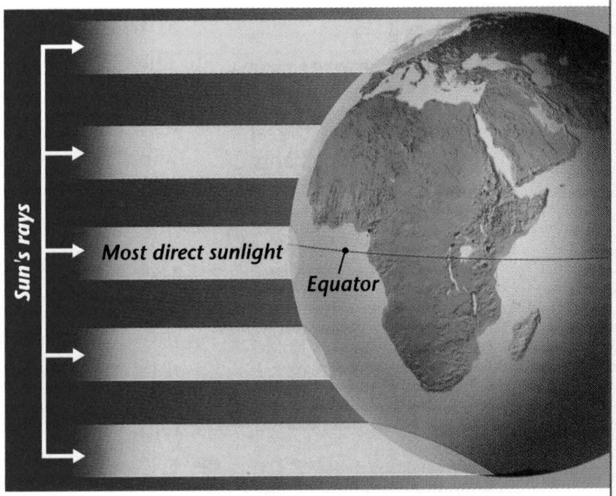

Figure 9 Near the equator, energy from the sun strikes Earth almost directly. Near the poles, the same amount of energy is spread out over a larger area.

Global Convection Currents Temperature differences between the equator and the poles produce giant convection currents in the atmosphere. Warm air rises at the equator, and cold air sinks at the poles. Therefore air pressure tends to be lower near the equator and greater near the poles, causing winds at Earth's surface to blow from the poles toward the equator. Higher in the atmosphere, air flows away from the equator toward the poles. **The movement of air between the equator and the poles produces global winds.**

The Coriolis Effect If Earth did not rotate, global winds would blow in a straight line from the poles toward the equator. Because Earth is rotating, global winds do not follow a straight path. As the winds move, Earth rotates from west to east underneath them, making it seem as if the winds have curved. The way Earth's rotation makes winds curve is called the **Coriolis effect** (kawr ee OH lis). It is named for the French mathematician who studied and explained it in 1835.

In the Northern Hemisphere, all global winds gradually turn toward the right. As you can see in Figure 10, a wind blowing toward the north gradually turns toward the northeast. In other words, a south wind gradually changes to a southwest wind. In the Southern Hemisphere, winds curve toward the left. A south wind becomes an southeast wind, and a north wind becomes a northwest wind.

Figure 10 As Earth rotates, the Coriolis effect turns winds in the Northern Hemisphere toward the right. *Interpreting Diagrams Which way do winds turn in the Southern Hemisphere?*

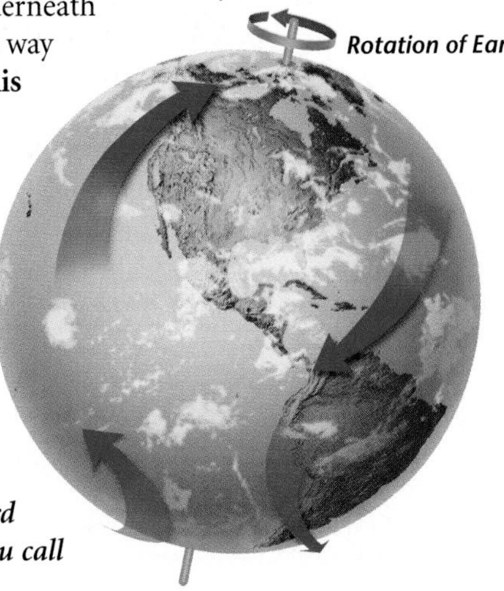

☑ *Checkpoint What happens to a wind blowing toward the south in the Northern Hemisphere? What would you call this wind?*

Global Winds

Demonstration

Materials *globe, small flashlight*
Time 5 minutes

ACTIVITY

Challenge a pair of students to model Earth and the sun using a globe and flashlight. *(One student should hold the globe, and the other student should shine the light on the equator, with the room lights dimmed.)* Call students' attention to the fact that the light is direct and bright over the equator but angled and dim at the poles. Ask: **How do these differences in energy cause global winds?** *(The more concentrated energy falling directly on the equator causes air over the equator to be warmer than air over the poles, leading to the convection currents that cause global winds.)* **learning modality: visual**

Answers to Self-Assessment

Caption Questions

Figure 7 A land breeze occurs at night.
Figure 10 In the Southern Hemisphere, winds turn toward the left.

☑ *Checkpoint*

A wind blowing toward the south in the Northern Hemisphere gradually turns toward the right. You would call it a northeast wind.

Ongoing Assessment

Drawing Have students make a sketch in their journals to show how the Coriolis effect influences global winds.

Global Wind Belts

Including All Students

Materials *globe*
Time 10 minutes

ACTIVITY

Give students who need extra help a chance to spin a globe in a counterclockwise direction while moving their finger over its surface from north to south. Ask: **How does the path you traced on the globe model global winds?** *(The path of global winds curves to the right in the same way.)* Then have students use the globe to locate a city or country that interests them. Ask: **Which major wind belt flows over that location?** *(Answers will vary depending on locations students choose.)* Suggest that students find the latitude of their location to determine which global wind belt flows over it. **learning modality: kinesthetic**

Social Studies CONNECTION

Make sure students realize that for the time period in question, ships had sails and depended on the wind to move. Suggest that they refer to the illustration on page 59 when doing this feature. From the figure, students should be able to identify which winds they would have used to sail east *(prevailing westerlies)* and which they would have used to sail west *(trade winds).*

In Your Journal Students should see from the figure on page 59 that making use of the trade winds to go west requires a more southern route across the Atlantic. They should write in their letter that the journey west takes almost twice as many weeks because the southern route is less direct and longer. **learning modality: verbal**

Social Studies CONNECTION

From colonial days to the late 1800s, American merchants traded new ships, lumber, cotton, tobacco, and furs for manufactured goods, such as textiles, from England. The eastbound voyage in the early 1800s took about three weeks. However, the westbound passage took almost twice as long—five to six weeks.

In Your Journal

Imagine that you are a sea captain making the voyage to England and back to America. Your family doesn't understand why your journey home takes almost twice as long as your journey to England. Write a letter to your family explaining why you have to travel farther south to take advantage of the prevailing winds on your return voyage.

Global Wind Belts

The Coriolis effect and other factors combine to produce a pattern of calm areas and wind belts around Earth. The calm areas include the doldrums and the horse latitudes. **The major global wind belts are the trade winds, the prevailing westerlies, and the polar easterlies.** As you read about each area, find it in *Exploring Global Winds.*

Doldrums Near the equator, the sun heats the surface strongly. Warm air rises steadily, creating an area of low pressure. Cool air moves into the area, but is warmed rapidly and rises before it moves very far. There is very little horizontal motion, so the winds near the equator are very weak. Regions near the equator with little or no wind are called the doldrums.

Horse Latitudes Warm air that rises at the equator divides and flows both north and south. **Latitude** is the distance from the equator, measured in degrees. At about 30° north and south latitudes, the air stops moving toward the poles and sinks. In each of these regions, another belt of calm air forms. Hundreds of years ago, sailors becalmed in these waters ran out of food and water for their horses and had to throw the horses overboard. Because of this, the latitudes 30° north and south of the equator are called the horse latitudes.

Trade Winds When the cold air over the horse latitudes sinks, it produces a region of high pressure. This high pressure causes surface winds to blow both toward the equator and away from it. The winds that blow toward the equator are turned west by the Coriolis effect. As a result, winds in the Northern Hemisphere between 30° north latitude and the equator blow generally from the northeast. In the Southern Hemisphere between 30° south latitude and the equator, the winds blow from the southeast. These steady easterly winds are called the trade winds. For hundreds of years, sailors relied on them to carry cargoes from Europe to the West Indies and South America.

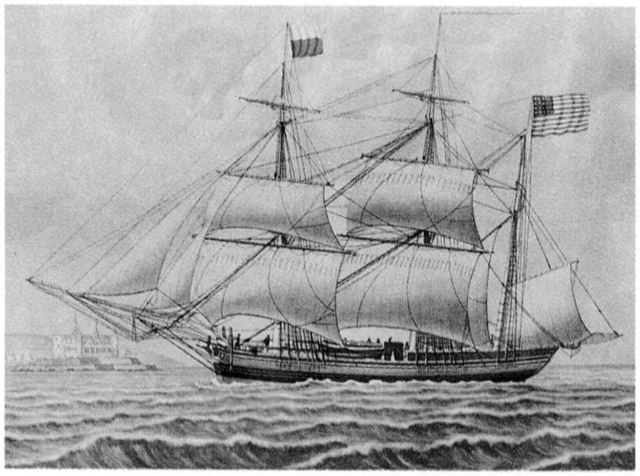

Figure 11 The bark *Patriot,* built in 1809, carried goods to many parts of the world. *Applying Concepts How much effect do you think the prevailing winds have on shipping today?*

Background

Integrating Science Like global winds, the surface currents of oceans are deflected by the Coriolis effect. They flow to the right in the Northern Hemisphere and to the left in the Southern Hemisphere.

The prevailing winds blow the surface waters of the oceans and contribute to the deflection of ocean currents caused by the Coriolis effect. For example, the prevailing westerlies, which blow across most of the United States, help make the Gulf Stream the largest, strongest surface current in the North Atlantic Ocean. The Gulf Stream flows from the Caribbean Sea northeast along the east coast of the United States until it reaches North Carolina. Then it veers off into the Atlantic Ocean. Eventually the Gulf Stream reaches the western coast of Europe, where its warm waters bring relatively mild, humid weather.

EXPLORING Global Winds

A series of wind belts circles Earth. Between the wind belts are calm areas where air is rising or falling.

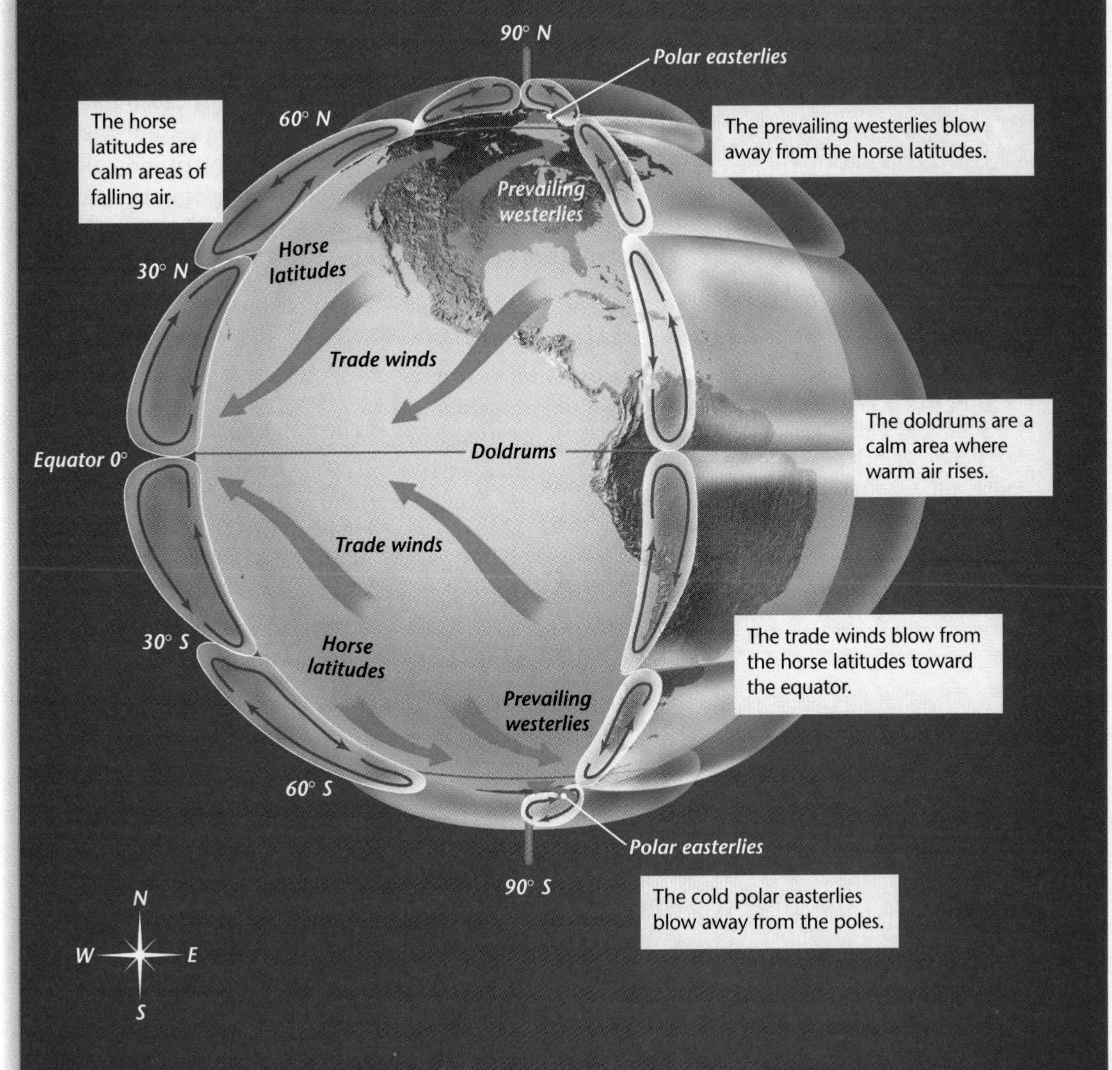

90° N
Polar easterlies
The horse latitudes are calm areas of falling air.
60° N
The prevailing westerlies blow away from the horse latitudes.
Prevailing westerlies
Horse latitudes
30° N
Trade winds
The doldrums are a calm area where warm air rises.
Equator 0°
Doldrums
Trade winds
The trade winds blow from the horse latitudes toward the equator.
30° S
Horse latitudes
Prevailing westerlies
60° S
Polar easterlies
90° S
The cold polar easterlies blow away from the poles.
N
W
E
S

Media and Technology

Transparencies "Global Winds," Transparency 7

Answers to Self-Assessment

Caption Question

Figure 11 Answers may vary. The most likely answer is that prevailing winds have little effect on shipping today because ships no longer depend on the winds to move.

EXPLORING

Global Winds

Make sure students understand that the spin of the planet in the figure is from left to right, or counterclockwise as seen from the North Pole. Check to see that students understand how the two different types of arrows are used in the diagram. Ask: **What do the small blue arrows pointing straight north or straight south represent?** *(The general direction of convection currents in the atmosphere due to unequal heating)* **What do the large red arrows represent?** *(The direction in which global winds blow because of the Coriolis effect)*

Tell students to assume they are planning a sailing trip from California to the tip of South America. Have them use the figure to trace with a finger the route they would take. Ask: **Which winds would help speed you on your way?** *(In the Northern Hemisphere the trade winds and in the Southern Hemisphere the prevailing westerlies)* **Which winds would slow you down?** *(In the Northern Hemisphere the prevailing westerlies and in the Southern Hemisphere the trade winds)*

Students may not understand why the two major global wind belts in each hemisphere blow in opposite north/south directions, even though both are turned in the same east/west direction by Earth's rotation. Explain that they blow in opposite directions because the convection currents that produce them flow in opposite directions. Point out in the figure how, in the Northern hemisphere, the convection currents in the region of the prevailing westerlies flow to the north, whereas in the region of the trade winds, the convection currents flow to the south. **learning modality: visual**

Ongoing Assessment

Oral Presentation Call on students at random to explain in their own words similarities and differences between the prevailing westerlies and the trade winds.

Jet Streams

Building Inquiry Skills: Inferring

Point out that the jet stream follows the boundary between the prevailing westerlies and polar easterlies. Ask: **Why do you think the jet stream is farther south in the winter?** *(As the sun's direct rays move south, the global wind belts also shift south.)* **learning modality: logical/mathematical**

3 Assess

Section 3 Review Answers

1. Unequal heating of air above Earth's surface causes winds because the warm air rises and cool air moves in to take its place.
2. Both local and global winds are caused by unequal heating of Earth's surface. Local winds cover small areas; global winds circle the globe. Local winds often change direction; global winds do not.
3. The major wind belts are trade winds, prevailing westerlies, and polar easterlies. Students' drawings should show the winds as pictured on page 59.
4. The pilot should set a course to the southeast because Earth's rotation will result in the plane going west relative to cities on the ground.

Check Your Progress CHAPTER PROJECT 2

Check that students continue to take accurate measurements. Make sure they are recording all the measurements in their weather log, including the units for each measurement.

Performance Assessment

Writing/Drawing Have students write a paragraph explaining what causes global winds and why they flow in the direction they do. Have them accompany their explanation with a clearly labeled diagram.

Figure 12 By traveling east in a jet stream, pilots can save time and fuel. *Predicting What would happen if a plane flew west in a jet stream?*

Prevailing Westerlies In the mid-latitudes, winds that blow toward the poles are turned toward the east by the Coriolis effect. Because they blow from the west to the east, they are called prevailing westerlies. The prevailing westerlies blow generally from the southwest between 30° and 60° north latitudes and from the northwest between 30° and 60° south latitudes. The prevailing westerlies play an important part in the weather of the United States.

Polar Easterlies Cold air near the poles sinks and flows back toward lower latitudes. The Coriolis effect shifts these polar winds to the west, producing winds called the polar easterlies. The polar easterlies meet the prevailing westerlies at about 60° north and 60° south latitudes, along a region called the polar front. The mixing of warm and cold air along the polar front has a major effect on weather changes in the United States.

☑ *Checkpoint* ***In what region do the polar easterlies meet the prevailing westerlies?***

Jet Streams

About 10 kilometers above Earth's surface are bands of high-speed winds called **jet streams.** These winds are hundreds of kilometers wide but only a few kilometers deep. Jet streams blow from west to east at speeds of 200 to 400 kilometers per hour. As jet streams travel around Earth, they wander north and south along a wavy path.

Airplanes are aided by a jet stream when traveling east. Pilots can save fuel and time by flying east in a jet stream. However, airplanes flying at jet stream altitudes are slowed down when traveling west against the jet stream winds.

Section 3 Review

1. How does the unequal heating of Earth's surface cause winds?
2. How are local winds and global winds similar? How are they different?
3. Name and draw the three major wind belts.
4. **Thinking Critically Applying Concepts** Imagine you are flying from Seattle to San Francisco, which is almost exactly due south of Seattle. Should the pilot set a course due south? Explain your answer.

Check Your Progress CHAPTER PROJECT 2

Check with your teacher to be sure you are using the weather instruments correctly. Are you recording units for each measurement? Collect and record measurements each day.

Answers to Self-Assessment

☑ *Checkpoint*

The polar easterlies meet the prevailing westerlies at about the 60° north and 60° south latitudes.

Caption Question

Figure 12 If a plane flew west in a jet stream, it would be slowed down by the winds flowing east.

Program Resources

- **Teaching Resources** 2-3 Review and Reinforce, p. 51; 2-3 Enrich, p. 52

Media and Technology

Interactive Student Tutorial CD-ROM I-2

SECTION 4 Water in the Atmosphere

DISCOVER — ACTIVITY

How Does Fog Form?

1. Fill a narrow-necked plastic bottle with hot tap water. Pour out most of the water, leaving about 3 cm at the bottom. **CAUTION:** *Avoid spilling hot water. Do not use water that is so hot that you cannot safely hold the bottle.*
2. Place an ice cube on the mouth of the bottle. What happens?
3. Repeat Steps 1 and 2 using cold water instead of hot water. What happens?

Think It Over

Developing Hypotheses How can you explain your observations? Why is there a difference between what happens with the hot water and with the cold water?

GUIDE FOR READING

- How is relative humidity measured?
- How do clouds form?
- What are the three main types of clouds?

Reading Tip **Before you read, write a definition of "cloud." Revise your definition as you read about clouds.**

During a rainstorm, the air feels moist. On a clear, cloudless day, the air may feel dry. As the sun heats the land and oceans, the amount of water in the atmosphere changes. Water is always moving between the atmosphere and Earth's surface.

This movement of water between the atmosphere and Earth's surface, called the water cycle, is shown in Figure 13. Water vapor enters the air by evaporation from the oceans and other bodies of water. **Evaporation** is the process by which water molecules in liquid water escape into the air as water vapor. Water vapor is also added to the air by living things. Water enters the roots of plants, rises to the leaves, and is released as water vapor.

As part of the water cycle, some of the water vapor in the atmosphere condenses to form clouds. Rain and other forms of precipitation fall from the clouds toward the surface. The water then runs off the surface, or moves through the ground, back into the oceans, lakes, and streams.

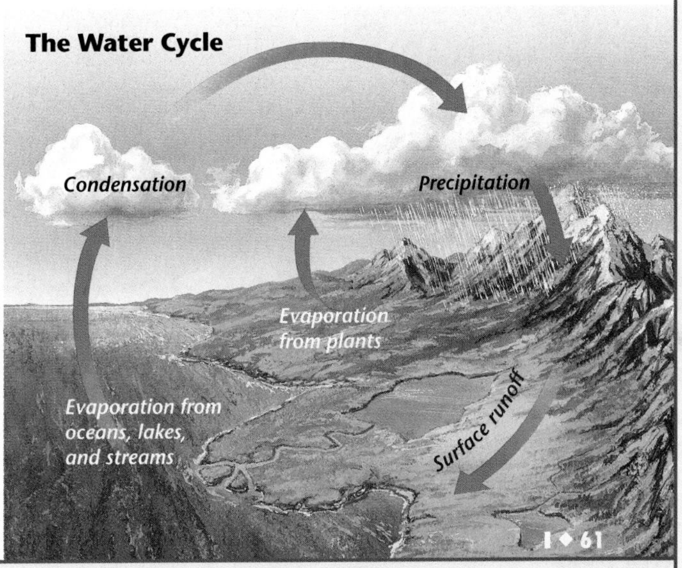

Figure 13 In the water cycle, water moves from lakes and oceans into the atmosphere and falls back to Earth.

READING STRATEGIES

Vocabulary Help students keep track of the complex names of clouds with these helpful hints. The words *cumulus, stratus,* and *cirrus* describe basic cloud shapes. If the word *nimbus* or the prefix *nimbo-* is added, it means that the cloud produces rain or snow. The prefix *alto-* means that the cloud is a medium-altitude cloud. The prefix *cirro-* means that the cloud is a high-altitude cloud.

Program Resources

- **Teaching Resources** 2-4 Lesson Plan, p. 53; 2-4 Section Summary, p. 54

Media and Technology

Audiotapes English-Spanish Summary 2-4

Transparencies "The Water Cycle," Transparency 8

SECTION 4 Water in the Atmosphere

Objectives

After completing the lesson, students will be able to

- describe how relative humidity is measured;
- explain how clouds form;
- name the three main types of clouds.

Key Terms evaporation, humidity, relative humidity, psychrometer, condensation, dew point, cumulus, stratus, cirrus

1 Engage/Explore

Activating Prior Knowledge

Help students recall seeing water vapor condense out of the air. Ask: **Have you ever noticed when you take a shower that the bathroom mirror clouds up?** *(Most students will have had this experience.)* **Do you know what causes this?** *(Students may say it is caused by moisture in the air from the shower.)* Explain that when warm moist air from the shower comes into contact with the cool surface of the mirror, the air cools and can hold less water vapor. As a result, water vapor condenses on the mirror. Point out that clouds form the same way: water vapor condenses when warm moist air cools in the atmosphere.

DISCOVER — ACTIVITY

Skills Focus developing hypotheses
Materials *narrow-necked plastic bottle, hot tap water, 2 ice cubes, cold tap water*
Time 10 minutes
Tips Make sure students let the bottle cool before repeating Steps 1 and 2 with cold water.
Expected Outcome Fog will form in the bottle when it contains hot water but not when it contains cold water.
Think It Over Fog forms in the bottle when warm moist air rises from the surface of the hot water and condenses as it cools near the ice cube. This does not occur when there is cold water in the bottle because the cold water does not produce warm moist air.

2 Facilitate

Humidity

Integrating Life Science

Help students appreciate how evaporation can cool the body by asking: **Did you ever step out of a swimming pool on a hot day and feel cold, even though the air was warmer than the water?** *(Most students will have experienced this.)* **Why did you feel cold?** *(As the water evaporated, it took heat from the body.)* Then help students appreciate the effect of high relative humidity on evaporative cooling. Ask: **What happens when you exercise on a hot, humid day?** *(You get wet with sweat, but the sweat doesn't evaporate and cool you down.)* **learning modality: verbal**

Measuring Relative Humidity

Inquiry Challenge

ACTIVITY

Materials *human hair, drinking straw, tape, glue, clay, shoebox, or other materials of students' choice*

Time 20 minutes for setup; 5 minutes for later observations

Tell students that human hair shrinks when the humidity is low and stretches when the humidity is high. Then challenge students to use a human hair to indicate changes in humidity. One way students might do this is by setting a shoebox on one of its long sides and taping one end of a drinking straw to the inside of this long side. The unattached end of the straw should be close, but not touching, the inside of a short side of the shoebox. Then attach a long human hair to the straw and to the inside of the opposite (top) long side of the shoebox so it suspends the unattached end of the straw, making it a pointer. Plug this end of the straw with a little clay so the hair remains taut. Students can calibrate this hair hygrometer by observing the straw pointer move up and down with changes in humidity. **learning modality: logical/mathematical**

Humidity

Humidity is a measure of the amount of water vapor in the air. The percentage of water vapor in the air compared to the maximum amount the air could hold is called the **relative humidity.** For example, at 10°C, 1 cubic meter of air can hold a maximum of 8 grams of water vapor. If there actually were 8 grams of water vapor in the air, then the relative humidity of the air would be 100 percent. If the air held 4 grams of water vapor, the relative humidity would be half, or 50 percent. The amount of water vapor that the air can hold depends on its temperature. Warm air can hold more water vapor than cool air.

INTEGRATING LIFE SCIENCE "It's not the heat, it's the humidity." What does this common expression mean? Even on a hot day, you can still feel comfortable if the air is dry. Evaporation of moisture from your skin removes heat and helps to keep your body's temperature comfortable. You feel less comfortable on a hot day if the relative humidity is high. When the relative humidity is high, evaporation slows down. Evaporation therefore has less cooling effect on your body.

Measuring Relative Humidity

Relative humidity can be measured with a psychrometer. A **psychrometer** (sy KRAHM uh tur) has two thermometers, a wet-bulb thermometer and a dry-bulb thermometer. The bulb of the wet-bulb thermometer has a cloth covering that is moistened with water. Air is then blown over both thermometers. Because the wet-bulb thermometer is cooled by evaporation, its reading drops below that of the dry-bulb thermometer.

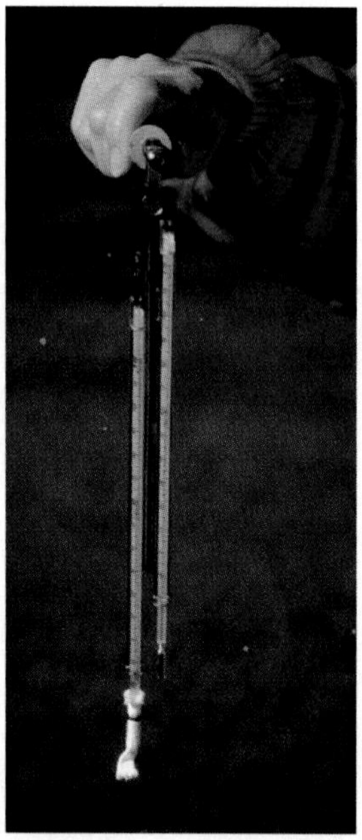

Relative Humidity

Dry-Bulb Reading (°C)	Difference Between Wet- and Dry-Bulb Readings (°C)				
	1	2	3	4	5
10	88	76	65	54	43
12	88	78	67	57	48
14	89	79	69	60	50
16	90	80	71	62	54
18	91	81	72	64	56
20	91	82	74	66	58
22	92	83	75	68	60
24	92	84	76	69	62
26	92	85	77	70	64
28	93	86	78	71	65
30	93	86	79	72	66

Figure 14 A sling psychrometer is used to measure relative humidity. First, find the wet-bulb and dry-bulb temperatures. Then find the dry-bulb temperature in the left column of the table. Find the difference between the wet- and dry-bulb temperatures across the top of the table. The number in the table where these two readings intersect indicates the relative humidity in percent.

Background

Facts and Figures The heat stress index tells you how much hotter it feels because of high humidity. For example, a temperature of 38°C (100°F) combined with a relative humidity of 50% gives a heat stress index of 49°C (120°F). In other words, the humidity makes it feel like it is 11°C (20°F) hotter than it actually is.

The dew point is a good indicator of relative humidity, because the higher the temperature at which water vapor starts condensing out of the air, the more saturated the air must be. When the dew point is 27°C (80°F) or higher, humidity is extremely high. When the dew point is around 10°C (50°F), humidity is moderate. When the dew point is below 4°C (40°F), humidity is very low.

If the relative humidity is high, the water on the wet bulb will evaporate slowly and the wet-bulb temperature will not change much. If the relative humidity is low, the water on the wet bulb will evaporate rapidly and the wet-bulb temperature will drop. The relative humidity can be found by comparing the temperatures of the wet-bulb and dry-bulb thermometers on a table like the one in Figure 14.

☑ *Checkpoint* ***What is the difference between humidity and relative humidity?***

How Clouds Form

What do clouds remind you of? They can look like people, animals, countries, and a thousand other fanciful forms. Of course, not all clouds are fluffy and white. Storm clouds can be dark and cover the whole sky.

Clouds of all kinds form when water vapor in the air becomes liquid water or ice crystals. The process by which molecules of water vapor in the air become liquid water is called **condensation.** How does water condense? As you know, cold air can hold less water vapor than warm air. As air cools, the amount of water vapor it can hold decreases. Some of the water vapor in the air condenses to form droplets of liquid water.

The temperature at which condensation begins is called the **dew point.** If the dew point is below the freezing point, the water vapor may change directly into ice crystals. When you look at a cloud, you are seeing millions of tiny ice crystals or water droplets.

For water vapor to condense, tiny particles must be present so the water has a surface on which to condense. Most of these particles are salt crystals, dust from soil, and smoke. Sometimes water vapor condenses onto solid surfaces, such as blades of grass, instead of particles. Water that condenses from the air onto a cold surface is called dew. Frost is ice that has been deposited directly from the air onto a cold surface.

Clouds form whenever air is cooled to its dew point and particles are present. But why does the air cool? If air is warmed near the ground, it

Figure 15 Dew forms when water vapor condenses out of the air onto a solid surface, such as this flower.

Sharpen your Skills

Interpreting Data

ACTIVITY

At lunchtime you use a psychrometer and get readings of 26°C on the dry-bulb thermometer and 21°C on the wet-bulb thermometer. Use Figure 14 to find the relative humidity.

Later in the day you use the psychrometer again and this time get readings of 20°C on the dry-bulb thermometer and 19°C on the wet-bulb thermometer. Find the new relative humidity. Is the relative humidity increasing or decreasing?

Program Resources

◆ **Integrated Science Laboratory Manual** I-2, "Using a Psychrometer to Determine Relative Humidity"

Science Explorer Series *Earth's Waters,* Chapter 1, has more information about the water cycle.

Answers to Self-Assessment

☑ *Checkpoint*

Humidity is a measure of the amount of water vapor in the air. Relative humidity is the percentage of water vapor in the air compared to the maximum amount the air could hold.

Sharpen your Skills

Interpreting Data

ACTIVITY

Time 10 minutes

Tips Remind students to subtract the wet-bulb reading from the dry-bulb reading and then find the difference between the two readings in the table.

Expected Outcome The first value for relative humidity is 64%, the second is 91%; relative humidity is increasing.

Extend Use the table to help students understand the relationship between temperature and relative humidity. Ask: **When the difference between wet- and dry-bulb readings is small, is the relative humidity high or low?** *(high)* **How is this relationship affected by air temperature?** *(The higher the air temperature, the higher the relative humidity for a given difference between wet- and dry-bulb readings.)* **learning modality: logical-mathematical**

How Clouds Form

Building Inquiry Skills: Measuring

ACTIVITY

Materials *beaker, room-temperature water, ice cubes, stirring rod, thermometer*

Time 10 minutes

Have students find the dew point in the classroom. Have them fill a beaker with room-temperature water and measure and record the water temperature. Then have them add a few ice cubes to the beaker and stir the ice water. As soon as moisture forms, have students measure and record the temperature of the water again. This temperature represents the dew point in the classroom. Ask: **Would the dew point be the same if you did this experiment on a different day?** *(Probably not, because the dew point depends on the temperature and relative humidity)* **learning modality: logical/mathematical**

Ongoing Assessment

Writing Have students explain in their own words how temperature, humidity, and dew point are related.

How Clouds Form, continued

Building Inquiry Skills: Inferring

ACTIVITY

Materials *water, gallon bottle with cap, bicycle pump*
Time 10 minutes

Show students how clouds form by making a cloud in a bottle. Explain that air gets warmer when compressed and cooler when allowed to expand. Cover the bottom of a gallon bottle with a few centimeters of water. Use a nail to punch holes in the cap, overlapping the holes to make an opening about 0.5 cm in diameter. Place the cap on the bottle and push the nozzle of a bicycle pump into the opening. Have a volunteer push down on the pump two or three times. Quickly release the cap, and a cloud will form inside the bottle. Ask: **Why did a cloud form inside the bottle?** *(Pumping air into the bottle compressed and warmed the air in the bottle, so it picked up moisture from the water. Letting air out of the bottle let the air in the bottle expand and cool, so it could hold less water. Water condensed out of the air, forming a cloud.)* **learning modality: logical/mathematical**

Types of Clouds

Including All Students

Help students become more familiar with the distinctive shapes of the main cloud types. Find and bring to class several drawings or photographs of different types of clouds. Challenge students to identify the types of clouds shown in the pictures. Ask: **How can you tell which of the three main types a cloud is?** *(by its shape)* **learning modality: visual**

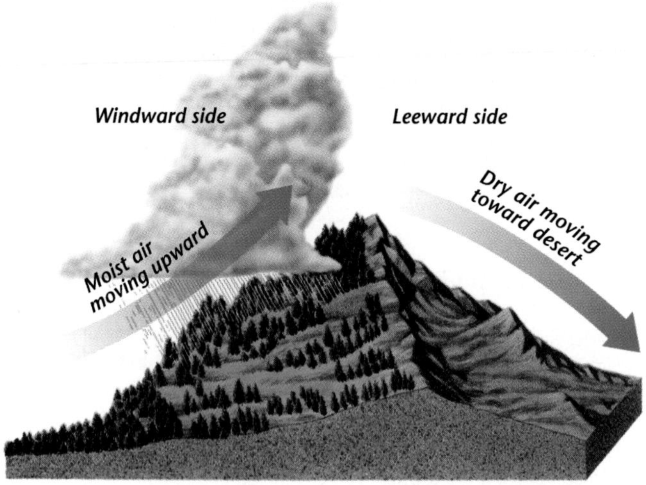

Figure 16 Humid air cools as it is blown up the side of a mountain. *Predicting What happens when water vapor condenses out of the air?*

becomes less dense and rises in a convection current. When the rising air expands and becomes cooler, clouds may form.

When wind strikes the side of a hill or mountain, the air is forced upward. As the air rises along the slope, the air cools. Rain or snow falls on the windward side of the mountains, the side facing the oncoming wind.

By the time the air reaches the other side of the mountains, it has lost much of its water vapor. The air is cool and dry. The land on the leeward side of the mountains—downwind—is in a rain shadow. Just as very little light falls in a sun shadow, very little rain falls in a rain shadow. Not only has the air lost its water vapor while crossing the mountains, but the air has also grown warmer while flowing down the mountainside. This warm, dry air creates a desert on the leeward side of the mountains.

***Checkpoint* Why are the tops of some mountains almost always covered by clouds?**

Types of Clouds

As you know, clouds come in different shapes. **Meteorologists classify clouds into three main types: cumulus, stratus, and cirrus.** Clouds are also classified by their altitude. Each type of cloud is associated with a different type of weather.

Clouds that look like fluffy, rounded piles of cotton are called **cumulus** (KYOO myuh lus) clouds. The word *cumulus* means "heap" or "mass." Cumulus clouds form less than 2 kilometers above the ground, but may grow in size and height until they extend upward as much as 18 kilometers. Cumulus clouds usually indicate fair weather. Towering clouds with flat tops, called cumulonimbus clouds, often produce thunderstorms. The suffix *-nimbus* comes from a Latin word meaning "rain."

Clouds that form in flat layers are called **stratus** (STRAT us) clouds. *Strato* means "spread out." Stratus clouds usually cover all or most of the sky. As stratus clouds thicken, they may produce drizzle, rain, or snow. They are then called nimbostratus clouds.

Wispy, feathery clouds are called **cirrus** (SEER us) clouds. Cirrus clouds form only at high levels, above about 6 kilometers, where temperatures are very low. As a result, cirrus clouds are made mostly of ice crystals.

Background

Facts and Figures The amount of water contained in a cloud may surprise students. A scientist with the National Center for Atmospheric Research, named Margaret LeMone, actually estimated the weight of a small cumulus cloud. The cloud was about 1,000 m wide, 1,000 m long, and 1,000 m high. Based on other studies of clouds of the same type, LeMone assumed that the cloud contained about 0.5 g of water per cubic meter. Given the size of the cloud, she concluded that it contained a total of 500 million g of water. This is about 550 tons of water, or about 100 tons heavier than a fully loaded jumbo jet.

Did you ever notice a ring around the sun or moon? Called halos, these rings are created when light passes through thin high clouds of ice crystals.

EXPLORING Clouds

The main types of clouds are cumulus, stratus, and cirrus. A cloud's name contains clues about its height and structure.

Cirrus clouds Cirrus, cirrostratus, and cirrocumulus clouds are made up mostly of ice crystals.

Cumulonimbus clouds Thunderstorms come from cumulonimbus clouds. For this reason cumulonimbus clouds are also called thunderheads.

Nimbostratus clouds Nimbostratus clouds may produce rain or snow.

Cumulus clouds Cumulus clouds are usually a sign of fair weather.

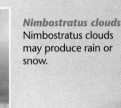

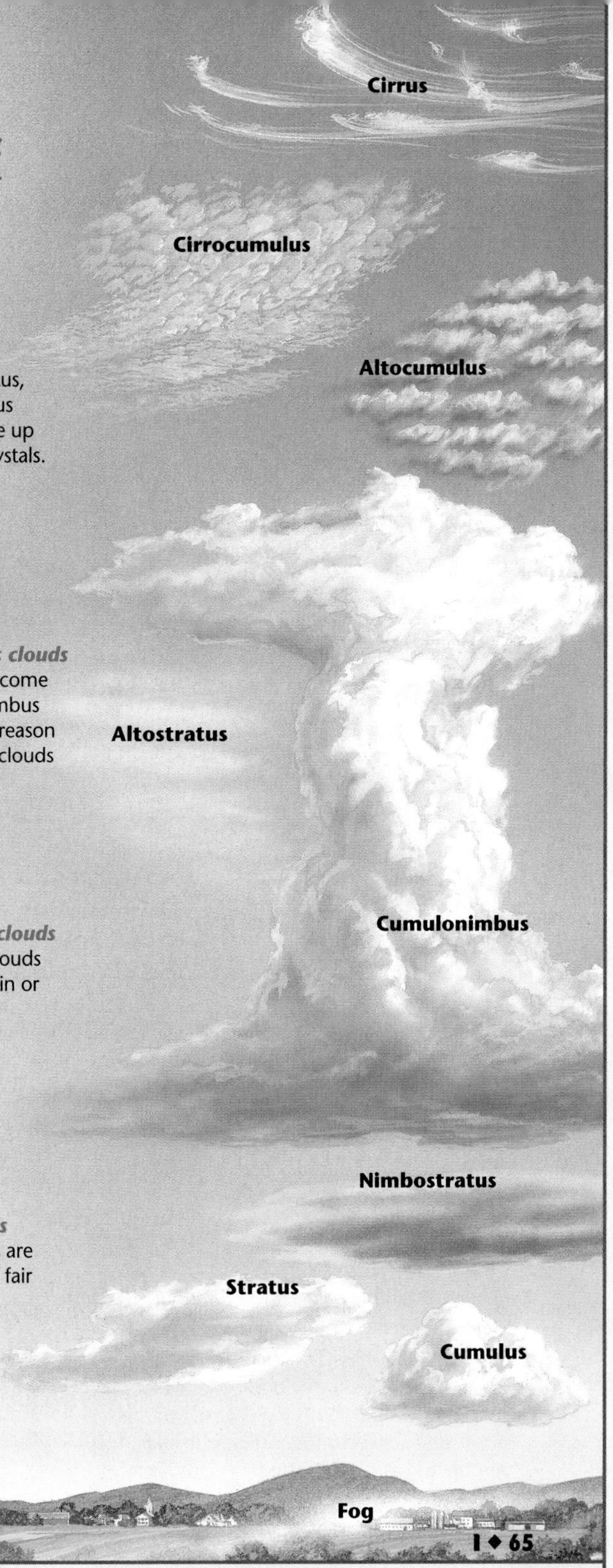

Media and Technology

Transparencies "Clouds," Transparency 9

Answers to Self-Assessment

Caption Question

Figure 16 When water vapor condenses out of the air, clouds form.

☑ Checkpoint

When warm, moist air moves upward over a mountain, it cools. This causes water vapor to condense out of the air and form clouds.

EXPLORING

Clouds

Extend the information in the Exploring feature by calling students' attention to each of the clouds pictured on the left, starting with cumulus clouds, and explaining how each type of cloud is formed. This will help students understand why the different cloud types have the shapes and other characteristics they do. Explain that cumulus clouds form during clear weather when warm air rises over small regions of Earth, such as plowed fields or paved parking lots, because these areas are heated more by the sun. Nimbostratus clouds are formed by warm air rising over a wide area, so they tend to cover the whole sky. Cumulonimbus clouds are formed when a lot of hot air rises very fast and towers upward for several kilometers. Strong winds at the bottom of the stratosphere flatten the tops of cumulonimbus clouds to give them their characteristic anvil shape. Cirrus clouds are formed high up in the atmosphere where it is very cold and there is little water vapor, making them thin and wispy. **learning modality: visual**

Building Inquiry Skills: Forming Operational Definitions

If students are having difficulty keeping cloud names straight, have them play a quiz game called "Name that Cloud." First have students find and list the definitions of basic cloud names (cumulus, stratus, cirrus, nimbus) and cloud prefixes (alto-, nimbo-, cirro-) on a set of index cards. Then have students use the definitions as the basis for the game. Students should provide a definition of a specific cloud type, and their partner must correctly name the cloud. The person with the most correct responses wins the game. **cooperative learning**

Ongoing Assessment

Drawing Have students draw and label each of the three main cloud types.

Types of Clouds, continued

Real-Life Learning

Point out that how large a cloud appears is a good indicator of its altitude. Tell students that in general fist-sized clouds are cumulus clouds, thumb-sized clouds altocumulus, and little-fingernail-sized clouds cirrocumulus. **learning modality: kinesthetic**

3 Assess

Section 4 Review Answers

1. The instrument is a psychrometer. It works by comparing the temperatures on a wet-bulb and a dry-bulb thermometer.
2. For clouds to form, air must be cooled to its dew point and particles must be present in the air.
3. Cumulus clouds look like fluffy, rounded piles of cotton. Stratus clouds form in flat layers. Cirrus clouds are wispy and feathery.
4. Low-level clouds are fog, cumulus, stratus, and nimbostratus. Medium-level clouds are altocumulus and altostratus. High-level clouds are cirrostratus and cirrus.

Science at Home

ACTIVITY

Materials *large glass, cold water, ice cubes*
Tips Tell students to use cold tap water for the activity, not cold water from the refrigerator, which may be cold enough to make water condense on the outside of the glass without adding ice. Students should explain that the water on the outside of the glass condensed from water vapor in the air. It only appeared after ice was added because water vapor condenses out of the air when the temperature falls below the dew point.

Performance Assessment

Skills Check Have students infer why they can see their breath on a cold day. *(Students should infer that water droplets condense out of their warm, moist breath when it hits the cold air.)*

Figure 17 Fog often forms at night over cool lakes. *Predicting What will happen as the sun rises and warms the air above the lake?*

Cirrus clouds that have feathery "hooked" ends are sometimes called mare's tails. Cirrocumulus clouds, which look like rows of cotton balls, often indicate that a storm is on its way.

Part of a cloud's name may be based on its height. The names of clouds that form between about 2 and 6 kilometers above Earth's surface have the prefix *alto-*, which means "high." The two main types of these clouds are altocumulus and altostratus.

Clouds that form at or near the ground are called fog. Fog often forms when the ground cools at night after a warm, humid day. The ground cools the air just above the ground to the air's dew point. The next day the heat of the morning sun "burns" the fog off as its water droplets evaporate.

Section 4 Review

1. What instrument is used to measure relative humidity? How does it work?
2. What conditions are needed for clouds to form?
3. Describe each of the three main types of clouds.
4. **Thinking Critically** **Classifying** Classify each of the following cloud types as low-level, medium-level, or high-level: altocumulus, altostratus, cirrostratus, cirrus, cumulus, fog, nimbostratus, and stratus.

Science at Home

Fill a large glass half-full with cold water. Show your family members what happens as you add ice cubes to the water. Explain to your family that the water that appears on the outside of the glass comes from water vapor in the atmosphere. Also explain why the water on the outside of the glass only appears after you add ice to the water in the glass.

Answers to Self-Assessment

Caption Question

Figure 17 The fog will "burn" off as its water droplets evaporate.

Program Resources

- **Teaching Resources** 2-4 Review and Reinforce, p. 55; 2-4 Enrich, p. 56

Media and Technology

Interactive Student Tutorial CD-ROM I-2

SECTION 5 Precipitation

DISCOVER ACTIVITY

How Can You Make Hail?

1. Put on your goggles.
2. Put 15 g of salt into a beaker. Add 50 mL of water. Stir the solution until most of the salt is dissolved.
3. Put 15 mL of cold water in a clean test tube.
4. Place the test tube in the beaker.
5. Fill the beaker almost to the top with crushed ice. Stir the ice mixture every minute for six minutes.

6. Remove the test tube from the beaker and drop an ice chip into the test tube. What happens?

Think It Over

Inferring Based on your observation, what conditions are necessary for hail to form?

In Arica, Chile, the average rainfall is less than 1 millimeter per year. Many years pass with no precipitation at all. On the other hand, the average rainfall on Mount Waialeale on the island of Kauai in Hawaii is about 12 meters per year. That's more than enough to cover a three-story house! As you can see, rainfall varies greatly around the world.

Water evaporates into the air from every water surface on Earth and from living things. This water eventually returns to the surface as precipitation. **Precipitation** (pree sip uh TAY shun) is any form of water that falls from clouds and reaches Earth's surface.

Precipitation always comes from clouds. But not all clouds produce precipitation. For precipitation to occur, cloud droplets or ice crystals must grow heavy enough to fall through the air. One way that cloud droplets grow is by colliding and combining with other cloud droplets. As the droplets grow larger, they fall faster and collect more and more small droplets. Finally, the droplets become heavy enough to fall out of the cloud as raindrops.

GUIDE FOR READING

- What are the main types of precipitation?
- How is precipitation measured?

Reading Tip As you read, make a list of the types of precipitation. Write a sentence describing how each type forms.

Types of Precipitation

In warm parts of the world, precipitation is almost always rain or drizzle. In colder regions, precipitation may fall as snow or ice. **Common types of precipitation include rain, sleet, freezing rain, hail, and snow.**

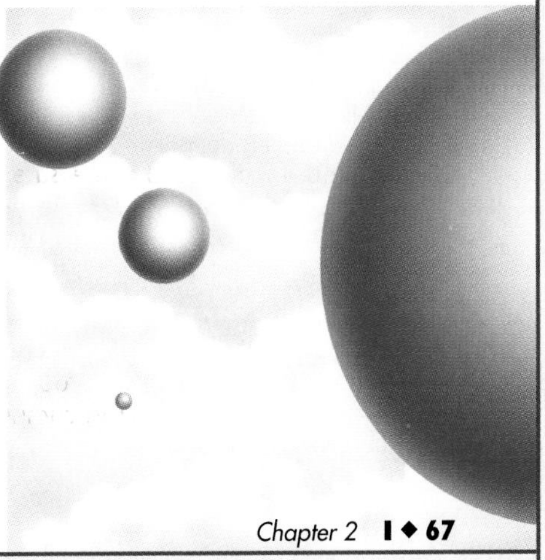

Figure 18 Droplets come in many sizes. Believe it or not, a raindrop has about one million times as much water in it as a cloud droplet.

READING STRATEGIES

Reading Tip Suggest to students that they save their sentences and use them as a study guide. Tell students that knowing how each type of precipitation forms will help them understand its characteristics.

Study and Comprehension Suggest to students that they make a concept map using the main concepts in the section.

Program Resources

- **Teaching Resources** 2-5 Lesson Plan, p. 57; 2-5 Section Summary, p. 58
- **Interdisciplinary Explorations Series** "Where River Meets Sea," pp. 24–25; "India Beyond the Golden Age," p. 33

Media and Technology

Audiotapes English-Spanish Summary 2-5

SECTION 5 Precipitation

Objectives

After completing the lesson, students will be able to

- identify the main types of precipitation;
- describe how precipitation is measured and ways that it might be controlled.

Key Terms precipitation, rain gauge, droughts

1 Engage/Explore

Activating Prior Knowledge

Stimulate students to think about precipitation by asking: **Did you ever hear the expression, "It's raining cats and dogs"?** *(Most students will say yes.)* **Do you know what it means?** *(That it's raining very hard)* **Where do you think the expression comes from?** *(Students probably will not know.)* Explain that the expression may come from old Norse myths, in which cats were identified with rain and dogs with winds. Tell the class they will learn more about rain and other types of precipitation in this section.

DISCOVER ACTIVITY

Skills Focus inferring
Materials *15 g salt, beaker, 50 mL water, stirrer, 15 mL cold water, clean test tube, crushed ice, watch or clock*
Time 15 minutes
Tips The inside of the test tube must be very clean. Have students measure the temperature of the water in the test tube before they add the ice chip. They may be surprised to find it is less than 0°C. (The freezing point of salt water is less than 0°C, the freezing point of fresh water.)
Expected Outcome When the ice chip is dropped into the test tube, the cold water in the test tube will crystalize into ice around it.
Think It Over For hail to form, it must be very cold and there must be particles on which water can crystalize into ice.

2 Facilitate

Types of Precipitation

Building Inquiry Skills: Observing

Materials *transparent plastic lid, dropper, pencil, water*
Time 10 minutes

Have student pairs do this activity to observe how tiny water droplets in clouds merge to form larger drops of water until the drops are heavy enough to fall as precipitation. Students should fill the dropper with water and squeeze many separate drops onto the inside of a transparent plastic lid. Then they should quickly turn the lid over and, holding it in the air by one side, use the point of a pencil from underneath the lid to move the tiny drops of water together. When the drops touch, they will appear to leap together to form larger drops, and when the drops get large enough they will fall like rain. Ask: **What causes the water drops in clouds to move around and bump into each other so they can merge into larger drops?** *(wind and gravity)* **learning modality: kinesthetic**

Using the Visuals: Figure 19

Call students' attention to the devastation caused by freezing rain that is shown in photo B. Ask: **How did freezing rain cause this kind of damage?** *(The weight of the accumulated ice broke tree branches and downed power lines.)* **How would the street pictured in the photo look if, instead of freezing rain, the same amount of snow or hailstones had fallen?** *(Snow is lighter than ice so it probably would not have broken branches or power lines, although it might have blocked the street. Hailstones, depending on their size, might have broken twigs and small branches and even the windshield of the car, but it probably would not have blocked the street with large branches or downed power lines.)* **learning modality: visual**

Figure 20 A. Snowflakes form in clouds that are colder than 0°C. B. Freezing rain coats objects with a layer of ice. C. Hailstones are formed inside clouds during thunderstorms.

Rain The most common kind of precipitation is rain. Drops of water are called rain if they are at least 0.5 millimeter in diameter. Precipitation made up of smaller drops of water is called mist or drizzle. Mist and drizzle usually fall from nimbostratus clouds.

Sleet Sometimes raindrops fall through a layer of air below 0°C, the freezing point of water. As they fall, the raindrops freeze into solid particles of ice. Ice particles smaller than 5 millimeters in diameter are called sleet.

Freezing Rain At other times raindrops falling through cold air near the ground do not freeze in the air. Instead, the raindrops freeze when they touch a cold surface. This is called freezing rain. In an ice storm, a smooth, thick layer of ice builds up on every surface. The weight of the ice may break tree branches onto power lines, causing power failures. Freezing rain and sleet can make sidewalks and roads slippery and dangerous.

Hail Round pellets of ice larger than 5 millimeters in diameter are called hailstones. Hail forms only inside cumulonimbus clouds during thunderstorms. A hailstone starts as an ice pellet inside a cold region of a cloud. Strong updrafts in the cloud carry the hailstone up and down through the cold region many times. Each time the hailstone goes through the cold region, a new layer of ice forms around the hailstone. Eventually the hailstone becomes heavy enough to fall to the ground. If you cut a hailstone in half, you can often see shells of ice, like the layers of an onion. Because hailstones can grow quite large before finally falling to the ground, hail can cause tremendous damage to crops, buildings, and vehicles.

68 ◆ I

Background

History of Science For centuries people have tried to increase the amount of precipitation that falls. From praying and dancing to sending up explosives into clouds, they have searched for ways to make rain. It wasn't until the 1940s, however, that Vincent Schaefer discovered how to make rain by seeding clouds. He discovered that a grain of dry ice dropped into a cloud led to the formation of millions of ice crystals, often leading to precipitation. Shortly after this discovery, Bernard Vonnegut discovered that silver iodide led to the production of even more ice crystals than dry ice. Since then, no other process has been found that is better at making rain than their cloud-seeding method. Rainmaking companies still use this method in many parts of the world.

Snow Often water vapor in a cloud is converted directly into ice crystals called snowflakes. Snowflakes have an endless number of different shapes and patterns, all with six sides or branches. Snowflakes often join together into larger clumps of snow in which the six-sided crystals are hard to see.

☑ *Checkpoint* *How do hailstones form?*

Measuring Precipitation

Meteorologists measure rainfall with a rain gauge. A **rain gauge** is an open-ended can or tube that collects rainfall. The amount of rainfall is measured by dipping a ruler into the water or by reading a marked scale. To increase the accuracy of the measurement, the top of a rain gauge may have a funnel that collects ten times as much rain as the tube alone. The funnel collects a greater depth of water that is easier to measure. But to get the actual depth of rain, it is necessary to divide by ten.

Snowfall is measured using a ruler or by melting collected snow and measuring the depth of water it produces. On average, 10 centimeters of snow contains about the same amount of water as 1 centimeter of rain. Of course, light, fluffy snow contains far less water than heavy, wet snow.

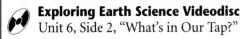

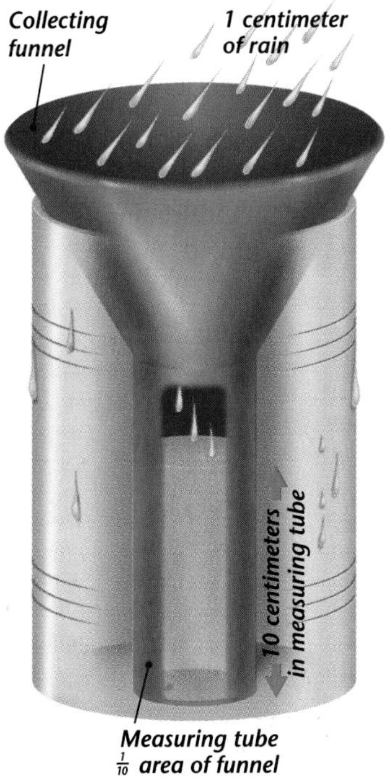

Figure 20 A rain gauge measures the depth of rain that falls. *Observing How much rain was collected in the measuring tube of this rain gauge?*

Sharpen your Skills

Calculating

ACTIVITY

Make your own rain gauge by putting a funnel into a narrow, straight-sided glass jar. Here's how to calculate how much more rain your funnel collects than the jar alone.

1. First measure the diameter of the top of the funnel and square it.
   Example: $4 \times 4 = 16$
2. Then measure the diameter of the top of the jar and square it.
   Example: $2 \times 2 = 4$
3. Divide the first square by the second square.
   Example: $\frac{16}{4} = 4$
4. To find the actual depth of rain that fell, divide the depth of water in the jar by the ratio from Step 3.
   Example: $\frac{8 \text{ cm}}{4} = 2 \text{ cm}$

Building Inquiry Skills: Measuring

ACTIVITY

Materials *shallow pan, flour, sieve*
Time 10 minutes to collect raindrops; 10 minutes to compare sizes

On a day when it is raining, challenge students to catch raindrops and estimate their size. Have each student hold a shallow pan containing a smooth layer of flour out in the rain for a second or two, just long enough for several raindrops to land in the pan and form little lumps in the flour. After at least 15-20 minutes when the lumps have dried, have students pour the flour through a sieve to separate the lumps. Ask: **How big are the raindrops you caught?** *(Students should estimate the size of the raindrops from the size of the lumps. The bigger the lumps, the larger the raindrops.)* **learning modality: visual**

Measuring Precipitation

Sharpen your Skills

Calculating

ACTIVITY

Time 15 minutes
Tips Explain that the amount of rain collected in the jar is the amount that fell over an area the size of the funnel opening. The calculations show how much smaller the area of the jar opening is than the area of the funnel opening. The total amount of rain collected must be reduced by this ratio to show how much would have fallen into the jar alone. Be sure students do not get confused by Figure 20, which shows a different ratio.
Expected Outcome Students should work through the calculations to make sure they also get a final answer of 2 cm.
Extend Ask: **What is the actual depth of the rain that fell if the diameter of the top of the funnel is 6 cm and the depth of water in the jar is 8 cm?** *(8 cm ÷ 36/4 = 0.89 cm)* **learning modality: logical/mathematical**

Ongoing Assessment

Drawing Have students draw diagrams showing how rain, sleet, and freezing rain form.

Media and Technology

Exploring Earth Science Videodisc
Unit 6, Side 2, "What's in Our Tap?"

Chapter 6

Answers to Self-Assessment

☑ *Checkpoint*

Hailstones form when pellets of ice inside cumulonimbus clouds are carried up and down many times, each time adding a new layer of ice, until they become heavy enough to fall to the ground.

Caption Question

Figure 20 Though one cm of rain fell into the gauge, 10 cm were collected.

Controlling Precipitation

Integrating Technology

Point out that rain-making technology could not be developed until scientists discovered how rain actually forms in clouds. In the early 1900s, a scientist named Alfred Wegener hypothesized that almost all precipitation, even rain, starts out as ice crystals. Explain that the condensation of water alone is a much slower process, and this is why Wegener believed correctly that it could not account for most precipitation. Ask: **How does Wegener's hypothesis relate to the cloud-seeding technology?** *(Clouds are seeded with crystals of dry ice and silver iodide because this quickly leads to the formation of ice crystals large enough to fall as precipitation.)* **learning modality: verbal**

3 Assess

Section 5 Review Answers

1. Rain, sleet, freezing rain, hail, and snow
2. rain gauge
3. Cloud droplets or ice crystals must grow heavy enough to fall through the air.
4. Cumulonimbus clouds produce hail.
5. The can with the larger diameter would collect more rain. However, the depth of the water in the two cans would be the same.

CHAPTER PROJECT 2

Check Your Progress

Suggest that students experiment with different types of graphs to display their weather data. Also require that they graph all or most of the weather factors on the same graph so they can see how the weather factors change together. This will help them see patterns in the data.

Performance Assessment

Skills Check Have students make a table comparing and contrasting the five common types of precipitation.

Figure 21 The corn in this photo was damaged by a long drought. *Applying Concepts* *How can cloud seeding be used to reduce the effect of droughts?*

Controlling Precipitation

In some regions, there may be periods that are much drier than usual. Long periods of unusually low precipitation are called **droughts.** Droughts can cause great hardship. In the farming regions of the Midwest, for example, droughts may cause entire crops to fail. The farmers suffer from lost income and consumers suffer from high food prices. In some less-developed countries, droughts can cause widespread hunger, or famine.

INTEGRATING TECHNOLOGY In recent years, scientists have been trying to produce rain during droughts. The most common method is called cloud seeding. In cloud seeding, tiny crystals of dry ice (solid carbon dioxide) and silver iodide are sprinkled into clouds from airplanes. Many clouds contain supercooled water droplets, which are actually below 0°C. The droplets don't freeze because there aren't enough particles around which ice crystals can form. Water vapor can condense on the particles of silver iodide, forming rain or snow. Dry ice works by cooling the droplets even further, so that they will freeze without particles being present.

Cloud seeding has also been used with some success to clear fog from airports. Dry ice is sprinkled into the fog, causing ice crystals to form. This removes some of the fog so pilots can see the runways. Unfortunately, cloud seeding clears only cold fogs, so its use for this purpose is limited.

Section 5 Review

1. Name the five common types of precipitation.
2. What device is used to measure precipitation?
3. What must happen before precipitation can fall from a cloud?
4. What kind of cloud produces hail?
5. **Thinking Critically Applying Concepts** If two open cans of different diameters were left out in the rain, how would the amount of water they collected compare? How would the depth of water in the cans compare?

CHAPTER PROJECT 2

Check Your Progress

Now you should be ready to begin graphing your weather data. Look for patterns in your graphs. Use your data to predict what the next day's weather will be. Compare your predictions with what actually happens the next day. Are you able to predict the weather with confidence?

Answers to Self-Assessment

Caption Question

Figure 21 Cloud seeding can be used to lessen the effect of droughts by sprinkling clouds with particles around which water droplets can condense to form rain.

Program Resources

- **Teaching Resources** 2-5 Review and Reinforce, p. 59; 2-5 Enrich, p. 60

Media and Technology

Interactive Student Tutorial CD-ROM I-2

STUDY GUIDE

Section 1 Energy in the Atmosphere

Key Ideas

- Energy from the sun travels to Earth as electromagnetic waves—mostly visible light, infrared radiation, and ultraviolet radiation.
- When Earth's surface is heated, it radiates some of the energy back into the atmosphere in the form of longer-wavelength radiation.

Key Terms

electromagnetic wave, radiation, infrared radiation, ultraviolet radiation, scattering, greenhouse effect

Section 2 Heat Transfer

Integrating Physics

Key Ideas

- The energy of motion in the molecules of a substance is called thermal energy.
- Three forms of heat transfer—radiation, conduction, and convection—work together to heat the troposphere.

Key Terms

thermal energy, temperature, thermometer, ✓heat 8, ✓conduction 3, ✓convection 4

Section 3 Winds

Key Ideas

- All winds are caused by differences in air pressure, which are the result of unequal heating of Earth's surface.
- Local winds are caused by unequal heating of Earth's surface within a small area.
- The movement of air between the equator and the poles produces global winds.

Key Terms

✓wind 14, ✓anemometer 1, ✓wind-chill factor 15, local wind, sea breeze, land breeze, monsoon, ✓global wind 7, Coriolis effect, latitude, ✓jet stream 10

Section 4 Water in the Atmosphere

Key Ideas

- Relative humidity is the percentage of water vapor in the air compared to the amount of water vapor the air could hold. It can be measured with a psychrometer.
- Clouds of all kinds form when water vapor in the air becomes liquid water or solid ice.
- Meteorologists classify clouds into three main types: cumulus, stratus, and cirrus.

Key Terms

evaporation, ✓humidity 9, ✓relative humidity 13, ✓psychrometer 12, ✓condensation 2, ✓dew point 5, cumulus, stratus, cirrus

Section 5 Precipitation

Key Ideas

- Common types of precipitation include rain, sleet, freezing rain, hail, and snow.
- Rain is measured with a rain gauge.
- Scientists have used cloud seeding to produce rain and to clear fog from airports.

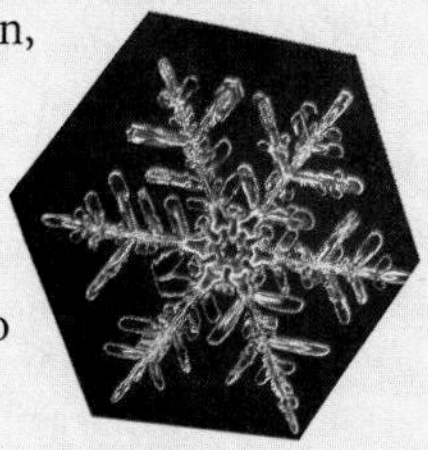

Key Terms

✓precipitation 11, rain gauge, ✓drought 6

ACTIVITY USING THE INTERNET
www.science-explorer.phschool.com

CHAPTER 2 REVIEW

Program Resources

- **Teaching Resources** Chapter 2 Project Scoring Rubric, p. 40; Chapter 2 Performance Assessment, pp. 141–143; Chapter 2 Test, pp. 144–147

Media and Technology

Interactive Student Tutorial CD-ROM I-2

Computer Test Bank Chapter 2 Test

1. anemometer
2. Condensation
3. Conduction
4. convection
5. dew point
6. drought
7. global wind
8. heat
9. humidity
10. jet stream
11. precipitation
12. psychrometer
13. relative humidity
14. wind
15. wind-chill factor

CHAPTER 2 REVIEW

Reviewing Content: Multiple Choice

1. a **2.** b **3.** b **4.** c **5.** c

True or False

6. visible light **7.** greenhouse effect
8. true **9.** anemometer **10.** true

Checking Concepts

11. The greenhouse effect is caused by the absorption of heat from Earth's surface by carbon dioxide, water vapor, and other gases in the atmosphere. It keeps Earth's atmosphere at a temperature that is warmer than it would be otherwise.

12. Convection causes most of the heating of the troposphere as the upward movement of warm air and the downward movement of cool air form convection currents.

13. Warm air rises at the equator and flows toward the poles. Cold air sinks at the poles and spreads out toward the equator. The movement of air between the equator and the poles produces global winds.

14. Clouds usually form high in the air instead of at Earth's surface because the air must be cold for water vapor to condense and form clouds and air at high altitudes usually is colder than air near the surface.

15. Sleet forms when raindrops fall through a layer of air below 0°C and freeze into small particles of ice. Hail forms when an ice pellet in a cumulonimbus cloud is carried up and down through the cold region of the cloud by strong updrafts, each time gathering another layer of ice until the hailstone is heavy enough to fall to the surface. Snow forms when water vapor in a cloud is converted directly into ice crystals.

16. Students' diary entries will vary, but they should reflect students' knowledge of the water cycle and include the terms *evaporation, condensation,* and *precipitation.*

Thinking Visually

17. a. Global winds **b.-c.** Sea breezes, Land breezes **d.-e.** Prevailing westerlies, Polar easterlies

CHAPTER 2 REVIEW

Reviewing Content

For more review of key concepts, see the Interactive Student Tutorial CD-ROM.

Multiple Choice

Choose the letter of the best answer.

1. Energy from the sun travels to Earth's surface by
   a. radiation.
   b. convection.
   c. evaporation.
   d. conduction.
2. Rising warm air transports heat energy by
   a. conduction.
   b. convection.
   c. radiation.
   d. condensation.
3. A psychrometer is used to measure
   a. rainfall.
   b. relative humidity.
   c. temperature.
   d. humidity.
4. Clouds form because water vapor in the air
   a. warms. b. conducts.
   c. condenses. d. evaporates.
5. Rain, sleet, and hail are all forms of
   a. evaporation.
   b. condensation.
   c. precipitation.
   d. convection.

True or False

If the statement is true, write true. If it is false, change the underlined word or words to make the statement true.

6. Infrared radiation and ultraviolet radiation make up most of the energy Earth receives from the sun.
7. The process by which gases hold heat in the atmosphere is called the wind-chill factor.
8. Water molecules in liquid water escape into the atmosphere as water vapor in the process of evaporation.
9. The instrument used to measure wind speed is a thermometer.
10. Clouds that form near the ground are called fog.

Checking Concepts

11. What causes the greenhouse effect? How does it affect Earth's atmosphere?
12. What form of heat transfer is most important in heating the troposphere?
13. Describe how the movements of hot air at the equator and cold air at the poles produce global wind patterns.
14. Why do clouds usually form high in the air instead of near Earth's surface?
15. Describe sleet, hail, and snow in terms of how each one forms.
16. **Writing to Learn** Imagine you are a drop of water in the ocean. Write a diary describing your journey through the water cycle. How do you become a cloud? What type of conditions cause you to fall as precipitation? Use descriptive words to describe your journey.

Thinking Visually

17. **Concept Map** Copy the concept map about winds onto a separate sheet of paper. Then complete the map and add a title. (For more on concept maps, see the Skills Handbook.)

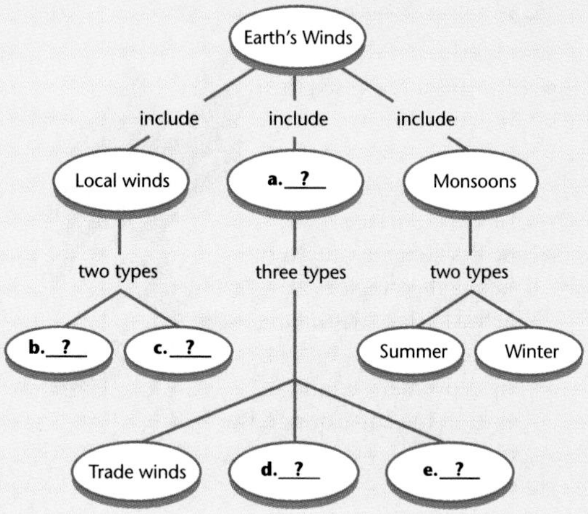

Applying Skills

18. Student's graphs should have one axis labeled "Month" and the other axis labeled "Average Monthly Rainfall (centimeters)." The bars should range from 1 centimeter in height (January, February, March, and December) to 57 centimeters in height (August).

19. 253 centimeters

20. *Dry:* January, February, March, April, November, and December; *Wet:* May, June, July, August, September, and October

21. Monsoons

Thinking Critically

22. A nighttime land breeze in a city near the ocean would be caused by the land cooling off more quickly than the water at night so that as warm air rose over the water, cool air would flow from the land to take its place.

23. The relative humidity is 100 percent because since both temperatures were the same, the water on the wet bulb must not have been able to evaporate, which would happen only when the relative humidity is that high.

24. Hail and sleet are both frozen rain. Sleet is

Applying Skills

Use the table below to answer Questions 18–21.

Average Monthly Rainfall

Month	Rainfall	Month	Rainfall
January	1 cm	July	49 cm
February	1 cm	August	57 cm
March	1 cm	September	40 cm
April	2 cm	October	20 cm
May	25 cm	November	4 cm
June	52 cm	December	1 cm

18. **Graphing** Use the information in the table to draw a bar graph that shows the rainfall each month at this location.
19. **Calculating** What is the total amount of rainfall each year at this location?
20. **Classifying** Which months of the year would you classify as "dry"? Which months would you classify as "wet"?
21. **Drawing Conclusions** The place represented by the rainfall data is in Southeast Asia. What do you think accounts for the extremely heavy rainfall that occurs during some months?

Thinking Critically

22. **Relating Cause and Effect** What circumstances could cause a nighttime land breeze in a city near the ocean?
23. **Problem Solving** If you use a psychrometer and get the same reading on both thermometers, what is the relative humidity?
24. **Comparing and Contrasting** How are hail and sleet alike? How are they different?
25. **Classifying** Classify the different types of clouds by the kind of weather associated with each type.
26. **Relating Cause and Effect** What is the source of the energy that powers Earth's winds?

CHAPTER 2 REVIEW

Performance Assessment

CHAPTER PROJECT 2

Wrap Up

Presenting Your Project Develop a way to present your findings to the class. For example, you could put your graphs and predictions on a poster. Are your graphs neatly drawn and easy to understand? Practice your presentation and make any needed improvements.

Reflect and Record How could you improve the accuracy of your observations? What did you learn about how easy or difficult it is to predict the weather?

Getting Involved

In Your Community Ask a family member if he or she remembers a time of extreme rainfall or drought in your region. When did it occur? Ask your librarian to help you find newspaper articles about the event. How much precipitation fell in that period? How did it affect people in the region? Write a brief summary that tells the significance of the event.

smaller than 5 millimeters in diameter, while hail is larger than 5 millimeters in diameter. Sleet forms anytime rain falls through a layer of air below 0°C; hail forms only inside cumulonimbus clouds during thunderstorms when layers of ice form around ice pellets as they are carried up and down through cold regions of a cloud.

25. Cumulus clouds are associated with fair weather. Cumulonimbus clouds are associated with thunderstorms. Nimbostratus clouds are associated with drizzle, rain, or snow. Cirrocumulus clouds are associated with approaching storms.

26. Earth's winds are powered by unequal heating of Earth's atmosphere by the sun.

Program Resources

- **Inquiry Skills Activity Book** Provides teaching and review of all inquiry skills

Performance Assessment

CHAPTER PROJECT 2

Wrap Up

Presenting Your Project

Make sure students have clearly-drawn graphs or other visuals to use for their presentations. Advise them to include in their presentations a description of when and where their measurements were made and the instruments that were used. They also should include a discussion of any patterns they see in their data.

Reflect and Record If students used instruments they made themselves, they may be able to improve the accuracy of their observations by using commercial instruments. Students probably will find that it is difficult to predict the weather because some of the patterns they observe in their data may not be significant for prediction. Help students focus on the most significant factors for predicting the weather, including air pressure, clouds, and wind direction.

Getting Involved

In Your Community If students' family members cannot remember a time of extreme rainfall or drought, or if they have forgotten the year in which it occurred, suggest to students that they look at rainfall records for their area and find a time when there was much more or less rain than average. Their librarian can help them find rainfall records as well as newspaper articles from the relevant time period. If heavy rains or drought were severe, local newspapers for the time period probably will contain stories about the weather itself as well as how farmers, consumers, homeowners, or other groups were affected by it. Point out to students that heavy rains are likely to cause flooding, so they should look for newspaper articles on floods as well as rain if they are researching a period of extreme rainfall.

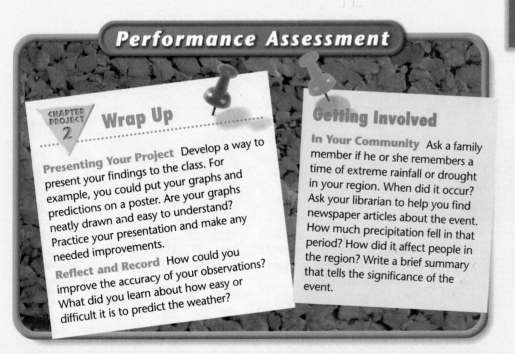

CHAPTER 3

Weather Patterns

Sections	Time	Student Edition Activities	Other Activities
CHAPTER PROJECT 3 **The Weather Tomorrow** p. 75	Ongoing (2–3 weeks)	Check Your Progress, p. 82 Check Your Progress, p. 98 Check Your Progress, p. 105 Wrap Up, p. 109	
1 Air Masses and Fronts pp. 76–82 ◆ Identify the major types of air masses that affect the weather in North America. ◆ Name the main types of fronts. ◆ Define cyclones and anticyclones.	2–3 periods/ 1–1½ blocks	**Discover** How Do Fluids of Different Densities Behave?, p. 76 **Sharpen Your Skills** Classifying, p. 81	**TE** Inquiry Challenge, p. 79 **TE** Including All Students, p. 79 **TE** Demonstration, p. 80 **TE** Including All Students, p. 81
2 Storms pp. 83–94 ◆ List the main kinds of storms and explain how they form. ◆ Describe measures you can take to ensure safety in a storm.	4–5 periods/ 2–2½ blocks	**Discover** Can You Make a Tornado?, p. 83 **Try This** Lightning Distances, p. 84 **Science at Home,** p. 91 **Real-World Lab: Careers in Science** Tracking a Hurricane, pp. 92–93	**TE** Demonstration, p. 84 **TE** Including All Students, p. 85 **IES** "India Beyond the Golden Age," pp. 31–32 **IES** "Back to the Thirties," pp. 10–12
3 *INTEGRATING HEALTH* **Floods** pp. 95–98 ◆ Identify the causes of flooding. ◆ Explain how the dangers of floods can be reduced.	1–2 periods/ ½–1 block	**Discover** What Causes Floods?, p. 95 **Sharpen Your Skills** Communicating, p. 96	**TE** Using the Visuals: Figure 15, p. 96
4 Predicting the Weather pp. 99–106 ◆ Explain how technology helps forecasters predict the weather. ◆ State the types of information shown on weather maps.	2–3 periods/ 1–1½ blocks	**Discover** What's the Weather?, p. 99 **Sharpen Your Skills** Interpreting Data, p. 102 **Skills Lab: Interpreting Data** Reading a Weather Map, p. 106	**TE** Inquiry Challenge, p. 101 **TE** Real-Life Learning, p. 104 **TE** Building Inquiry Skills: Calculating, p. 104 **TE** Exploring Newspaper Weather Maps, p. 105 **ISLM** I-3, "Investigating Weather Maps"
Study Guide/Chapter Review pp. 107–109	1 period/ ½ block		

For Standard or Block Schedule The Resource Pro® CD-ROM gives you maximum flexibility for planning your instruction for any type of schedule. Resource Pro® contains Planning Express®, an advanced scheduling program, as well as the entire contents of the Teaching Resources and the Computer Test Bank.

CHAPTER PLANNING GUIDE

Program Resources	Assessment Strategies	Media and Technology
TR Chapter 3 Project Teacher Notes, pp. 66–67 **TR** Chapter 3 Project Student materials, pp. 68–71 **TR** Chapter 3 Project Scoring Rubric, p. 72	**SE** Performance Assessment: Chapter 3 Project Wrap Up, p. 109 **TE** Check Your Progress, pp. 82, 98, 105 **TR** Chapter 3 Project Scoring Rubric, p. 72	Science Explorer Internet Site
TR 3-1 Lesson Plan, p. 73 **TR** 3-1 Section Summary, p. 74 **TR** 3-1 Review and Reinforce, p. 75 **TR** 3-1 Enrich, p. 76	**SE** Section 1 Review, p. 82 **TE** Ongoing Assessment, pp. 77, 79, 81 **TE** Performance Assessment, p. 82 **TR** 3-1 Review and Reinforce, p. 75	Exploring Earth Science Videodisc, Unit 4 Side 2, "Heating the Earth" Audiotapes, English-Spanish Summary 3-1 Transparencies 10, "North American Air Masses"; 11, "Cold Front"; 12, "Warm Front"; 13, "Occluded Front" Interactive Student Tutorial CD-ROM, I-3
TR 3-2 Lesson Plan, p. 77 **TR** 3-2 Section Summary, p. 78 **TR** 3-2 Review and Reinforce, p. 79 **TR** 3-2 Enrich, p. 80 **TR** Real-World Lab blackline masters, pp. 89–91	**SE** Section 2 Review, p. 91 **SE** Analyze and Conclude, p. 93 **TE** Ongoing Assessment, pp. 85, 87, 89 **TE** Performance Assessment, p. 91 **TR** 3-2 Review and Reinforce, p. 79	Exploring Earth Science Videodisc, Unit 4 Side 2, "Violent Storms" Audiotapes, English-Spanish Summary 3-2 Transparency 14, "Clouds and Winds in a Hurricane" Interactive Student Tutorial CD-ROM, I-3
TR 3-3 Lesson Plan, p. 81 **TR** 3-3 Section Summary, p. 82 **TR** 3-3 Review and Reinforce, p. 83 **TR** 3-3 Enrich, p. 84	**SE** Section 3 Review, p. 98 **TE** Ongoing Assessment, p. 97 **TE** Performance Assessment, p. 98 **TR** 3-3 Review and Reinforce, p. 83	Audiotapes, English-Spanish Summary 3-3 Interactive Student Tutorial CD-ROM, I-3
TR 3-4 Lesson Plan, p. 85 **TR** 3-4 Section Summary, p. 86 **TR** 3-4 Review and Reinforce, p. 87 **TR** 3-4 Enrich, p. 88 **TR** Skills Lab blackline masters, pp. 92–93 **SES** Book H, *Earth's Waters,* Chapter 4	**SE** Section 4 Review, p. 105 **SE** Analyze and Conclude, p. 106 **TE** Ongoing Assessment, pp. 101, 103 **TE** Performance Assessment, p. 105 **TR** 3-4 Review and Reinforce, p. 87	Exploring Earth Science Videodisc, Unit 4 Side 2, "Never Put Up the Umbrella Until It Starts to Rain" Audiotapes, English-Spanish Summary 3-4 Transparencies 15, "Weather Map"; 16, "Newspaper Weather Map" Interactive Student Tutorial CD-ROM, I-3
TR Chapter 3 Performance Assessment, pp. 148–150 **TR** Chapter 3 Test, pp. 151–154	**SE** Chapter 3 Review, pp. 107–109 **TR** Chapter 3 Performance Assessment, pp. 148–150 **TR** Chapter 3 Test, pp. 151–154 **CTB** Chapter 3 Test	Interactive Student Tutorial CD-ROM, I-3 Computer Test Bank, Chapter 3 Test

Key: **SE** Student Edition
CTB Computer Test Bank
ISAB Inquiry Skills Activity Book
TE Teacher's Edition
SES Science Explorer Series Text
PTA Product Testing Activities by *Consumer Reports*
TR Teaching Resources
ISLM Integrated Science Laboratory Manual
IES Interdisciplinary Explorations Series

Meeting the National Science Education Standards and AAAS Benchmarks

National Science Education Standards	Benchmarks for Science Literacy	Unifying Themes
Science As Inquiry (Content Standard A) ◆ **Use appropriate tools and techniques to gather, analyze, and interpret data** Students make weather forecasts. Students use data to predict the path of a hurricane. Students interpret a weather map. *(Chapter Project; Real-World Lab; Skills Lab)* **Earth and Space Science** (Content Standard D) ◆ **Structure of the Earth system** An air mass is a huge body of air that has similar temperature, humidity, and air pressure throughout. A storm is a violent disturbance in the atmosphere. Floods occur when so much water pours into a stream or river that it overflows its banks. *(Sections 1, 2, 3)* **Science in Personal and Social Perspectives** (Content Standard F) ◆ **Personal health** There are various measures to take to ensure safety during storms and floods. *(Sections 2, 3)* ◆ **Natural hazards** Unanticipated storms have even changed the course of history. *(Science & History)* ◆ **Risks and benefits** Students analyze the controversy around hurricane evacuations. *(Science and Society)* ◆ **Science and technology in society** Technology helps meteorologists predict the weather. *(Section 4)*	**1B Scientific Inquiry** Students make weather forecasts. Students use data to predict the path of a hurricane. Students interpret a weather map. *(Chapter Project; Real-World Lab; Skills Lab)* **3A Technology and Science** Technology helps meteorologists predict the weather. *(Section 4)* **4B The Earth** An air mass is a huge body of air that has similar temperature, humidity, and air pressure throughout. A storm is a violent disturbance in the atmosphere. Floods occur when so much water pours into a stream or river that it overflows its banks. *(Sections 1, 2, 3)* **6E Physical Health** There are various measures to take to ensure safety during storms and floods. *(Sections 2, 3)* **7C Social Change** Unanticipated storms have even changed the course of history. *(Science & History)* **7D Social Trade-Offs** Students analyze the controversy around hurricane evacuations. *(Science and Society)*	◆ **Energy** A storm is a violent disturbance in the atmosphere. Rushing water in a flood has tremendous power. *(Sections 2, 3)* ◆ **Patterns of Change** Students look for patterns in the weather to make weather forecasts. As an air mass moves into an area, it changes the weather there. Students use data to predict the path of a hurricane. Meteorologists interpret weather data to prepare weather forecasts. *(Chapter Project; Sections 1, 4; Real-World Lab)* ◆ **Scale and Structure** An air mass is a huge body of air that has similar temperature, humidity, and air pressure throughout. A typical hurricane is about 600 kilometers across. *(Sections 1, 2)* ◆ **Systems and Interactions** Four major types of air masses influence the weather in North America. Different atmospheric conditions cause different kinds of storms. A warm-water event, known as El Niño, affects global weather. Students interpret a weather map to describe weather conditions. *(Sections 1, 2, 4; Skills Lab)* ◆ **Unity and Diversity** Air masses are classified as tropical, polar, maritime, or continental and fronts as cold, warm, stationary, or occluded. Four kinds of storms are thunderstorms, tornadoes, hurricanes, and winter storms. *(Sections 1, 2)*

Media and Technology

Exploring Earth Science Videodiscs

◆ **Section 1** "Heating the Earth" gives examples of conduction, convection, and radiation.

◆ **Section 2** "Violent Storms" examines thunderstorms, tornadoes, and hurricanes.

◆ **Section 4** "Never Put Up the Umbrella Until It Starts to Rain" explains the factors that interact to produce weather.

Interactive Student Tutorial CD-ROM

◆ **Chapter Review** Interactive questions help students self-assess their mastery of key chapter concepts.

Student Edition Connection Strategies

◆ **Section 2** **Integrating Health,** pp. 85, 87, 90, 91
Science & History, pp. 86–87
Visual Arts Connection, p. 90
Science and Society, p. 94

◆ **Section 3** **Integrating Health,** pp. 95–98

◆ **Section 4** **Integrating Technology,** p. 101

ACTIVITY

USING THE INTERNET

www.science-explorer.phschool.com

Visit the Science Explorer Internet site to find an up-to-date activity for Chapter 3 of *Weather and Climate.*

ACTIVITY	Time (minutes)	Materials *Quantities for one work group*	Skills
Section 1			
Discover, p. 76	10	**Consumable** cardboard divider, red food coloring, 1 L warm water, 100 mL table salt, blue food coloring, 1 L cold water **Nonconsumable** plastic shoe box	Developing Hypotheses
Sharpen Your Skills, p. 81	home	No special materials required.	Classifying
Section 2			
Discover, p. 83	10	**Consumable** water, liquid dish detergent **Nonconsumable** large plastic jar with lid, penny or marble	Observing
Try This, p. 84	10	**Nonconsumable** watch or stopwatch, calculator	Calculating
Science at Home, p. 91	home	No special materials required.	Communicating
Real-World Lab, pp. 92–93	40	**Consumable** tracing paper **Nonconsumable** ruler; red, blue, green, and brown pencils	Interpreting Data, Predicting
Section 3			
Discover, p. 95	10	**Consumable** water **Nonconsumable** cup, funnel, basin	Inferring
Sharpen Your Skills, p. 96	10	No special materials required.	Communicating
Section 4			
Discover, p. 99	10	**Nonconsumable** local newspaper weather report	Observing
Sharpen Your Skills, p. 102	10	No special materials required.	Interpreting Data
Skills Lab, p. 106	30	No special materials required.	Interpreting Data, Drawing Conclusions

A list of all materials required for the Student Edition activities can be found on pages T14–T15. You can order Materials Kits by calling 1-800-828-7777 or by accessing the Science Explorer Internet site at **www.science-explorer.phschool.com.**

CHAPTER 3

Weather Patterns

A lightning bolt tears through the dark sky, illuminating a field of wheat.

WHAT'S AHEAD

CHAPTER PROJECT 3

The Weather Tomorrow

People often complain about the unreliability of weather forecasts. For example, they may blame their local weather forecaster when an unexpected thunderstorm ruins their picnic. Yet predicting the weather is something that interests most people because the weather influences so many things that we do. In this chapter, students will learn what causes changes in the weather and how the information recorded on weather maps can be used to make weather predictions.

Purpose In this project, students will get a chance to predict the weather and then evaluate how well they have done compared with the actual weather and with professional forecasts.

Skills Focus After completing this project, students will be able to

- ◆ interpret the symbols in newspaper weather maps;
- ◆ compare weather maps from day to day to find patterns in the weather;
- ◆ predict the weather for tomorrow based on the weather today;
- ◆ draw weather maps to show their weather predictions;
- ◆ compare their own predictions with professional forecasts and the next day's weather.

Project Time Line The entire project will take at least two weeks. Students should start collecting newspaper weather maps immediately. They should also read about weather maps in Section 4, paying special attention to *Exploring Newspaper Weather Maps* on page 105. As soon as students have finished reading Section 1 on air masses and fronts, they can start analyzing their weather maps. They should be looking for patterns in the weather by comparing the maps from day to day. Check students' progress at this point and give extra guidance to any students who are having problems.

Students should continue collecting and comparing weather maps over the next week or so. Check their progress when they finish Section 3 by having them predict the next day's weather at their own location and two other locations of their choice that are at least 1,000 km apart. Students should draw a weather map to show their weather predictions. After a week of predicting the weather in this way, have students compare their own predictions to the next days' weather maps and to professional forecasts.

When students have finished reading the chapter, give them a day or two to organize their presentations. They should display their newspaper weather maps and the weather maps they made to predict the weather. They should also include commentary, written or oral, about the patterns they observed in the weather and how they made their predictions.

For more detailed information on planning and supervising the chapter project, see Chapter 3 Project Teacher Notes, pages 66–67 in Teaching Resources.

Suggested Shortcuts You can reduce the scope of the project by requiring students to select just one location instead of three. Another shortcut is to have students work in groups. If you do, make sure groups divide tasks in such a way that each student makes a

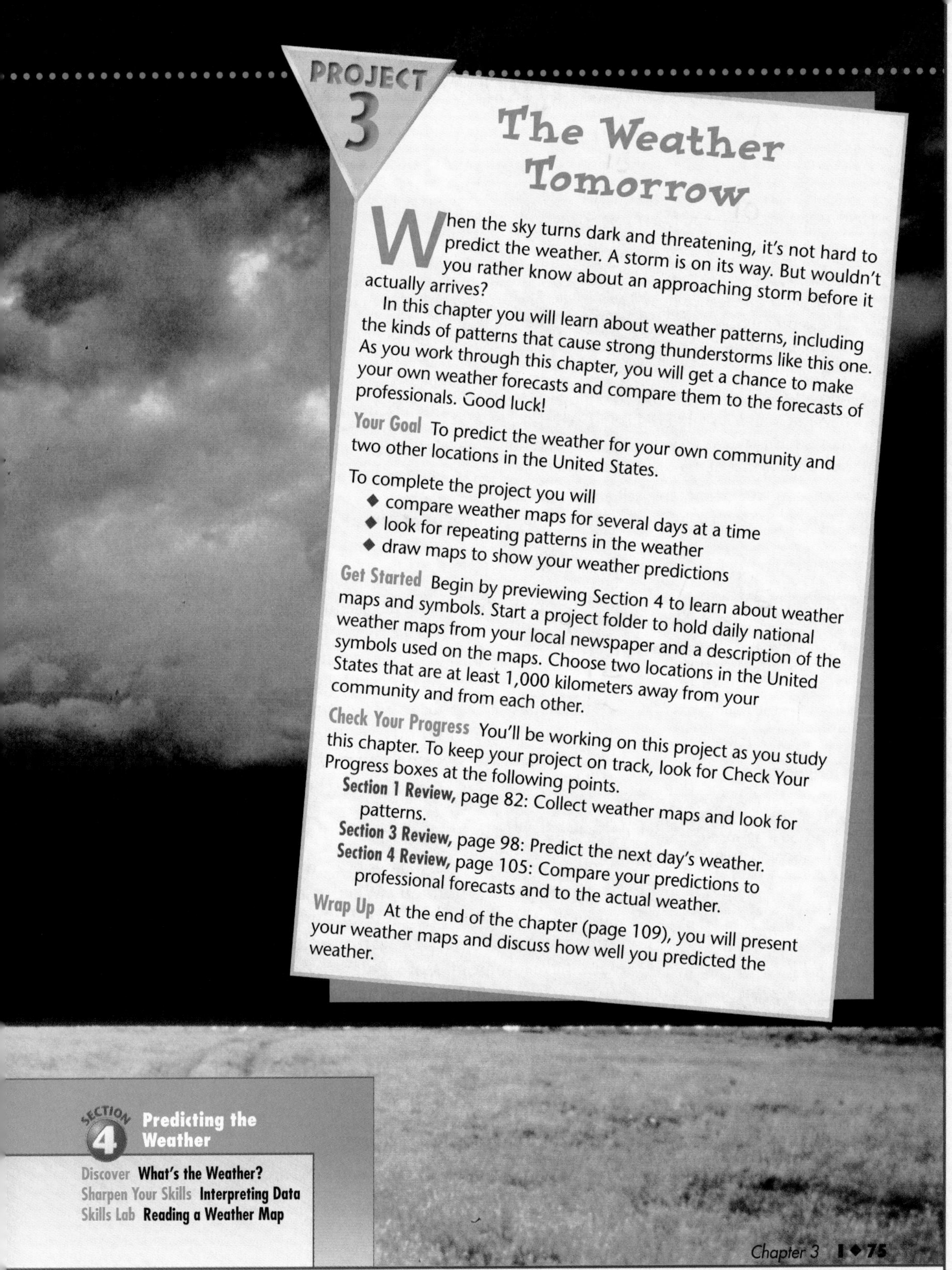

PROJECT 3

The Weather Tomorrow

When the sky turns dark and threatening, it's not hard to predict the weather. A storm is on its way. But wouldn't you rather know about an approaching storm before it actually arrives?

In this chapter you will learn about weather patterns, including the kinds of patterns that cause strong thunderstorms like this one. As you work through this chapter, you will get a chance to make your own weather forecasts and compare them to the forecasts of professionals. Good luck!

Your Goal To predict the weather for your own community and two other locations in the United States.

To complete the project you will
- compare weather maps for several days at a time
- look for repeating patterns in the weather
- draw maps to show your weather predictions

Get Started Begin by previewing Section 4 to learn about weather maps and symbols. Start a project folder to hold daily national weather maps from your local newspaper and a description of the symbols used on the maps. Choose two locations in the United States that are at least 1,000 kilometers away from your community and from each other.

Check Your Progress You'll be working on this project as you study this chapter. To keep your project on track, look for Check Your Progress boxes at the following points.

Section 1 Review, page 82: Collect weather maps and look for patterns.

Section 3 Review, page 98: Predict the next day's weather.

Section 4 Review, page 105: Compare your predictions to professional forecasts and to the actual weather.

Wrap Up At the end of the chapter (page 109), you will present your weather maps and discuss how well you predicted the weather.

SECTION 4 **Predicting the Weather**

Discover **What's the Weather?**
Sharpen Your Skills **Interpreting Data**
Skills Lab **Reading a Weather Map**

significant contribution to the overall effort. Urge groups to divide tasks according to students' specific abilities and interests, if possible.

This chapter project can also be done as a class project. Spend a few minutes at the beginning of class each day reviewing with students that day's newspaper weather map. If possible, make an overhead transparency of the map so you can point out details on the map as you discuss it. Also spend a few minutes each day comparing that day's weather map with the weather map from the day before. At the end of a week, have students start trying to predict the next day's weather.

Possible Materials Newspaper weather maps are readily available and easy to work with as long as students always use the same source so the maps have the same format. This makes them easier to compare and creates less confusion. A good source for weather maps regardless of where you live is *USA Today.*

Launching the Project Introduce students to weather maps by handing out copies of a national weather map showing today's weather. Have students find their own state on the map, and then challenge them to use the map to learn as much as they can about their state's weather. For example, ask: **What does the map tell you about the temperature in our state today?** Make sure all the students know how to find this and other weather factors for their state on the map. If necessary, call their attention to the map key and point out the relevant symbols and numbers on the map. Tell students they will be collecting and comparing maps like this one for the Chapter 3 Project. They will use the maps to learn how weather changes and how to predict tomorrow's weather from weather conditions today. Point out, however, that students will make their weather predictions without using the weather forecasts that are often included in weather information in newspapers and on radio and television.

Program Resources

- **Teaching Resources** Chapter 3 Project Teacher Notes, pp. 66–67; Chapter 3 Project Student Materials, pp. 68–71; Chapter 3 Project Scoring Rubric, p. 72

Performance Assessment

To assess students' performance in this project, use the Chapter 3 Project Scoring Rubric on page 72 of Teaching Resources.

Students will be assessed on
- their collection and interpretation of weather maps;
- their weather predictions;
- their class presentation;
- their group participation, if they worked in groups.

SECTION 1 Air Masses and Fronts

Objectives

After completing the lesson, students will be able to

- ◆ identify the major types of air masses that affect the weather in North America;
- ◆ name the main types of fronts;
- ◆ define cyclones and anticyclones.

Key Terms air mass, tropical, polar, maritime, continental, front, occluded, cyclone, anticyclone

1 Engage/Explore

Activating Prior Knowledge

Help students recall the properties of air they learned about in Chapter 2. Ask: **Which is denser, warm air or cold air?** *(cold air)* **What do you think would happen if a large mass of cold air came into contact with a large mass of warm air?** *(The cold air would sink and the warm air would rise.)* Tell students that large masses of cold and warm air often do meet in the atmosphere. Point out that the meeting of large air masses with different temperatures causes most of our weather.

DISCOVER ACTIVITY

Skills Focus developing hypotheses
Materials *cardboard divider, plastic shoe box, red food coloring, 1 L warm water, 100 mL table salt, blue food coloring, 1 L cold water*
Time 10 minutes
Tips The more salt students use, the denser the cold water will be and the more obvious the outcome.
Expected Outcome The red water and the blue water will not mix. Instead, they will form separate layers, with the blue water on the bottom and the red water on top.
Think It Over Students should hypothesize that the cold air mass would move underneath the warm air mass and the warm air mass would rise.

SECTION 1 Air Masses and Fronts

DISCOVER ACTIVITY

How Do Fluids of Different Densities Behave?

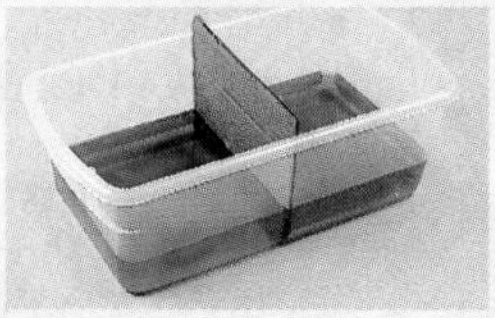

1. Put on your apron. Place a cardboard divider across the middle of a plastic shoe box.
2. Add a few drops of red food coloring to a liter of warm water. Pour the red liquid, which represents low-density warm air, into the shoe box on one side of the divider.
3. Add about 100 mL of table salt and a few drops of blue food coloring to a liter of cold water. Pour the blue liquid, which represents high-density cold air, into the shoe box on the other side of the divider.
4. What do you think will happen if you remove the divider?
5. Now quickly remove the divider. Watch carefully from the side. What happens?

Think It Over
Developing Hypotheses Based on this activity, write a hypothesis stating what would happen if a mass of cold air ran into a mass of warm air.

GUIDE FOR READING

- ◆ What are the major types of air masses that affect the weather in North America?
- ◆ What are the main types of fronts?
- ◆ What are cyclones and anticyclones?

Reading Tip Before you read, use the headings to make an outline about air masses and fronts. Leave space to fill in details as you read.

Listen to the evening news and you may hear a weather forecast like this: "A huge mass of Arctic air is moving our way, bringing freezing temperatures." Today's weather is influenced by air from thousands of kilometers away—perhaps from Canada or the Caribbean Sea. A huge body of air that has similar temperature, humidity, and air pressure throughout it is called an **air mass.** A single air mass may spread over an area of millions of square kilometers and be up to 10 kilometers high.

Types of Air Masses

Scientists classify air masses according to two characteristics: temperature and humidity. Whether an air mass is warm or cold depends on the temperature of the region over which the air mass forms. **Tropical,** or warm, air masses form in the tropics and have low air pressure. **Polar,** or cold, air masses form north of 50° north latitude and south of 50° south latitude. Polar air masses have high air pressure.

Whether an air mass is humid or dry depends on whether it forms over water or land. **Maritime** air masses form over oceans. Water evaporates from the oceans, so the air can become very humid. **Continental** air masses form over land, in the middle of continents, and are dry.

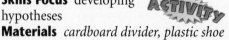

READING STRATEGIES

Study and Comprehension Help students avoid confusion about the different types of air masses and fronts described in this section. Have them make a table in which they contrast air masses in terms of their temperature and humidity and another table in which they contrast fronts in terms of how they form and the type of weather they bring.

Vocabulary Point out to students that the term *cyclone,* as it is used in this section, has a somewhat different meaning than its common usage. Many people use the term *cyclone* to mean a tornado, a type of severe storm students will learn about in Section 2. In this section, the term *cyclone* is used to refer to any large, swirling air mass that has low pressure at the center. This is why a cyclone is also called a "low." Unlike a tornado, a cyclone may cover thousands of kilometers.

Four major types of air masses influence the weather in North America: maritime tropical, continental tropical, maritime polar, and continental polar.** *Exploring North American Air Masses* on the next page shows where these air masses come from and what parts of North America they affect.

Maritime Tropical Warm, humid air masses form over oceans near the tropics. Maritime tropical air masses that form over the Gulf of Mexico and the Atlantic Ocean move first into the southeastern United States. These air masses then move north and northeast, where they influence weather in the central and eastern United States. In the west, maritime tropical air masses form over the Pacific Ocean. They affect mainly the weather on the West Coast. As they cross the coastal mountain ranges, the Pacific air masses lose moisture. They bring dry air to the eastern slopes.

In summer, maritime tropical air masses usually bring hot, humid weather. Most summer showers and thunderstorms in the United States develop in air masses that have formed over the Gulf of Mexico. In winter, a humid air mass can bring heavy rain or snow.

Maritime Polar Cool, humid air masses form over the icy cold North Pacific and North Atlantic oceans. Maritime polar air masses affect the West Coast more than the East Coast. Even in summer, these masses of cool, humid air often bring fog, rain, and cool temperatures to the West Coast.

Figure 1 This beach is on the southern Oregon coast. *Applying Concepts How does maritime polar air affect the weather at this location?*

2 Facilitate

Types of Air Masses

Building Inquiry Skills: Applying Concepts

Some students may need to review concepts covered in earlier chapters to understand the material presented in this section. Check their comprehension of relevant concepts by asking: **How does warm ocean water or a warm land surface heat the air above it?** *(By radiation and conduction of heat from the surface to the air above it and by convection, which carries the heated air high up into the atmosphere in air currents)* **Which type of air mass would you expect to contain more moisture, a maritime air mass or a continental air mass?** *(A maritime air mass, because it forms over the ocean)* **Would a maritime tropical air mass or a maritime polar air mass have more moisture?** *(A maritime tropical air mass, because it is warmer and warm air can hold more moisture than cold air)* **learning modality: verbal**

Including All Students

Help students distinguish among the different types of air masses covered in this section. Challenge them to create crossword puzzles incorporating the terms *tropical, polar, maritime,* and *continental.* After students have created their puzzles, urge them to exchange puzzles with a partner and try to solve them. **learning modality: limited English proficiency**

Media and Technology

Audiotapes English-Spanish Summary 3-1

Exploring Earth Science Videodisc Unit 4, Side 2, "Heating the Earth"

Chapter 1

Answers to Self-Assessment

Caption Question

Figure 1 It causes the weather to be cool and humid and often foggy and rainy.

Program Resources

- **Teaching Resources** 3-1 Lesson Plan, p. 73; 3-1 Section Summary, p. 74

Ongoing Assessment

Writing Have students explain the similarities and differences between polar and tropical air masses and between maritime and continental air masses.

Types of Air Masses, continued

EXPLORING

North American Air Masses

Invite students to apply the information in the feature by having them identify the types of air masses that affect different locations, such as different regions of the United States, different states, or different cities. Include the location where students live. For each location, ask: **What type of air are you likely to find there, and where does it come from?** *(Answers will depend on the locations chosen. For example, northern California receives cool, humid air due to maritime polar air masses from the northern Pacific Ocean.)* **learning modality: visual**

Building Inquiry Skills: Predicting

Point out that when air masses move from where they originate, they tend to be modified by the terrain they pass over. For example, the cold, dry air of continental polar air masses is warmed and moistened when it passes over the Great Lakes. Ask: **How would you predict that the other three North American air masses would be modified by the terrain they usually pass over?** *(Continental tropical air masses would be cooled, maritime polar air masses would be warmed and dried, maritime tropical air masses would be cooled and dried.)* **learning modality: logical/mathematical**

EXPLORING North American Air Masses

Air masses can be warm or cold, and humid or dry. As an air mass moves into an area, it changes the weather there.

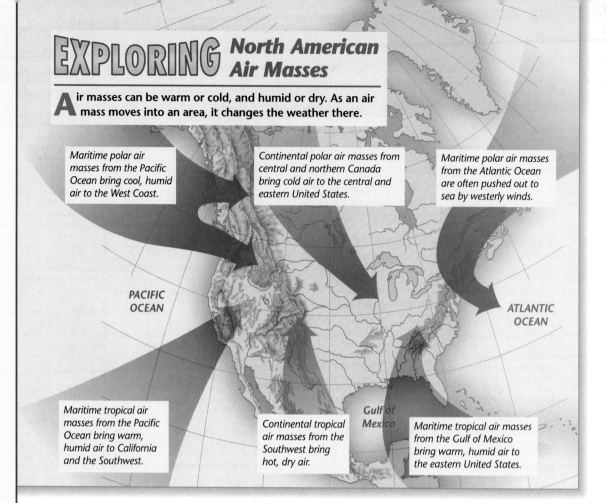

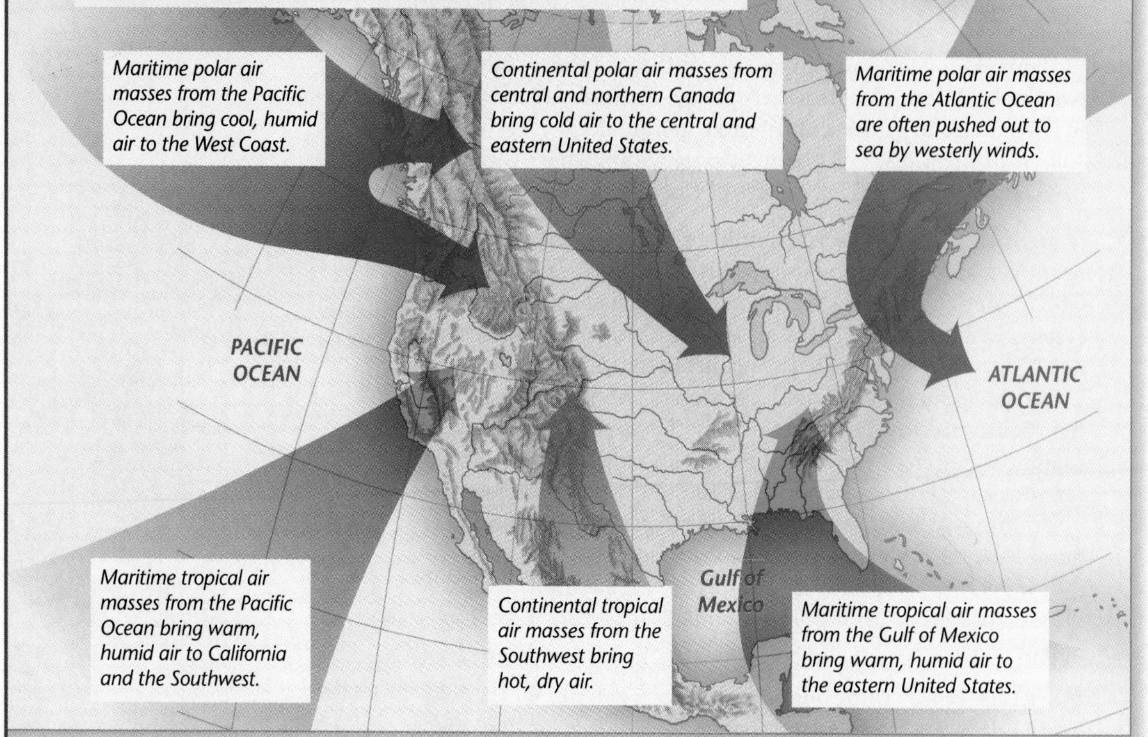

Maritime polar air masses from the Pacific Ocean bring cool, humid air to the West Coast.
Continental polar air masses from central and northern Canada bring cold air to the central and eastern United States.
Maritime polar air masses from the Atlantic Ocean are often pushed out to sea by westerly winds.
PACIFIC OCEAN
ATLANTIC OCEAN
Maritime tropical air masses from the Pacific Ocean bring warm, humid air to California and the Southwest.
Continental tropical air masses from the Southwest bring hot, dry air.
Gulf of Mexico
Maritime tropical air masses from the Gulf of Mexico bring warm, humid air to the eastern United States.

Continental Tropical Hot, dry air masses form only in summer over dry areas of the Southwest and northern Mexico. Continental tropical air masses cover a smaller area than other air masses. They occasionally move northeast, bringing hot, dry weather to the southern Great Plains.

Continental Polar Large continental polar air masses form over central and northern Canada and Alaska. As you would expect, continental polar air masses bring cool or cold air. In winter, continental polar air masses bring clear, cold, dry air to much of North America. Air masses that form near the Arctic Circle can bring bitterly cold weather with very low humidity. In summer, storms may occur when continental polar air masses move south and meet maritime tropical air masses moving north.

☑ *Checkpoint* *Where do continental polar air masses come from?*

Background

History of Science Up until the early 1900s, scientists thought that storms were caused by low air pressure. This conclusion was based on the fact that storms always seemed to occur in low-pressure areas. Then, in the early twentieth century, a Norwegian meteorologist named Vilhelm Bjerknes and a group of his colleagues deduced that storms are caused by the collision of large air masses that differ from one another in temperature and humidity. Although storms do occur in low-pressure areas, the low pressure is not their cause. Rather, low pressure areas, like storms, are a result of the collision of different air masses. This finding is now accepted as one of the most important principles of modern meteorology, and it is the basic principle underlying weather forecasting today.

How Air Masses Move

Recall that the prevailing westerlies are the major wind belts in the continental United States. The prevailing westerlies generally push air masses from west to east. For example, maritime polar air masses from the Pacific Ocean are blown onto the West Coast, bringing heavy rain or snow. Continental polar air masses from central Canada enter the United States between the Rocky Mountains and the Great Lakes. These cold, dry air masses are then blown east, where they affect the weather of the central and eastern United States.

Fronts

As huge masses of air move across the land and the oceans, they bump into each other. But the air masses do not easily mix. Why don't they? Think about a bottle of oil-and-vinegar salad dressing. The less dense oil floats on top of the more dense vinegar.

Something similar happens when two air masses with different temperatures and densities collide. The area where the air masses meet and do not mix becomes a **front.** The term *front,* which is borrowed from military language, means a battle area where opposing armies meet to fight. When air masses meet at a front, the collision often causes storms and changeable weather. A front may be 15 to 200 kilometers wide and extend as much as 10 kilometers up into the troposphere.

There are four types of fronts: cold fronts, warm fronts, stationary fronts, and occluded fronts. The kind of front that develops depends on the characteristics of the air masses and how they are moving. How does each type of front affect your local weather?

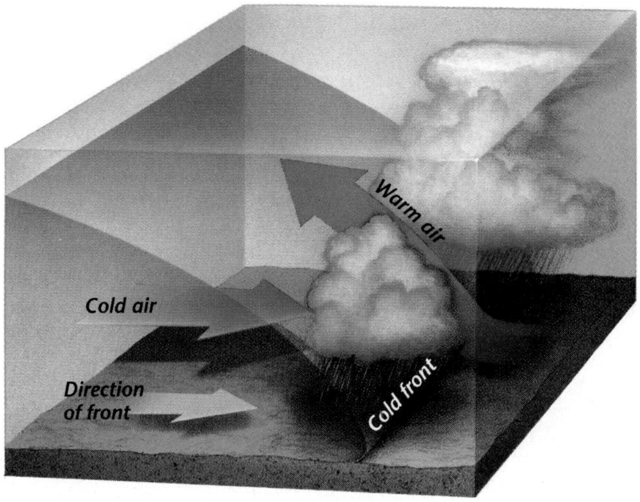

Figure 2 A cold front forms when cold air moves underneath warm air, forcing the warm air to rise.

How Air Masses Move

Inquiry Challenge

Material *world map or globe*
Time 10 minutes

ACTIVITY

Based on what they have just learned about the movement of air masses in North America, challenge students to infer which types of air masses are likely to affect the weather of Europe. First provide students with a world map or globe, and then ask: **Where do you think air masses come from that move over the European continent?** *(The Atlantic Ocean, northern Eurasia, and the African continent)* **What type of air do you think they bring to Europe?** *(Cool humid air from the Atlantic Ocean, cold dry air from northern Eurasia, and hot dry air from Africa)* **learning modality: logical/mathematical**

Fronts

Including All Students

Materials *red and green modeling clay*
Time 5 minutes

ACTIVITY

Give hands-on learners an opportunity to model the formation of warm and cold fronts using wedges of red and green modeling clay to represent warm and cold air masses, respectively. For each type of front that students model, ask: **In which direction is the front moving?** *(For the cold front, toward the warm air mass; for the warm front, toward the cold air mass)* **learning modality: kinesthetic**

Media and Technology

Transparencies "North American Air Masses," Transparency 10; "Cold Front," Transparency 11

Answers to Self-Assessment

☑ *Checkpoint*

Continental polar air masses come from central and northern Canada and Alaska.

Ongoing Assessment

Oral Presentation Call on students to name the four types of air masses that influence weather in North America. Then call on other students to state where each type of air mass forms, whether it is warm or cold, and whether it is humid or dry.

Fronts, continued

Using the Visuals: Figure 3

Help students understand the similarities and differences between warm and cold fronts by having them compare and contrast illustrations of each type of front. Ask: **How does Figures 3, which shows the formation of a warm front, differ from Figure 2, which shows the formation of a cold front?** *(In Figure 3, the warm air mass moves up over the cold air mass; in Figure 2, the cold air mass moves underneath the warm air mass.)* **How are the two figures similar?** *(In both cases, the warm air rises and cools, causing water vapor to condense out of it and form clouds.)* **learning modality: visual**

Demonstration

Materials *tall heat-resistant jar or beaker, cold water, pepper, stirrer, container of hot water, food coloring, candle, matches*
Time 15 minutes

ACTIVITY

Do this demonstration to show students how fronts form. Half-fill a tall, heat-resistant jar or beaker with cold water. Stir pepper into the water until it is mixed throughout. Add food coloring to a container of hot water, mix well, and then gently pour the hot water into the jar of cold water. The two layers of water should remain separate and mix only slightly. Light a candle and hold the jar above it. As the cold water in the bottom of the jar heats up, the pepper will move upward due to convection. However, the pepper will not penetrate the top layer of colored water but instead collect at the "front" between the two layers of water. Ask: **Why doesn't the pepper rise up through the top layer of water?** *(Because the top layer of water is warmer and will not mix with the cooler layer of water containing the pepper)* **learning modality: visual**

Cold Fronts As you know, cold air is dense and tends to sink. Warm air is less dense and tends to rise. When a rapidly moving cold air mass runs into a slowly moving warm air mass, the denser cold air slides under the lighter warm air. The warm air is pushed upward, as shown in Figure 2. The front that forms is called a cold front.

As the warm air rises, it cools. Remember that warm air can hold more water vapor than cool air. The rising air soon reaches the dew point, the temperature at which the water vapor in the air condenses into droplets of liquid water. Clouds form. If there is a lot of water vapor in the warm air, heavy rain or snow may fall. What will happen if the warm air mass contains only a little water vapor? In this case, the cold front may be accompanied by only cloudy skies.

Cold fronts move quickly, so they can cause abrupt weather changes, including violent thunderstorms. After a cold front passes through an area, cool, dry air moves in, often bringing clear skies and cooler temperatures.

Warm Fronts Clouds, storms, and rain also accompany warm fronts. At a warm front, a moving warm air mass collides with a slowly moving cold air mass. Because cold air is more dense than warm air, the warm air moves over the cold air, as shown in Figure 3. If the warm air is humid, showers and light rain fall along the front where the warm and cold air meet. If the warm air is dry, scattered clouds form. Because warm fronts move more slowly than cold fronts, the weather may be rainy or foggy for several days. After a warm front passes through an area, the weather is likely to be warm and humid. In winter, warm fronts bring snow.

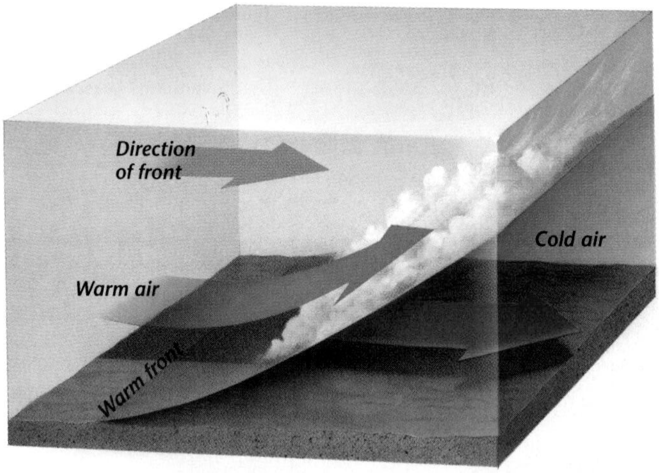

Figure 3 A warm front forms when warm air moves over cold air.
Interpreting Diagrams What kind of weather forms at a warm front?

Background

Facts and Figures Like fingerprints or snowflakes, no two fronts are exactly alike. For example, the slope of a front can vary considerably, from about 1:100 (1 km of vertical distance covers 100 km of horizontal distance) for a cold front to about 1:200 for a warm front.

The slope of a front is an important determinant of the type of weather the front brings. A cold front with a very steep slope is likely to bring a narrow band of violent storms extending less than 100 km. A warm front with a very gradual slope, on the other hand, is likely to bring cloudy weather but no storms. However, the area affected by the cloudy weather may extend for many hundreds of kilometers.

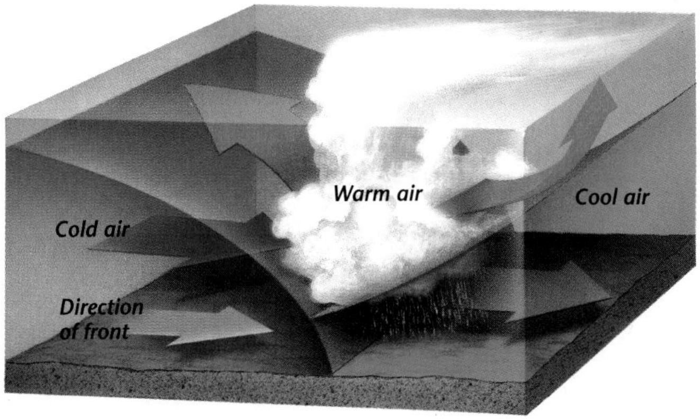

Figure 4 When a cold air mass and a cool air mass come together, the warm air caught between them is forced upward. The result is an occluded front.

Stationary Fronts Sometimes cold and warm air masses meet, but neither one has enough force to move the other. The two air masses face each other in a "standoff." In this case, the front is called a stationary front. Where the warm and cool air meet, water vapor in the warm air condenses into rain, snow, fog, or clouds. If a stationary front remains stalled over an area, it may bring many days of clouds and precipitation.

Occluded Fronts The most complex weather situation occurs at an occluded front, shown in Figure 4. At an occluded front, a warm air mass is caught between two cooler air masses. The denser cool air masses move underneath the less dense warm air mass and push it upward. The two cooler air masses meet in the middle and may mix. The temperature near the ground becomes cooler. The warm air mass is cut off, or **occluded,** from the ground. As the warm air cools and its water vapor condenses, the weather may turn cloudy and rainy or snowy.

☑ *Checkpoint* *What type of front forms when two air masses meet and neither one can move?*

Cyclones and Anticyclones

If you look at a weather map, you will see areas marked with an L. The L is short for "low," and indicates an area of relatively low air pressure. A swirling center of low air pressure is called a **cyclone,** from a Greek word meaning "wheel."

As warm air at the center of a cyclone rises, the air pressure decreases. Cooler air blows toward this low-pressure area from nearby areas where the air pressure is higher. Winds spiral inward toward the center of the system. Recall that in the Northern Hemisphere the Coriolis effect deflects winds to the right.

Sharpen your Skills

Classifying

At home, watch the weather forecast on television. Make a note of each time the weather reporter mentions a front. Classify the fronts mentioned or shown as cold, warm, stationary, or occluded. Also, note what type of weather is predicted to occur when the front arrives. Is each type of front always associated with the same type of weather?

Media and Technology

Transparencies "Warm Front," Transparency 12; "Occluded Front," Transparency 13

Answers to Self-Assessment

Caption Question

Figure 3 Clouds, storms, and precipitation form at a warm front.

☑ **Checkpoint**

A stationary front forms when two air masses meet and neither one can move.

Sharpen your Skills

Classifying

Tips Have students continue this activity over several days in order to observe at least three different types of fronts.

Expected Outcome Students should find that all types of fronts are associated with clouds and precipitation. However, cold fronts tend to be associated with more abrupt changes in the weather.

Extend Have students continue to monitor weather changes after the fronts pass through their area. Ask: **What type of weather follows each type of front?** *(Cold and occluded fronts are followed by cool, clear weather, warm fronts by warm, humid weather.)* **learning modality: logical/mathematical**

Cyclones and Anticyclones

Including All Students

Materials *two balloons, pencil, thread, ruler*
Time 5 minutes

Instruct students to inflate two balloons to 10 cm in diameter and tie them to the opposite ends of a pencil with pieces of thread 30 cm long. Then have them hold the pencil level, with the balloons 8 cm from their faces, and blow gently between the balloons. Ask: **Why did the balloons move closer together?** *(Blowing away the air between the balloons decreased the air pressure between them. The higher air pressure on the opposite side of the balloons then pushed the two balloons closer together.)* Ask: **How is this like a cyclone?** *(In a cyclone, winds blow in toward the center because there is low pressure there.)* **learning modality: kinesthetic**

Ongoing Assessment

Drawing Have students create drawings to represent a warm front and a cold front. They should label the air masses as "cold" or "warm" and use arrows to indicate the direction the air masses are moving.

3 Assess

Section 1 Review Answers

1. temperature and humidity
2. A front is the area where two air masses meet and do not mix. A cold front forms when cold air moves underneath warm air. A warm front forms when warm air moves over cold air. A stationary front forms when a warm and a cold air mass meet but neither can move the other. An occluded front forms when a warm air mass is caught between two cool air masses and cut off from the ground.
3. A swirling center of low air pressure; storms and precipitation
4. Because East Coast maritime polar air masses are blown out to sea by prevailing westerlies
5. Maritime tropical and polar air masses are humid; continental tropical and polar air masses are dry.

Check Your Progress (Chapter Project 3)

Check that each student has started to collect weather maps. Comparisons of weather in the three locations should include all the weather factors represented on the maps.

Performance Assessment

Skills Check Have students describe the direction of winds in cyclones and anticyclones in the Southern Hemisphere.

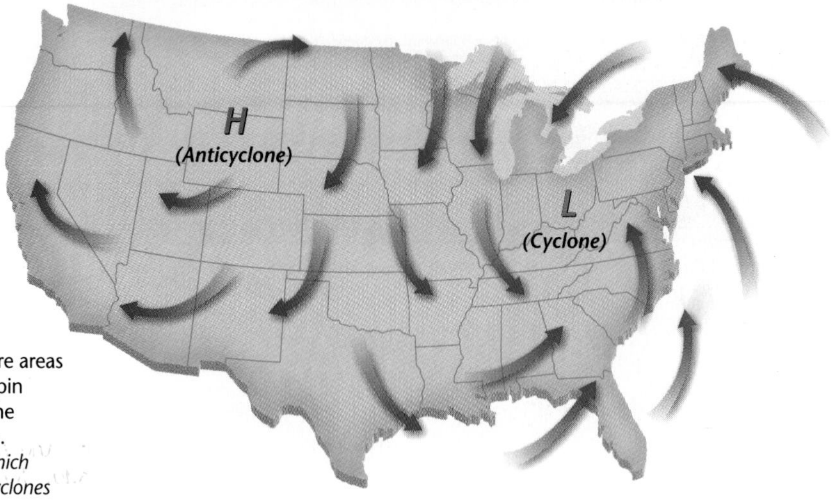

Figure 5 Cyclones are areas of low pressure that spin counterclockwise in the Northern Hemisphere. *Interpreting Maps* *Which way do winds in anticyclones spin?*

Because of this, winds in a cyclone spin counterclockwise in the Northern Hemisphere, as shown in Figure 5.

Cyclones play a large part in the weather of the United States. As air rises in a cyclone, the air cools, forming clouds and precipitation. **Cyclones and decreasing air pressure are associated with storms and precipitation.**

As its name suggests, an anticyclone is the opposite of a cyclone in most ways. **Anticyclones** are high-pressure centers of dry air. Anticyclones are also called "highs"—H on a weather map. Winds spiral outward from the center of an anticyclone, moving toward areas of lower pressure. Because of the Coriolis effect, winds in an anticyclone spin clockwise in the Northern Hemisphere. Because air moves out from the center of the anticyclone, cool air moves downward from higher in the troposphere. As the cool air falls, it warms up, so its relative humidity drops. The descending air in an anticyclone causes dry, clear weather.

Section 1 Review

1. What two main characteristics are used to classify air masses?
2. What is a front? Name and describe four types of fronts.
3. What is a cyclone? What type of weather does it bring?
4. Why do maritime polar air masses have more effect on the West Coast than the East Coast?
5. **Thinking Critically** **Classifying** Classify the four major types of air masses according to whether they are dry or humid.

Check Your Progress (Chapter Project 3)

Collect newspaper weather maps for about a week, and arrange them in order. Look carefully at how symbols on the map have moved from one day to the next. What patterns do you see from day to day in different weather factors? How does the weather in your community differ from the weather in the two other locations you selected?

Answers to Self-Assessment

Caption Question

Figure 5 Winds in anticyclones spin clockwise in the Northern Hemisphere.

Program Resources

- **Teaching Resources** 3-1 Review and Reinforce, p. 75; 3-1 Enrich, p. 76

Media and Technology

Interactive Student Tutorial CD-ROM I-3

SECTION 2 Storms

DISCOVER ACTIVITY

Can You Make a Tornado?

1. Fill a large plastic jar three-quarters full with water. Add a drop of liquid dish detergent and a penny or marble.
2. Put the lid on the jar tightly. Now move the jar in a circle until the water inside begins to spin.

Think It Over

Observing What happens to the water in the jar? Describe the pattern that forms. How is it like a tornado? Unlike a tornado?

GUIDE FOR READING

- What are the main kinds of storms? How do they form?
- What measures can you take to ensure safety in a storm?

Reading Tip As you read, create a table comparing thunderstorms, tornadoes, hurricanes, and snowstorms. Include temperature, precipitation, and safety rules.

Early in 1998, a series of powerful tornadoes roared through central Florida. With winds as high as 210 miles per hour, the tornadoes dropped cars into living rooms, crumpled trailers, and destroyed businesses and school buildings. They were the deadliest tornadoes ever to hit Florida. These tornadoes were not the only violent weather that year. In California the problem was rain. Record rainfalls brought devastating floods and mudslides.

What was causing these disasters? Meteorologists had an answer: El Niño. El Niño is a weather pattern related to the temperature of the water in the tropical Pacific Ocean. When temperatures there rise, they set off a series of events that can influence weather half a world away.

Have you ever experienced a tornado, hurricane, or other severe storm? When rain pours down, thunder crashes, or snowdrifts pile up, it may be hard to think about the actions of air pressure and air masses. Yet these are the causes of severe storms as well as the weather you experience every day.

A **storm** is a violent disturbance in the atmosphere. Storms involve sudden changes in air pressure, which in turn cause rapid air movements. Conditions that bring one kind of storm often cause other kinds of storms in the same area. For example, the conditions that cause thunderstorms can also cause tornadoes.

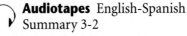

Figure 6 Tornadoes caused tremendous damage in Florida and other parts of the southeastern United States in 1998.

READING STRATEGIES

Reading Tip Urge students to add columns to their tables for recording such factors as wind speed, size of storm, length of time the storm lasts, and the type of damage it does. Have students save their tables for review. Students needing extra credit can copy their tables onto poster board and illustrate them with drawings and photographs. Display their posters in the classroom.

Program Resources

- **Teaching Resources** 3-2 Lesson Plan, p. 77; 3-2 Section Summary, p. 78

Media and Technology

Audiotapes English-Spanish Summary 3-2

SECTION 2 Storms

Objectives

After completing the lesson, students will be able to

- list the main kinds of storms and explain how they form;
- describe measures they can take to ensure safety in a storm.

Key Terms storm, lightning, tornado, hurricane, storm surge, evacuate

1 Engage/Explore

Activating Prior Knowledge

Introduce students to tornadoes and other storms by asking: **Did you ever see a dust devil, a spinning wind that picks up and carries dust, dead leaves, and other debris?** *(Most students probably will say "yes.")* **What did it look like?** *(a funnel)* **What do think causes dust devils?** *(Air swirling in a circle)* Point out that dust devils resemble small tornadoes. Explain that they are caused by hot air rising rapidly from the heated ground. As the hot air rises, the wind blows it into a spinning motion and it picks up loose material. Add that most dust devils last just a few seconds, rise only a few meters, and cause no damage. Tell students that the same type of air movement also causes tornadoes, as they will learn in this section.

DISCOVER ACTIVITY

Skills Focus observing
Materials *large plastic jar with lid, water, liquid dish detergent, penny or marble*
Time 10 minutes
Tips Tell students not to shake the jar or slosh the water back and forth to create bubbles. Instead, they should swirl the water gently with a circular motion.
Expected Outcome The water should swirl around in the jar like a tornado.
Think It Over Students should say that the water swirls in a funnel-shaped spiral. It is like a tornado because the water spins around in a circle. It is unlike a tornado because it occurs in water instead of air.

2 Facilitate

Thunderstorms

Demonstration

ACTIVITY

Materials *bottle with plastic cap, copper wire, aluminum foil, plastic comb, wool fabric*
Time 10 minutes

Show the class how lightning occurs with this demonstration. Push a short piece of copper wire through a small hole in the cap of a bottle. Form the bottom end of the wire into a hook and hang a small strip of aluminum foil over it. Put the cap on the bottle with the hook and foil inside. Rub a comb on wool fabric to give it an electrical charge and then touch the comb to the end of the wire protruding from the top of the bottle cap. Students will see the ends of the foil strip move apart from one another. Ask: **Why did the ends of the foil strip move?** *(Students may not know.)* Explain that the foil became charged with electricity, which was transmitted through the wire from the comb, causing the two ends of the foil strip to repel each other. Ask: **How is this like lightning?** *(A charge is built up when particles in clouds rub together, and when the electricity is discharged from one part of the cloud to another or to the ground, lightning occurs.)* **learning modality: visual**

TRY THIS

ACTIVITY

Skills Focus calculating
Materials *watch with second hand*
Time 10 minutes

Expected Outcome The number of seconds between the lightning flash and the sound of the thunder will depend on how far away the lightning is. If the lightning is very close, the thunder will occur just a split second later. If the lightning is very far away, the thunder may not even be audible. If the length of time between the lightning and thunder is increasing, the storm is moving away from you. If the length of time is decreasing, the storm is moving toward you. **learning modality: logical/mathematical**

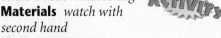

Figure 7 The anvil shape of this cloud is typical of cumulonimbus clouds that produce thunderstorms. *Applying Concepts Why do cumulonimbus clouds often form along cold fronts?*

TRY THIS

Lightning Distances

ACTIVITY

Because light travels faster than sound, you see a lightning flash before you hear the clap of thunder. Here's how to calculate your distance from a thunderstorm.

CAUTION: *Do this activity inside a building only.*

1. Count the number of seconds between the moment when you see the lightning and when you hear the thunder.
2. Divide the number of seconds you counted by three to get the distance in kilometers. Example:

$$\frac{15 \text{ s}}{3 \text{ s/km}} = 5 \text{ km}$$

Calculating Wait for another flash of lightning and calculate the distance again. How can you tell whether a thunderstorm is moving toward you or away from you?

Thunderstorms

Do you find thunderstorms frightening? Exciting? A little of both? As you watch the brilliant flashes of lightning and listen to long rolls of thunder, you have probably wondered what caused them.

How Thunderstorms Form Thunderstorms are heavy rainstorms accompanied by thunder and lightning. **Thunderstorms form within large cumulonimbus clouds, or thunderheads.** Most cumulonimbus clouds and thunderstorms form when warm air is forced upward at a cold front. Cumulonimbus clouds also form on hot, humid afternoons in the spring and summer. In both cases, the warm, humid air rises rapidly. As the air rises, it cools, forming dense thunderheads. Heavy rain falls, sometimes along with hail.

Thunderstorms produce strong upward and downward winds—updrafts and downdrafts—inside clouds. When a downdraft strikes the ground, the air spreads out in all directions, producing bursts of wind called wind shear. Wind shear has caused a number of airplane accidents during takeoff or landing.

Lightning and Thunder During a thunderstorm, areas of positive and negative electrical charges build up in the storm clouds. **Lightning** is a sudden spark, or energy discharge, as these charges jump between parts of a cloud or between the cloud and the ground. Lightning is similar to the shocks you sometimes feel when you touch a metal object on a very dry day, but on a much larger scale.

What causes thunder? A lightning bolt can heat the air near it to as much as 30,000°C, much hotter than the surface of the sun. The rapidly heated air expands suddenly and explosively. Thunder is the sound of the explosion. Because light travels faster than sound, you see lightning before you hear thunder.

84 ◆ I

Background

Facts and Figures Just how serious a threat do thunderstorms pose? At any given moment, about 1,800 thunderstorms are occurring somewhere on Earth. That's a total of 16 million thunderstorms a year worldwide, of which an estimated 100,000 occur in the United States. Every second about 100 bolts of lightning strike Earth's surface. About 80 people in the United States are killed by lightning each year (more than are typically killed each year by tornadoes). Over the last 10 years, lightning started more than 15,000 fires in the United States and caused hundreds of millions of dollars in damage each year and the destruction of two million acres of forest. The high winds that often accompany thunderstorms can be even more damaging. Thunderstorm winds can exceed 160 km/h, which is as fast as the winds of a hurricane.

Thunderstorm Safety When lightning strikes the ground, the hot, expanding air can shatter tree trunks or start forest fires. When lightning strikes people or animals, it acts like a powerful electric shock. Being struck by lightning can cause unconsciousness, serious burns, or even heart failure.

INTEGRATING HEALTH

What should you do to remain safe if you are caught outside during a thunderstorm? **During thunderstorms, avoid touching metal objects because they can conduct electricity from lightning into your body.** Lightning usually strikes the tallest nearby object, such as a tree, house, or flagpole. To protect buildings from lightning, people install metal lightning rods at the highest point on a roof. Lightning rods intercept a lightning stroke and conduct the electricity through cables safely into the ground.

In open spaces, such as a golf course, people can be in danger because they are the tallest objects in the area. It is equally dangerous to seek shelter under a tree, because lightning may strike the tree and you at the same time. Instead, find a low area away from trees, fences, and poles. Crouch with your head down and your hands on your knees. If you are swimming or in a boat, get to shore and find shelter away from the water.

If you are inside a house during a thunderstorm, avoid touching telephones, electrical appliances, or plumbing fixtures, all of which can conduct electricity into the house. It is usually safe to stay in a car with a hard top during a thunderstorm because the electricity will move along the metal skin of the car and jump to the ground. However, do not touch any metal inside the car.

Figure 8 Lightning occurs when electricity jumps within clouds or between a cloud and the ground.

☑ *Checkpoint* *Why is lightning dangerous?*

Tornadoes

A tornado is one of the most frightening and destructive types of storms. A **tornado** is a rapidly whirling, funnel-shaped cloud that reaches down from a storm cloud to touch Earth's surface. If a tornado occurs over a lake or ocean, it is known as a waterspout. Tornadoes are usually brief, but can be deadly. They may touch the ground for 15 minutes or less and be only a few hundred meters across, but wind speeds may approach 480 kilometers per hour.

Integrating Health

There are many naive conceptions about lightning that may cause people to take needless risks in thunderstorms. Address some of these naive conceptions by first asking: **Do you think the old saying is true that lightning never strikes twice in the same place?** *(Students may say "yes".)* Tell students that the chance of lightning striking the same place twice is very small, but there is no reason it cannot happen. In fact, some buildings and even people have been struck by lightning repeatedly. Other myths about lightning include that there is no danger from lightning if it is not raining and that rubber-soled shoes will protect you from being struck by lightning.
learning modality: verbal

Tornadoes

Including All Students

ACTIVITY

Materials *raw potato, plastic drinking straw*
Time 5 minutes

Tell students that the force of the wind in a tornado may be great enough to drive a drinking straw through a board. If students find this hard to believe, this activity will help them appreciate just how strong the wind can be. Have students place the end of a plastic drinking straw against a raw potato and push as hard as they can. The straw will bend and scarcely penetrate the potato. Now have students hold the straw at least half a meter away from the potato and drive it into the potato as fast as possible. This time the straw will penetrate the potato without bending. Ask: **Why did the straw go through the potato when you drove it in from a distance?** *(It was pushed harder.)* Add that winds in a tornado can push with such force that a blade of grass may be driven into a tree trunk.
learning modality: kinesthetic

Media and Technology

Exploring Earth Science Videodisc
Unit 4, Side 2,
"Violent Storms"

Chapter 4

Answers to Self-Assessment

Caption Question

Figure 7 Cumulonimbus clouds often form along cold fronts because warm air is forced upward. As the warm air rises, it cools, forming dense thunderheads.

☑ *Checkpoint*

Lightning acts like a powerful shock and can cause unconsciousness, serious burns, or even heart failure.

Ongoing Assessment

Writing Challenge students to write a public service announcement for television or radio that spells out the precautions people should take to remain safe in a thunderstorm.

SCIENCE & History

Call students' attention to the feature and then ask: **What types of storms are described in the feature?** *(Thunderstorms and hurricanes)* Point out that tornadoes are not included, and then ask: **Why might tornadoes have less impact on history?** *(A tornado's path of destruction tends to be narrow and short lived.)* Inform students that there are some notable exceptions to the brief, local nature of most tornadoes. For example, the Great Tri-State Tornado of March 18, 1925, killed almost 700 people in three states, and the Superoutbreak Tornadoes of April 3–4, 1974, killed more than 300 people and injured over 5,500 others in 12 states in 24 hours. Add that, unlike thunderstorms and hurricanes, exactly when and where a tornado will touch down is still difficult to predict. Suggest to students who need an extra challenge that they research other examples of tornadoes, thunderstorms, and hurricanes that had an impact, great or small, on the course of history. Urge them to share what they learn with the rest of the class.

In Your Journal Students' paragraphs will vary depending on the specific event they choose. If they choose the storms that affected the *Mayflower*, for example, they may say that, with advance warning, the settlers might have delayed their landing until the storms had passed and then settled in what is now New York City instead of Plymouth. **learning modality: verbal**

How Tornadoes Form **Tornadoes develop in low, heavy cumulonimbus clouds—the same clouds that bring thunderstorms.** Tornadoes are most likely to occur when thunderstorms are likely—in spring and early summer, often late in the afternoon when the ground is warm. The Great Plains often have the kind of weather pattern that is likely to create tornadoes: a warm, humid air mass moves north from the Gulf of Mexico into the lower Great Plains. A cold, dry air mass moves south from Canada. When the air masses meet, the cold air moves under the warm air, which rises. A squall line of thunderstorms is likely to form, with storms traveling from southwest to northeast. A single squall line can cause 10 or more tornadoes.

Tornadoes occur more often in the United States than in any other country. About 800 tornadoes occur in the United States

SCIENCE & History

Weather That Changed History

Unanticipated storms have caused incredible damage, killed numbers of people, and even changed the course of history.

1281 Japan

In an attempt to conquer Japan, Kublai Khan, the Mongol emperor of China, sent a fleet of ships carrying a huge army. A hurricane from the Pacific brought high winds and towering waves that sank the ships. The Japanese named the storm *kamikaze*, meaning "divine wind."

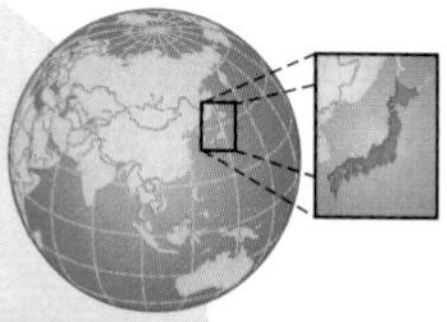

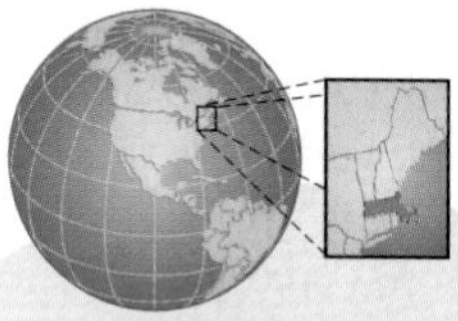

1620 Massachusetts

English Pilgrims set sail for the Americas in the *Mayflower*. They had planned to land near the mouth of the Hudson River, but turned back north because of rough seas and storms. When the Pilgrims landed farther north, they decided to stay and so established Plymouth Colony.

1300 | 1400 | 1500 | 1600

1588 England

King Philip II of Spain sent the Spanish Armada, a fleet of 130 ships, to invade England. Strong winds in the English Channel trapped the Armada near shore. Some Spanish ships escaped, but storms wrecked most of them.

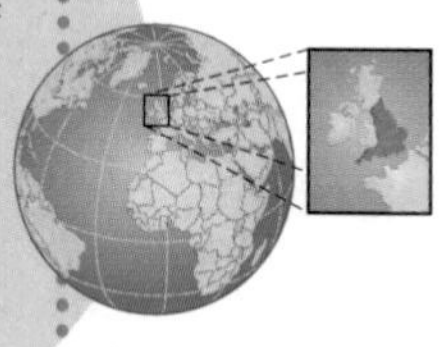

Background

Facts and Figures Tornadoes are commonly classified according to the following scale, which is called the Fujita-Pearson Tornado Intensity Scale after its inventors:

F0 Light (under 116 km/h)
F1 Moderate (116–180 km/h)
F2 Considerable (181–253 km/h)
F3 Severe (254–332 km/h)
F4 Devastating (333–419 km/h)
F5 Incredible (over 419 km/h)

The winds of tornadoes have done some amazing things. In Bedfordshire, England, in May of 1950, a tornado is reported to have plucked the feathers off several chickens, who amazingly were otherwise unharmed. Tornadoes also have lifted frogs and fish from ponds and then dropped them elsewhere, leading to the saying, "a tornado may rain frogs."

every year. Weather patterns on the Great Plains result in a "tornado alley," shown in Figure 9, that runs from north-central Texas across central Oklahoma, Kansas, and Nebraska. However, tornadoes can and do occur in nearly every part of the United States.

☑ *Checkpoint* *Where do tornadoes form?*

Tornado Safety A tornado can level houses on one street, but **INTEGRATING HEALTH** leave neighboring houses standing. Tornado damage comes from both strong winds and flying debris. The low pressure inside the tornado sucks up dust and other objects into the funnel. Tornadoes can move large objects—sheds, trailers, cars—and scatter debris many miles away. One tornado tore off a motel sign in Broken Bow, Oklahoma, and dropped it 30 miles away in Arkansas!

In Your Journal

Some of these events happened before forecasters had the equipment to predict weather scientifically. Choose one of the events in the time line. Write a paragraph describing how history might have different if the people involved had had accurate weather predictions.

1870 Great Lakes

Learning that more than 1,900 boats had sunk in storms on the Great Lakes in 1869, Congress decided to set up a national weather service, the Army Signal Corps. In 1891 the job of issuing weather warnings and forecasts went to a new agency, the U.S. Weather Bureau.

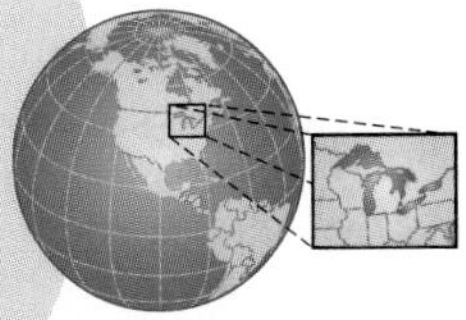

1700 **1800** **1900**

1837 North Carolina

The steamship *Home* sank during a hurricane off Ocracoke, North Carolina. In one of the worst storm-caused disasters at sea, 90 people died. In response, the U.S. Congress passed a law requiring seagoing ships to carry a life preserver for every passenger.

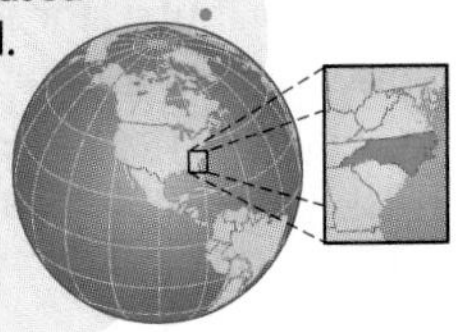

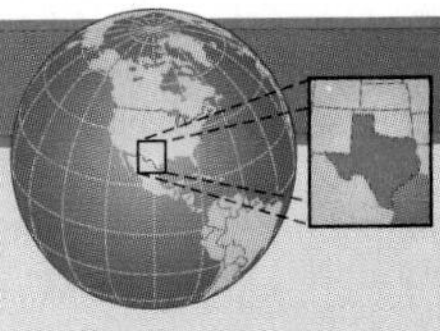

1915 Texas

When a hurricane struck the port city of Galveston in 1900, it killed 6,000 people and destroyed much of the city. As a result, a seawall 5 meters high and 16 kilometers long was built. When another hurricane struck in 1915, the seawall greatly reduced the amount of damage.

Answers to Self-Assessment

☑ *Checkpoint*

Tornadoes form in low, heavy cumulonimbus clouds.

Integrating Health

To help students take the danger of tornadoes seriously, tell them that tornadoes cause damage and take lives in three ways: the direct force of the wind, the twisting force of the wind, and the lift and drop force at the center of the tornado. Ask a volunteer to record ideas as students brainstorm specific ways that these three tornado forces can cause damage and claim lives. *(Possible ways might include: the direct force of the wind can turn over cars, knock down buildings, and blow debris that smashes windows and kills people; the twisting force of the wind can twist signs off buildings and twist trees and power poles out of the ground; and the lift and drop force at the center of the tornado can suck people and objects high into the air and drop them down elsewhere.)* **cooperative learning**

Ongoing Assessment

Skills Check Have students compare and contrast tornadoes and thunderstorms.

Tornadoes, continued

Using the Visuals: Figure 9

Use the map in Figure 9 to help students understand why the central part of the United States has so many tornadoes. Ask: **What is the reddish shaded area called?** *(Tornado Alley)* **Why is it called that?** *(More tornadoes occur there than anywhere else in the United States.)* **Why do you think so many tornadoes occur there?** *(Because cold and warm air masses meet there)* **learning modality: visual**

Addressing Naive Conceptions

Ask students if the following statements are true or false: **If you don't have a basement, the safest place in your home in the event of a tornado is the southwest corner.** *(False. The safest place is a small windowless room or closet in the center of the house.)* **If a tornado catches you on the road, it is best to stay in your car.** *(False. A tornado can overturn a car or pick it up and drop it elsewhere. You should leave the car and go to a well-built building or lie flat in a low place with your head covered.)* Based on how students respond, discuss any misconceptions they may hold. For example, if students believe that the safest place in a home without a basement is an outside corner, explain that an outside room is more at risk of damage from the wind, and windows in outside rooms put you at risk of flying glass. **learning modality: verbal**

Hurricanes

Including All Students

Explain to students that hurricanes are given names according to certain rules. They are named alphabetically, alternating between masculine and feminine names. For example, in 1996, the first storm of the season was named Arthur, the second Bertha, the third Cesar, and so on. Challenge the class to come up with their own list of names for 15 hurricanes. Give each student a number from 1 to 15 and have the student apply the rules to name the hurricane of that number. **limited English proficiency**

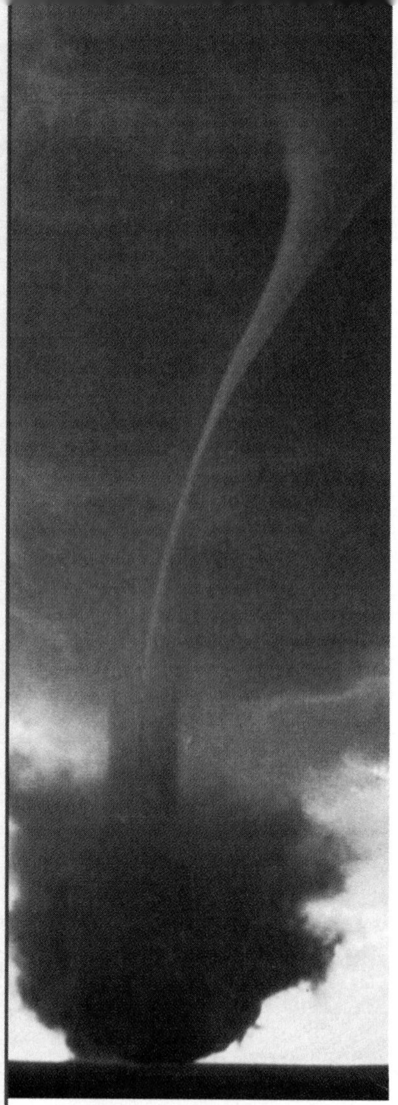

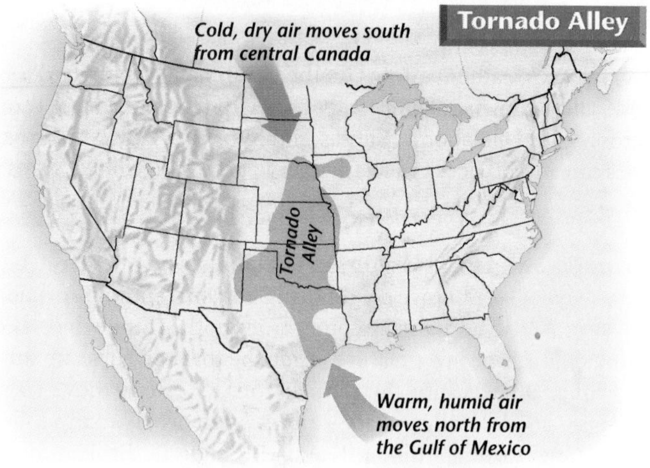
Tornado Alley
Cold, dry air moves south from central Canada
Tornado Alley
Warm, humid air moves north from the Gulf of Mexico

Figure 9 A tornado can cause a lot of damage in a short period of time. The map shows where tornadoes are most likely to occur in the United States.
Interpreting Maps Which states are partially located in "tornado alley"?

What should you do if a tornado is predicted in your area? A "tornado watch" is an announcement that tornadoes are possible in your area. Watch for approaching thunderstorms. A "tornado warning" is an announcement that a tornado has been seen in the sky or on weather radar. If you hear a tornado warning, move to a safe area as soon as you can. Do not wait until you actually see the tornado.

The safest place to be during a tornado is in the basement of a well-built building. If the building you are in does not have a basement, move to the middle of the ground floor. Stay away from windows and doors that could break and fly through the air. Lie on the floor under a sturdy piece of furniture, such as a large table. If you are outdoors or in a car or mobile home, move to a building or lie flat in a ditch.

☑ *Checkpoint* *What is the difference between a tornado watch and a tornado warning?*

Hurricanes

Between June and November, people who live in the eastern United States hear weather reports much like this: "A hurricane warning has been issued for the Atlantic coast from Florida to North Carolina. Hurricane Michael has winds of over 160 kilometers per hour and is moving north at about 65 kilometers per hour." A **hurricane** is a tropical storm that has winds of 119 kilometers per hour or higher. A typical hurricane is about 600 kilometers across.

Hurricanes also form in the Pacific and Indian oceans. In the western Pacific Ocean, hurricanes are called typhoons. Although hurricanes may be destructive, they bring much-needed rainfall to South Asia and Southeast Asia.

Background

Facts and Figures Hurricanes are ranked on a scale called the Saffir-Simpson Scale, which is based on maximum wind speed:
1 Minimal (119–153 km/h)
2 Moderate (154–177 km/h)
3 Extensive (178–209 km/h)
4 Extreme (210–250 km/h)
5 Catastrophic (over 250 km/h)

Two recent devastating hurricanes were Agnes and Andrew. Agnes, which occurred in June of 1972, caused severe flooding from North Carolina to New York and spawned 17 tornadoes in Florida and Georgia. Andrew, which occurred in August of 1992, caused over $25 billion worth of damage, making it the most expensive hurricane in the history of the United States up to that date.

How Hurricanes Form A typical hurricane that strikes the United States forms in the Atlantic Ocean north of the equator in August, September, or October. **A hurricane begins over warm water as a low-pressure area, or tropical disturbance.** If the tropical disturbance grows in size and strength, it becomes a tropical storm, which may then become a hurricane.

A hurricane gets its energy from the warm, humid air at the ocean's surface. As this air rises and forms clouds, more air is drawn into the system. As with other storm systems, winds spiral inward toward the areas of low pressure. Inside the storm are bands of very high winds and heavy rains. The lowest air pressure and warmest temperatures are at the center of the hurricane. The lower the air pressure at the center of a storm, the faster the winds blow toward the center. Hurricane winds may be as strong as 320 kilometers per hour.

The Eye of the Hurricane The center of a hurricane is a ring of clouds surrounding a quiet "eye," as shown in Figure 10. If you were in the path of a hurricane, you would notice that the wind gets stronger as the eye approaches. When the eye arrives, the weather changes suddenly. The winds grow calm and the sky may clear. After the eye passes, the storm resumes, but the wind blows from the opposite direction.

How Hurricanes Move Hurricanes last longer than other storms, usually a week or more. Hurricanes that form in the Atlantic Ocean are steered by easterly trade winds toward the Caribbean islands and the southeastern United States. After a hurricane passes over land, it no longer has warm, moist air to draw energy from. The hurricane gradually slows down and loses strength, although heavy rainfall may continue for a number of days.

Figure 10 In a hurricane, air moves rapidly around a low-pressure area called the eye. *Observing Where is the eye of the hurricane in the photograph?*

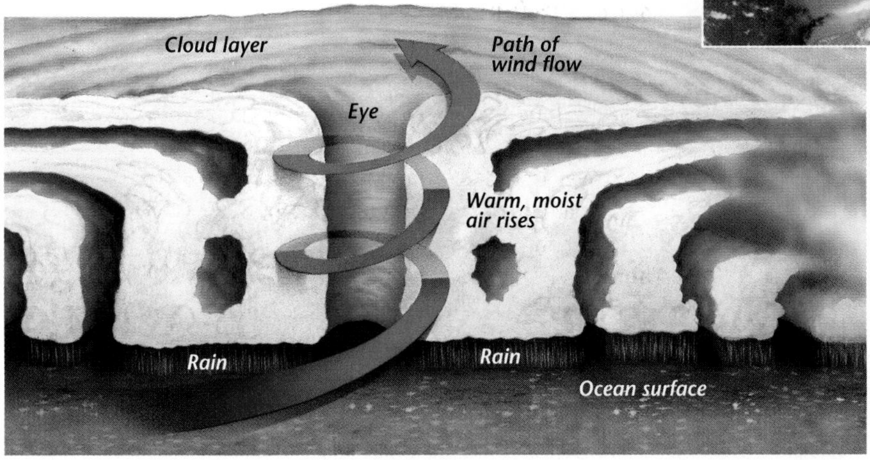

Real-Life Learning

If it is hurricane season, have groups of students monitor tropical disturbances, watch for those that develop into hurricanes, and note where the hurricanes reach land. Groups should gather information from newspapers, television, or the Internet and, at the end of hurricane season, present the information to the class. Challenge groups to use a diversity of ways to record and present the information. **cooperative learning**

Using the Visuals: Figure 10

Call students' attention to the figure, then check to be sure that they understand how the two parts of the figure are related, by asking: **In which illustration are you looking down at a hurricane from above?** *(The photograph on the right)* **From which direction are you looking at the hurricane in the drawing?** *(From the side)* **In which direction is the wind blowing in both illustrations?** *(Counterclockwise around the eye of the hurricane)* **learning modality: visual**

Building Inquiry Skills: Problem Solving

Challenge students to solve the following problem. Tell them to assume they have been caught in the path of a hurricane and the eye of the storm is predicted to pass over their town. Now, after two days of high winds and waves and severe thunderstorms with torrential rain, the storm has died down and the sky has cleared. Ask: **Should you assume the storm has passed and start unboarding the windows and cleaning up the debris? Why or why not?** *(No, because this may be a temporary calm due to the eye of the storm. If so, after the eye passes, the storm will return.)* **How could you find out?** *(Listen to weather bulletins on radio or television)* **learning modality: logical/mathematical**

Media and Technology

Transparencies "Clouds and Winds in a Hurricane," Transparency 14

Answers to Self-Assessment

Checkpoint

Tornado watch: tornadoes are possible. Tornado warning: a tornado has been seen in the sky or on weather radar.

Caption Questions

Figure 9 South Dakota, Iowa, Nebraska, Kansas, Missouri, Oklahoma, Texas, New Mexico, Arkansas
Figure 10 In the center of the clouds

Ongoing Assessment

Oral Presentation Call on students at random to name the parts of the country where hurricanes occur. Call on other students to explain in their own words why hurricanes occur only in those places.

Hurricanes, continued

Integrating Health

Divide the class into groups and challenge the groups to brainstorm a list of actions people in hurricane-prone areas should take: (1) at the beginning of hurricane season *(Trim dead branches from trees, learn safe routes inland)*; (2) if a hurricane watch is issued *(Keep tuned to radio or television for storm updates, check radio and flashlight for batteries, stock up on canned food)*; and (3) if a hurricane warning is issued *(Leave mobile homes, unplug appliances and turn off gas tanks, board up glass windows and doors, listen to radio or television for orders to evacuate and do so immediately when instructed)*. When groups have completed their lists, have them share their ideas with the class. **cooperative learning**

Winter Storms

Visual Arts CONNECTION

Challenge students talented in art to create their own artwork depicting a snowstorm or other storm. Invite them to share their artwork with the class.

In Your Journal Students should comment on how well the words made them see, hear, and feel a snowstorm. **learning modality: visual**

Building Inquiry Skills: Inferring

Towns in the Rocky Mountains get even more snow than Buffalo and Rochester, New York. **Why do you think the high mountain areas of the West receive so much snow?** *(Because warm, moist air from the Pacific Ocean is cooled and drops its moisture as snow when it rises up over the Rocky Mountains)* **How are the Rocky Mountains similar to areas bordering the Great Lakes that receive lake-effect snow?** *(Both areas receive warm, moist west winds that are cooled to produce large amounts of snow.)* **learning modality: logical/mathematical**

Visual Arts CONNECTION

Weather and storms are favorite subjects for artists. "Snow Storm" is an oil painting by English artist J.M.W. Turner (1775–1851). To convey a mood or feeling, artists choose certain colors and textures. How does Turner's choice of colors enhance the mood of the painting? What texture do you see in the sea and sky? How does the texture support the feeling of the painting?

In Your Journal

Write a paragraph or two about the mood of this painting. Describe how you would feel being out in the wind and waves. Before you begin writing, jot down words that describe what you would see, hear, touch, taste, and smell. Exchange your descriptive writing with a partner to get feedback.

Hurricane Damage When a hurricane comes ashore, it brings high waves and severe flooding as well as wind damage. Hurricanes uproot trees, smash buildings, and destroy power lines. Heavy rains flood roads.

One of the most dangerous features of a hurricane is the storm surge. The low pressure and high winds of the hurricane over the ocean raise the level of the water up to six meters above normal sea level. The result is a **storm surge,** a "dome" of water that sweeps across the coast where the hurricane lands. As the hurricane comes onshore, the water comes with it. Storm surges can cause great damage, washing away beaches and destroying buildings along the coast.

Hurricane Safety Until the 1950s, a fast-moving hurricane could strike with little warning. Since then, advances in communications and satellite tracking have made hurricanes less deadly. People now receive information well in advance of an approaching hurricane.

INTEGRATING HEALTH

A "hurricane watch" is an announcement that hurricane conditions are *possible* in your area within the next 36 hours. People should be prepared to **evacuate** (ee VAK yoo ayt), or move away temporarily.

A "hurricane warning" means that hurricane conditions are *expected* within 24 hours. **If you hear a hurricane warning and are told to evacuate, leave the area immediately.** If you must stay in a house, move to the interior of the building, away from windows.

☑ *Checkpoint* *What is a storm surge?*

Winter Storms

In the winter in the northern United States, much precipitation falls as snow. **Snow falls when humid air cools below 0°C.** Heavy snowfalls can block roads, trapping people in their homes and making it hard for emergency vehicles to move. Extreme cold can damage crops and cause water pipes to freeze and burst.

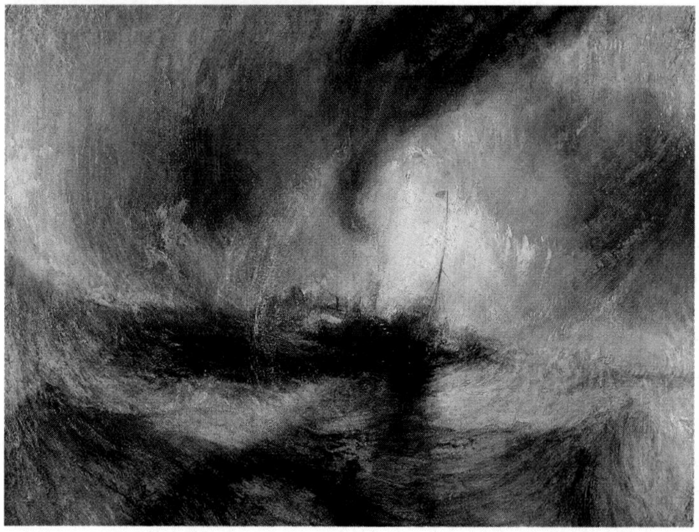

Figure 11 The British artist J.M.W. Turner painted "Snow Storm" in 1842.

Background

Integrating Science Two serious health dangers of winter storms are frostbite and hypothermia. Frostbite is damage to body tissue, usually in the nose, ears, fingers, or toes, due to freezing of the tissue. Symptoms include a loss of feeling and a white appearance in the affected area. If you think you have frostbite, slowly rewarm the affected area and get medical help right away.

Hypothermia is a fall in body temperature below normal. Symptoms include shivering, disorientation, slurred speech, and drowsiness. Hypothermia is a life-threatening emergency. If someone shows signs of hypothermia, seek medical help immediately.

Lake-effect Snow Two of the snowiest cities in the United States are Buffalo and Rochester in upstate New York. On average, nearly three meters of snow falls on each of these cities every winter. Why do Buffalo and Rochester get so much snow?

Study Figure 12. Notice that Buffalo is located to the east of Lake Erie, and Rochester is located to the south of Lake Ontario. In the fall and winter, the land near these lakes cools much more rapidly than the water in the lakes. Although the water in these lakes is cold, it is still much warmer than the surrounding land and air. When a cold, dry air mass moves from central Canada southeast across one of the Great Lakes, it picks up water vapor and heat from the lake. As soon as the air mass reaches the other side of the lake, the air rises and cools again. The water vapor condenses and falls as snow, usually within 40 kilometers of the lake.

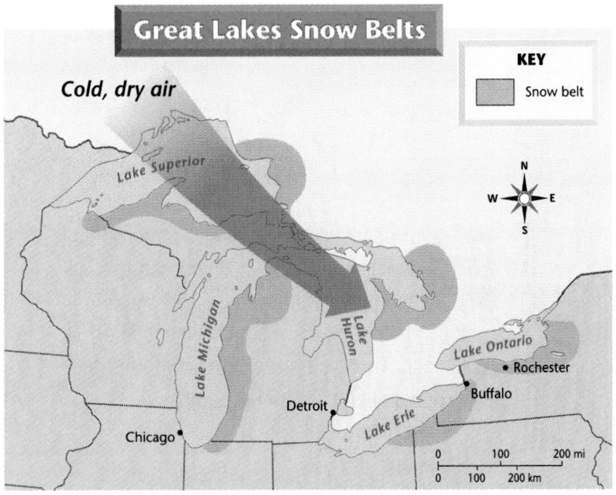

Figure 12 As cold dry air moves across the warmer water, it picks up water vapor. When the air reaches land and cools, lake-effect snow falls. *Interpreting Maps Which two cities receive large amounts of snow?*

Snowstorm Safety Imagine being out in a snowstorm when *INTEGRATING HEALTH* the wind suddenly picks up. High winds can blow falling snow sideways or pick up snow from the ground and suspend it in the air. This situation can be extremely dangerous because the blowing snow makes it easy to get lost. Also, strong winds cool a person's body rapidly. **If you are caught in a snowstorm, try to find shelter from the wind.** Cover exposed parts of your body and try to stay dry. If you are in a car, the driver should keep the engine running only if the exhaust pipe is clear of snow.

Section 2 Review

1. What weather conditions are most likely to cause thunderstorms and tornadoes?
2. What is the most common path for the hurricanes that strike the United States?
3. What safety precautions should you take if a tornado is predicted in your area? If a hurricane is predicted?
4. **Thinking Critically** **Applying Concepts** In the winter, cool, humid air from the Pacific Ocean blows across the cold land of southern Alaska. What kind of storm do you think this causes?

Science at Home

Interview a family member or other adult about a dramatic storm that he or she has experienced. Before the interview, make a list of questions you would like to ask. For example, how old was the person when the storm occurred? When and where did the storm occur? Write up your interview in a question-and-answer format, beginning with a short introduction.

Program Resources

- **Teaching Resources** 3-2 Review and Reinforce, p. 79; 3-2 Enrich, p. 80
- **Interdisciplinary Exploration Series** "India Beyond the Golden Age," pp. 31–32; "Back to the Thirties," pp. 10–12

Media and Technology

Interactive Student Tutorial CD-ROM I-3

Answers to Self-Assessment

Checkpoint

A storm surge is a "dome" of water that sweeps across the coast where a hurricane lands.

Caption Question

Figure 12 Buffalo and Rochester in upstate New York receive large amounts of snow.

Integrating Health

Tell students that the winds of snowstorms make them even more dangerous because they lead to low wind-chill temperatures. Wind chill is how cold it feels because of the wind. For example, if the air temperature is -8°C and the wind is blowing at 50 km/h, the wind-chill temperature is -31°C. Ask: **Why does the wind make you feel colder than the cold air temperature alone?** *(Because it blows the heat away from your body)* **learning modality: logical/mathematical**

3 Assess

Section 2 Review Answers

1. Warm air being forced upward at a cold front to form large cumulonimbus clouds
2. From the Atlantic Ocean westward toward the Caribbean islands and the southeastern United States
3. If a tornado is predicted, go to the basement of a well-built building. If a hurricane is predicted, leave the area immediately.
4. A heavy snowstorm, because the moisture in the cool humid air from the Pacific would condense and fall as snow when it reached the cold land of southern Alaska

Science at Home

Tips Encourage students to tape record or videotape their interview. They might want to present it to the class in the form of a newspaper article or television news report. Suggest that they use drawings or photographs to illustrate their presentation.

ACTIVITY

Performance Assessment

Skills Check Have students make a table comparing and contrasting thunderstorms, tornadoes, hurricanes, and snowstorms.

Real-World Lab

Careers in Science

Tracking a Hurricane

Preparing for Inquiry

Key Concept The path of a hurricane is not always easy to predict, making it difficult to issue hurricane warnings.

Skills Objectives Students will be able to

- ◆ interpret data on a map representing the location of a hurricane at repeated intervals;
- ◆ interpret additional data in tables to plot the continued path of the hurricane;
- ◆ use the data to predict when and where the hurricane will come ashore;
- ◆ make a judgement about when and for what area a hurricane warning should be issued.

Time 40 minutes

Advance Planning Students will have to press down hard to mark clearly on the tracing paper with the colored pencils, so have a pencil sharpener and extra pencils on hand. Students may need to trace additional maps, so have extra sheets of tracing paper on hand as well. You may wish to make a copy of the map from the student text as an overhead transparency. Use it to show students how to read latitude and longitude and plot the path of the hurricane.

Alternative Materials Instead of having students use tracing paper to trace the map in their text, you may want to provide each student with a photocopy of the map to mark on directly. If so, make copies of the map in advance.

Guiding Inquiry

Invitation To give the lab a context, point out that today hurricanes cause an average of only 17 deaths each year in the United States. Explain that the relatively low death rate is due to early warnings of when and where hurricanes are coming ashore. Earlier in this century, before the knowledge and technology needed for early warnings were available, the death rate from hurricanes was much higher. Add that one of the main jobs of some meteorologists during hurricane season is to track the storms so warnings can be issued in time to save lives.

Introducing the Procedure
Have students read through the steps of the procedure. Clear up any questions they may have. If necessary, review how to find latitude and longitude. Emphasize to students that they will be plotting the eye of the hurricane as it travels across the water. Ask: **How far on either side of the eye of the hurricane is the storm likely to extend?** *(A typical hurricane is 600 km wide, so the storm may extend 300 km on either side of the eye.)* **Why is this important to know for issuing a hurricane warning?** *(The area affected by the hurricane when it comes ashore will be as wide as the storm, and this is the area for which a hurricane warning should be issued.)*

Real-World Lab

Careers in Science

Tracking a Hurricane

Hurricane alert! You work at the National Hurricane Center. It is your job to track the paths of hurricanes and try to predict when and where a hurricane is likely to strike land. Then you must decide whether to warn people in the area to evacuate.

Problem

How can you predict when and where a hurricane will come ashore?

Skills Focus

interpreting data, predicting

Materials

ruler
red, blue, green, and brown pencils
tracing paper

Procedure

1. Look at the plotted path of the hurricane on the map. Each dot represents the location of the eye of the hurricane at six-hour intervals. The last dot shows where the hurricane was located at noon on August 30.
2. Predict the path you think the hurricane will take. Place tracing paper over the map below. Using a red pencil, place an X on your tracing paper where you think the hurricane will first reach land. Next to your X, write the date and time you think the hurricane will come ashore.

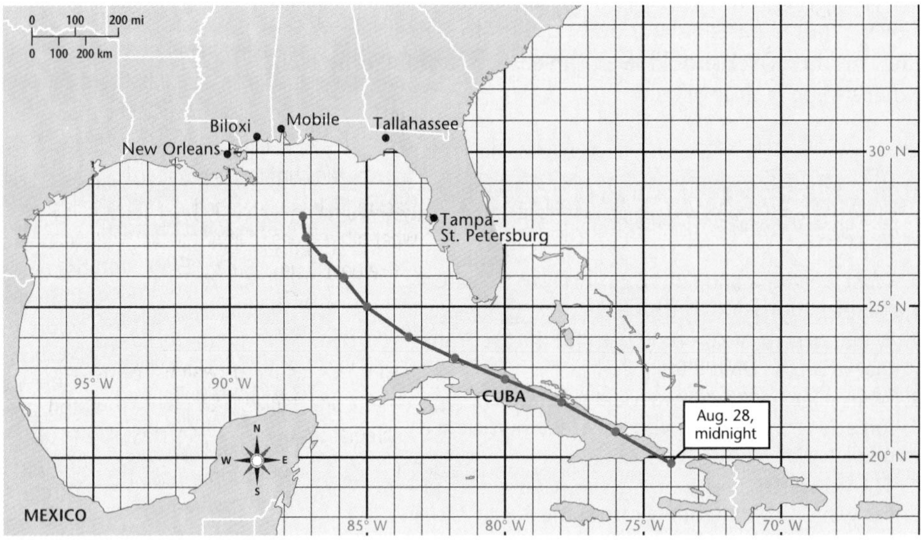

3. Hurricane warnings are issued for an area that is likely to experience a hurricane within 24 hours. On your tracing paper, shade in red the area for which you would issue a hurricane warning.
4. Using the following data table, plot the next five positions for the storm using a blue pencil. Use your ruler to connect the dots to show the hurricane's path.

Date and Time	Latitude	Longitude
August 30, 6:00 P.M.	28.3° N	86.8° W
August 31, midnight	28.4° N	86.0° W
August 31, 6:00 A.M.	28.6° N	85.3° W
August 31, noon	28.8° N	84.4° W
August 31, 6:00 P.M.	28.8° N	84.0° W

5. Based on the new data, decide if you need to change your prediction of where and when the hurricane will come ashore. Mark your new predictions in blue pencil on your tracing paper.
6. During September 1, you obtain four more positions. (Plot these points only after you have completed Step 5.) Based on these new data, mark in green pencil when and where you now think the hurricane will come ashore.

Date and Time	Latitude	Longitude
September 1, midnight	28.8° N	83.8° W
September 1, 6:00 A.M.	28.6° N	83.9° W
September 1, noon	28.6° N	84.2° W
September 1, 6:00 P.M.	28.9° N	84.8° W

7. The next day, September 2, you plot four more positions using a brown pencil. (Plot these points only after you have completed Step 6.)

Date and Time	Latitude	Longitude
September 2, midnight	29.4° N	85.9° W
September 2, 6:00 A.M.	29.7° N	87.3° W
September 2, noon	30.2° N	88.8° W
September 2, 6:00 P.M.	31.0° N	90.4° W

Analyze and Conclude

1. Describe in detail the complete path of the hurricane you tracked. Include where it came ashore and identify any cities that were in the vicinity.
2. How did your predictions in Steps 2, 5, and 6 compare to what actually happened?
3. What was unusual about your hurricane's path?
4. How do you think hurricanes with a path like this one affect the issuing of hurricane warnings?
5. Why do you have to be so careful when issuing warnings? What problems might be caused if you issued an unnecessary hurricane warning? What might happen if a hurricane warning were issued too late?
6. **Think About It** In this activity you only had data for the hurricane's position. If you were tracking a hurricane and issuing warnings, what other types of information would help you make decisions about the hurricane's path?

More to Explore

With your teacher's help, search the Internet for more hurricane tracking data. Map the data and try to predict where the hurricane will come ashore.

Troubleshooting the Experiment

- Point out to students that the lines of latitude and longitude on the map are in one-degree increments. Therefore, students will have to estimate where to plot the points because these are given in tenths of a degree of latitude or longitude.
- Use an overhead transparency of the map to show students how to plot the first point in the table as an example.
- If students think they are plotting incorrectly, advise them that hurricanes can change direction.
- As the hurricane changes direction, students' maps may become too crowded and difficult to read. If so, suggest that they trace a new map.

Program Resources

- **Teaching Resources** Real-World Lab blackline masters, pp. 89–91

Expected Outcome

Students' maps should show that the hurricane changed direction twice, once to the east and then to the west, before finally coming ashore near Biloxi, Mississippi, on September 2.

Analyze and Conclude

1. The hurricane first appeared to be moving north toward southern Louisiana. It then turned east toward central Florida, before reversing direction and heading northwest toward the panhandle of Florida. It continued to move west or northwest until it came ashore near Biloxi, Mississippi.
2. Students' predictions will vary. They are likely to have predicted that the storm would come ashore near Mobile in Step 2, between Tallahassee and Tampa-St. Petersburg in Step 5, and near New Orleans in Step 6. The hurricane actually came ashore somewhat east of New Orleans at Biloxi.
3. The path of the hurricane was unusual because it reversed direction.
4. Hurricanes with a path like this one make it difficult to issue accurate warnings because where the hurricane actually comes ashore is different from where it appears to be headed.
5. You have to be careful when you issue hurricane warnings because unnecessary warnings can disrupt lives, put people in danger, and cause economic losses, whereas warnings that come too late can result in needless loss of life and damage to property.
6. Other types of information that would help you make decisions about the hurricane's path and when and where to issue hurricane warnings would include how fast the hurricane is moving, the speed of its winds, and other indicators of the severity of the storm.

Extending the Inquiry

More to Explore A good Internet site for hurricane tracking data is the National Hurricane Center at **www.nhc.noaa.gov.**

SCIENCE AND SOCIETY

Hurricane Alert: To Stay or Not To Stay?

Purpose To inform students of the pros and cons of evacuation in a hurricane and help them decide whether or not the government should have the power to force people to evacuate.

Role-Play

Time a day to prepare; 15 minutes for role-play

Choose several students to role-play a family discussion in which family members argue over whether or not they should evacuate after a hurricane warning has been issued. Instruct some of the students to take the position that the family should evacuate and others to take the opposite position. Urge students to support their arguments with facts from the feature.

Extend Before the role-play is presented to the class, take a poll of students to see how many would and how many would not evacuate in a hurricane. After the role-play has been presented, take the poll again. Call on any students who changed their minds to explain why.

You Decide

1. The government can order but not enforce evacuations in a hurricane. Some people do not want to evacuate. Other people believe that the government should have the right to force people to evacuate for public safety.
2. Forcing people to evacuate may prevent injuries and save lives by getting people to safety. People who benefit are those who would have been killed or injured had they not been evacuated. People who might be harmed include people who need to protect their homes, businesses, or animals. Government officials might try to increase public awareness of the dangers of not evacuating. Citizens could become better informed about the reasons for evacuating.
3. Make sure students' arguments are well reasoned.

SCIENCE AND SOCIETY

Hurricane Alert: To Stay or Not To Stay?

When a hurricane sweeps in from the ocean, the National Hurricane Center tracks the storm's course. Radio stations broadcast warnings. Sirens blow, and people in the storm path take steps to protect their homes and families.

State and local governments may try to keep people safe by closing state offices, setting up emergency shelters, and alerting the National Guard. As the danger increases, a state's governor can order the evacuation of people from dangerous areas. These actions are meant to protect public safety.

But not everyone wants to evacuate. Some people believe they have the right to stay. And officials cannot make people obey an evacuation order. How much can—or should—the government do to keep people safe?

The Issues

Why Play It Safe? Hurricanes can be extremely dangerous. High winds blow off roofs and shatter windows. Flash floods and storm surges can wash away houses. Even after the storm blows away, officials may need to keep people from returning home because of flooded sewers or broken power lines and gas mains.

In recent years, earlier and more accurate forecasts have saved lives. People now have time to prepare and to get out of the hurricane's path. Emergency officials urge people—especially the elderly, sick, or disabled—to leave early while the weather is still good. Most casualties happen when people are taken by surprise or ignore warnings. Those who decide to stay may later have to be rescued by boat or helicopter. These rescues add to the expense of the storm and may put the lives of rescuers in danger.

Why Ride Out the Storm? People have different reasons for not wanting to evacuate. Some want to protect their homes or businesses. Others don't want to leave pets or farm animals or go to public shelters. Store owners may stay open to sell disaster supplies. In addition, warnings may exaggerate the potential danger, urging people to leave when they might actually be safe. Since leaving can be expensive and disruptive, residents have to carefully evaluate the risks.

Is It a Matter of Rights? Should a government have the power to make people evacuate? Some citizens argue that the government should not tell them what to do as long as they are not harming others. They believe that individuals should have the right to decide for themselves. What do you think?

You Decide

1. Identify the Problem
In your own words, explain the controversy around hurricane evacuations.

2. Analyze the Options
Review and list the pros and cons of forcing people to evacuate. What people benefit? Who might be harmed? What more, if anything, should government officials do? What more could citizens do?

3. Find a Solution
Imagine that the radio has broadcast a hurricane warning. Write a dialogue in which you and members of your family discuss the options and decide whether or not to evacuate.

94 ◆ I

Background

Many of the severe hurricanes that struck the United States earlier in the twentieth century had high fatality rates. For example, in 1900, a hurricane that struck Texas killed 6,000 people. In 1919, a hurricane that struck the Florida Keys killed 900 people. More recent hurricanes have led to less loss of life, primarily because of early warnings. For example, in 1989, hurricane Hugo killed fewer than 30 people in the United States, even though it was a severe storm. However, recent hurricanes have caused huge amounts of property damage. Hugo, for example, caused an estimated $10.5 billion worth of damage. The increased cost of hurricanes is partly due to an influx of population to the coast. With more houses, businesses, and other types of property along the shore, there is much greater potential for property damage due to hurricanes.

SECTION 3 Floods

DISCOVER ACTIVITY

What Causes Floods?

1. Fill a cup with water. Hold a funnel above a basin and pour the water very slowly into the funnel.
2. Refill the cup with the same amount of water you used in Step 1. Hold the funnel above the basin and this time pour the water rapidly into the funnel. What happens?

Think It Over

Inferring How is a funnel like a river valley? What do you think would happen if a large amount of water entered a river valley in a short period of time?

GUIDE FOR READING

- What causes flooding?
- How can the dangers of floods be reduced?

Reading Tip **As you read, draw a flowchart showing what can happen during a flood and how people should respond to it.**

Antelope Canyon in the northern Arizona desert is only a few meters wide in places. On August 12, 1997, a group of 12 hikers entered the dry, narrow canyon. That afternoon a severe thunderstorm dropped several inches of rain on the Kaibeto Plateau, 24 kilometers away. Dry stream channels that drain into Antelope Canyon quickly filled with rainwater. The water rushed into the canyon, creating a wall of water over 3 meters high. Tourists at the top of the canyon watched in horror as the water swept the hikers away. Only one hiker survived.

Are you surprised that floods can occur in a desert? Actually, floods like this are more common in the dry Southwest than in areas with more rain.

Figure 13 From the top, Antelope Canyon looks like a narrow slit in the ground.

READING STRATEGIES

Reading Tip A sample flowchart is: rain falls→river rises→land floods→people evacuate. You might want to have students add the words *dam* and *ice jam* to their flowcharts as additional causes of floods.

Study and Comprehension As students read the last two pages of the section, have them summarize flood safety rules in two brief lists, one a list of what *to* do, the other a list of what *not* to do, in a flood.

Program Resources

◆ **Teaching Resources** 3-3 Lesson Plan, p. 81; 3-3 Section Summary, p. 82

Media and Technology

Audiotapes English-Spanish Summary 3-3

SECTION 3 Floods

Objectives

After completing the lesson, students will be able to

◆ identify the causes of flooding;
◆ explain how the dangers of floods can be reduced.

Key Term flash flood

1 Engage/Explore

Activating Prior Knowledge

Introduce the section by having students apply what they know about watches and warnings to floods. Ask: **What do you think is the difference between a flood watch and a flood warning?** *(Students may say a flood watch means floods are possible and a flood warning means floods have already started to occur.)* **What should people do if a flood watch has been issued?** *(Stay tuned to radio or television.)* **What should people do if a flood warning has been issued?** *(Listen for further instructions, evacuate if ordered to do so.)*

DISCOVER ACTIVITY

Skills Focus inferring
Materials *cup, water, funnel, basin*
Time 10 minutes
Tips The funnel should be smaller than the cup so it overflows when students fill it rapidly.
Expected Outcome In Step 1, all the water will flow through the funnel. In Step 2, some of the water will overflow the funnel.
Think It Over Both a funnel and a river valley are narrow channels that collect water from much larger areas. The river might overflow its banks, similar to the way the water overflowed the funnel, and this would create a flood.

2 Facilitate

Flash Floods

Building Inquiry Skills: Inferring

Point out that flash floods are more likely in hilly areas, such as Antelope Canyon in Arizona, which is described in the text. Ask: **Why do you think flash floods are more likely in hilly areas?** *(Rain water quickly runs off hills and is channeled into narrow valleys and canyons that cannot hold all the water.)* **learning modality: logical/ mathematical**

Flood Safety Measures

Sharpen your Skills

ACTIVITY

Skills Focus communicating
Time 10 minutes
Tips Invite students to read their announcements to the class.
Expected Outcome Dangers include high rushing water, uprooted power poles, landslides, mudslides, washed out roads, and contaminated food and drinking water. Steps to follow in case of a flood include moving to higher ground, staying away from flood waters, leaving a flooded car, and boiling water before drinking.
Extend Have interested students use the Internet to contact the National Weather Service at **www.nws.noaa.gov/er/nerfc/floodinfo.html** for more information on flood safety. **learning modality: verbal**

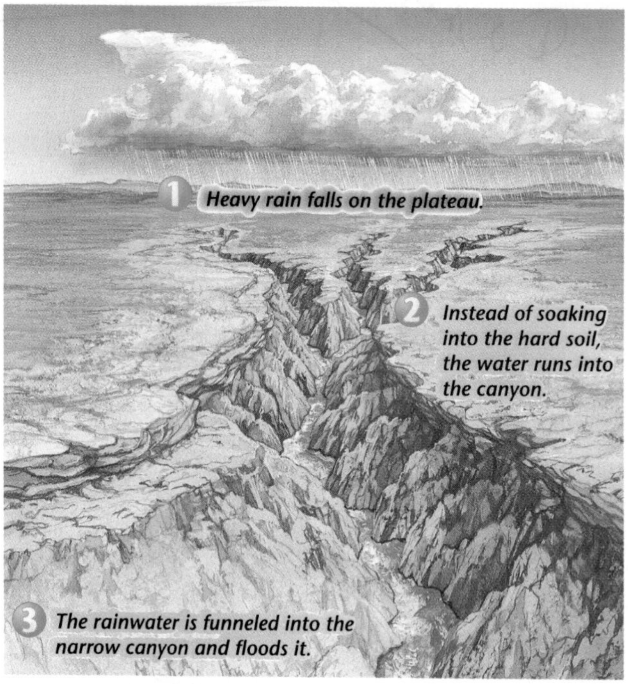

1 Heavy rain falls on the plateau.
2 Instead of soaking into the hard soil, the water runs into the canyon.
3 The rainwater is funneled into the narrow canyon and floods it.

Figure 14 Flash floods occur when large amounts of rain are funneled into a narrow valley. This drawing shows what happened in the Antelope Canyon flood.

Flash Floods

Although movies feature the violent winds of tornadoes and hurricanes, floods are the most dangerous weather-related events in the United States. **Floods occur when so much water pours into a stream or river that it overflows its banks and covers the land on either side of the channel.** People who live along certain rivers know that melting snow and spring rains are likely to bring floods.

Unexpected floods are the most dangerous. Floods like the Antelope Canyon flood are called flash floods because the water rises very rapidly—"in a flash"—after it begins to rain heavily. A **flash flood** is a sudden, violent flood that occurs within a few hours, or even minutes, of a storm.

Most flash floods are due to large amounts of rain. For example, a line of thunderstorms may remain over an area, dropping heavy rain for several hours or days. Hurricanes or tropical storms bring downpours that quickly fill stream channels. A flash flood can also be caused by a dam breaking, releasing millions of liters of water all at once. Similarly, if ice that has jammed a river breaks free, the sudden rush of water can cause a flash flood.

☑ *Checkpoint Why are flash floods so dangerous?*

Sharpen your Skills

Communicating ACTIVITY

Write a script for a 30-second public service radio announcement in which you tell about the dangers of floods. Include recommended safety steps to follow in case of a flood.

Flood Safety Measures

If you've never been in a flood, it's hard to imagine the awesome power of rushing water. What can people do to protect themselves and their homes?

Predicting Floods Advance warnings can help reduce flood damage and loss of life. Weather satellites supply information about snow cover so that scientists can estimate how much water will run into rivers when the snow melts. Radar can track and measure the size of an approaching rainstorm. Scientists check river gauges that measure water levels. With this information, forecasters can predict flood heights at different points along a river. Their goal is to issue warnings early enough to help people prepare and evacuate if necessary.

Background

Facts and Figures Flooding causes almost half of all weather fatalities, and most flood fatalities occur during flash floods. The worst flash flood in United States history was caused by a dam break in Johnstown, Pennsylvania, in May of 1889. A wall of water 12 m high washed over the city, killing 2,200 people.

It isn't dam breaks that cause most flash floods, but heavy rains. One of the worst flash floods in United States history due to heavy rain occurred in Rapid City, South Dakota, in June of 1972. About 38 cm of rain fell in five hours, and the resulting flood killed 238 people. More recently, Shadyside, Ohio, received 10 cm of rain in just two hours. A torrent 12 m high flooded the town, leaving 26 people dead.

The car stalls in the water.

Moving water pushes against the car.

As the water rises, the car begins to float.

Sixty centimeters of water can wash a car away.

Figure 15 These drawings show what can happen to a car in a flood. *Applying Concepts Why is it dangerous to stay in a car in a flood?*

A "flood watch" is an announcement describing the area in which flooding is possible. Stay alert for more news. A "flood warning" is an announcement that floods have already been reported or are about to occur. It's time to take action!

Emergency Safety What should *you* do in case of a flood? When the danger becomes too great or the water rises too high, people are usually evacuated. **The first rule of flood safety: Move to higher ground and stay away from flood waters.** Don't try to cross streams and rivers that look as if they're flooded. Playing in flood waters may look like fun, but it's dangerous. A few centimeters of fast-moving water can sweep you off your feet. Even the storm drain on a city street can draw you in.

If your family is in a car, the driver shouldn't try to drive on a flooded road. Sometimes less than 60 centimeters of fast-moving water can sweep a car away, as shown in Figure 15. Everyone should leave the car and move to higher ground.

Using the Visuals: Figure 15

ACTIVITY

Materials *small watertight metal container, pebbles or gravel, basin, water*
Time 5 minutes

Point out that a car, like the one pictured in the figure, can float in about 60 cm of water, even though it may have a mass of more than 1,000 kg. The car displaces more and more water as the water rises, until it has displaced its own weight in water. When that occurs, the car floats. To convince students how little water is needed for a car to float, simulate the sequence of events shown in the figure. To model the car, use a small, rectangular, watertight metal container, weighted down with a few pieces of gravel. Place the container in a basin and slowly add water to the basin. By the time the water level is about halfway up the side of the container, the container should start to float. Ask: **What do you think would happen if the water in the basin had a current?** *(The current would push against the container and sweep it away as soon as it floated.)* **learning modality: visual**

Real-Life Learning

Point out that floods can be a big problem in urban areas. Ask: **Why do you think cities might be especially prone to flooding when heavy rains occur?** *(Much of the surface is covered with buildings and pavement that cannot absorb water, so there is a lot of run off, all of which is channeled into drains and sewers. They may not be able to hold all the water when the rain is unusually heavy.)* **Why are urban areas likely to suffer a greater loss of life and property due to floods?** *(Because they have a greater concentration of people, cars, and buildings and other structures)* **learning modality: logical/mathematical**

Answers to Self-Assessment

☑ Checkpoint

Flash floods are so dangerous because the water rises very rapidly in a sudden violent flood.

Caption Question

Figure 15 It is dangerous to stay in a car in a flood because the water can wash the car away.

Ongoing Assessment

Oral Presentation Call on various students to describe in their own words one of the ways that flash floods can occur.

3 Assess

Section 3 Review Answers

1. By pouring so much water into a stream or river that it overflows its banks and covers the land on either side of the channel
2. Move to higher ground, stay away from flood waters, do not try to cross streams and rivers that look flooded, do not play in flood waters, avoid driving on flooded roads, abandon a flooded car and move to higher ground, be careful with food and water that flood waters have touched, and boil water before drinking it to be sure it is safe.
3. A flood watch means flooding is possible, whereas a flood warning means floods have already been reported or are about to occur.
4. Weather satellites, radar, and river gauges
5. Possible answers include a hurricane or tropical storm, a very heavy rain, or melting spring snow.

CHAPTER PROJECT 3

Check Your Progress

Make sure students use standard weather symbols on their maps. Remind them to include air masses and fronts and to keep in mind the type of weather usually associated with each kind of front.

Figure 16 In the spring of 1997, the Red River of the North flooded regions of North Dakota and Minnesota. A large part of flooded downtown Grand Forks burned down because fire trucks could not get to the scene of the fire or connect to any fire hydrants.

Other Flood Hazards High water is not the only hazard in a flood. Floods can knock down electrical poles and wires, cutting off power supplies. Flood waters can also saturate soil, causing landslides or mudslides. If roads have been flooded or washed away, emergency vehicles such as fire trucks and ambulances may not be able to get through.

Flood waters can wash into wells and water treatment plants, polluting the water. Therefore, be careful with food and water that flood waters have touched. Boil water before drinking it to be sure it is safe.

Section 3 Review

1. How can precipitation cause flooding?
2. What should you do to stay safe during a flood?
3. What is the difference between a flood watch and a flood warning?
4. Name three tools that supply information used in forecasting floods and providing flood information.
5. **Thinking Critically** **Predicting** Describe two weather situations in which you would expect floods to occur.

CHAPTER PROJECT 3

Check Your Progress

Now you are ready to predict tomorrow's weather. Look at today's weather map. Then predict tomorrow's weather both where you live and in the two other locations you selected. (*Project Hint:* Refer to the weather patterns you have been observing.) Decide what symbols you will need to use. Then, on an outline map of the United States, draw symbols to show what you think tomorrow's weather will be. Continue to make predictions every day for at least a week.

Program Resources

◆ **Teaching Resources** 3-3 Review and Reinforce, p. 83; 3-3 Enrich, p. 84

Media and Technology

Interactive Student Tutorial CD-ROM I-3

Performance Assessment

Writing Have students write a list of rules people should follow to ensure safety in a flood.

Portfolio Students can save their list of rules in their portfolio.

SECTION 4

Predicting the Weather

DISCOVER ACTIVITY

What's the Weather?

1. Look at the weather report in your local newspaper. Note what weather conditions are predicted for your area today, including temperature, precipitation, and wind speed.
2. Look out the window or think about what it was like the last time you were outside. Write down the actual weather conditions where you are.

Think It Over

Observing Does the weather report match what you observe? What is the same? What is different?

GUIDE FOR READING

- How does technology help forecasters predict the weather?
- What types of information are shown on weather maps?

Reading Tip Before you read, preview Figure 19 and *Exploring Newspaper Weather Maps.* Write a list of any questions you have about weather maps.

For centuries, people have tried to predict the weather. Every nation's folklore includes weather sayings. Many of these sayings are based on long-term observations. Sailors, pilots, farmers, and others who work outdoors are usually careful observers of clouds, winds, and other signs of coming changes in the weather. Here are two examples:

Evening red and morning gray
Will send the traveler on his way;
Evening gray and morning red
Will bring down rain upon his head.

Red sky in the morning,
sailors take warning;
Red sky at night, sailor's delight.

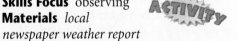

Why do these two weather sayings agree that a red morning sky means bad weather? Recall that in the United States storms usually move from west to east. Clouds in the west indicate an advancing low-pressure area, bringing stormy weather. If there are high clouds in the west in the morning, the rising sun in the east turns these clouds red. The reverse is true at sunset. As the sun sets in the west, it turns clouds in the east red. Clouds in the east indicate that a storm is moving away to the east.

READING STRATEGIES

Reading Tip Urge students to answer their own questions as they read the section. Give them feedback on their answers to check their comprehension.

Vocabulary Help students understand the terms *isobar* and *isotherm* by explaining that the prefix *iso-* means "the same", the root *-bar* means "air pressure" (as in *barometer*), and the root *-therm* means "temperature" (as in *thermometer*).

Program Resources

- **Teaching Resources** 3-4 Lesson Plan, p. 85; 3-4 Section Summary, p. 86

Media and Technology

Audiotapes English-Spanish Summary 3-4

SECTION 4

Predicting the Weather

Objectives

After completing the lesson, students will be able to

- explain how technology helps forecasters predict the weather;
- state the types of information shown on weather maps.

Key Terms meteorologist, El Niño, isobar, isotherm

1 Engage/Explore

Activating Prior Knowledge

Help students recall occasions when they wanted to know what the next day's or the weekend's weather would be. Ask: **Did you ever wonder how warm or cold it would be the next day so you could plan what to wear to school, or whether it would rain on Saturday and wash out your ball game?** *(Most students will say "yes.")* Point out that the major job of meteorologists, or weather scientists, is predicting the weather. Add that, with modern technology, meteorologists can now predict the weather in the near future quite accurately. Tell students that, in this section, they will learn tips that will also help them predict the weather.

DISCOVER ACTIVITY

Skills Focus observing
Materials *local newspaper weather report*
Time 10 minutes
Tips Suggest to students that they consider each of the weather factors reported on in the newspaper before deciding whether or not the actual weather matches the predicted weather.
Expected Outcome The newspaper weather report may or may not match actual conditions, but it probably will be close.
Think It Over The newspaper weather report may match the actual weather in general but not in every detail. For example, the actual temperature may differ from the predicted temperature by a few degrees or showers may be light instead of moderate.

2 Facilitate

Weather Forecasting

Real-Life Learning

Call students' attention to the example of weather folklore given in the opening paragraph of the section. Ask: **Do you know any other weather folklore?** *(Students may give familiar examples, such as a groundhog seeing its shadow meaning that there will be six more weeks of winter.)* Point out that long-term weather predictions, such as a groundhog's shadow predicting a longer winter, usually are unreliable. However, short-term predictions, such as the ones in the text, often are reliable because they are based on scientifically valid observations about the weather. Share other examples of reliable weather folklore with students such as the following: "Mackerel sky, mackerel sky, not long wet, not long dry." (High cirrus clouds that look like fish scales usually mean a change in the weather.) "When the sun or moon is in its house, it will rain soon." (The "house" refers to a ring around the sun or moon, which means clouds are thickening and rain is near.) "The north wind does blow, and we will have snow." (A north wind usually brings cold weather and thus a chance for snow.) **learning modality: verbal**

Building Inquiry Skills: Controlling Variables

Stress that today meteorologists rely on information from many different sources to predict the weather. Therefore, it is important to have standard ways of measuring weather factors. For example, wind speed varies with height, so meteorologists set a standard of 10 m above the ground for recording winds. Ask: **How do you think temperature might be standardized?** *(Students may say that temperature varies by time of day so it should be measured at the same time.)* Inform students that the lowest temperature of the day usually occurs near sunrise and the highest temperature between 1:00 and 4:00 p.m. **learning modality: logical/mathematical**

Weather Forecasting

You can make many predictions from your own observations. For example, if a barometer shows that the air pressure is falling, you can expect a change in the weather. Falling air pressure usually indicates an approaching low-pressure area, possibly bringing rain or snow.

You can read weather signs in the clouds, too. Cumulus clouds often form on warm afternoons when warm air rises. If you see these clouds growing larger and taller, you can expect them to become cumulonimbus clouds, which may bring a thunderstorm. If you see thin cirrus clouds high in the sky, a low-pressure area may be approaching.

Even careful weather observers often turn to professional meteorologists for television weather information. You may hear the person who gives the television weather report referred to as a meteorologist. Despite their name, meteorologists don't study meteors. **Meteorologists** (mee tee uh RAWL uh jists) are scientists who study the causes of weather and try to predict it.

Figure 17 These meteorologists are releasing a weather balloon. The box attached to the balloon contains instruments that will record weather data—such as temperature, pressure, and humidity—high in the atmosphere.

Meteorologists interpret information from a variety of sources, including local weather observers, instruments carried by balloons, satellites, and weather stations around the world. They use maps, charts, and computers to analyze the data and to prepare weather forecasts. Meteorologists use radar to track areas of rain or snow, so that forecasters can follow the path of a storm system.

Where do television and radio weather reporters get their information? A lot of weather information comes from the National Weather Service. However, weather forecasts for the general public may not have enough detail to be useful to farmers and pilots. There are also private weather-forecasting services, many of which use advanced, high-technology equipment. Private forecasting services are useful to people who need to answer questions like these: "Will the frost hurt the oranges in my orchard?" "Will the airport be fogged in?" "Will the trucks need to spread sand on the roads today?"

☑ *Checkpoint* ***Where do meteorologists get weather information?***

Background

History of Science Samuel Morse's invention of the telegraph in 1844 revolutionized meteorology. By 1849, scientists at the Smithsonian Institute started gathering weather reports from telegraph operators around the country, and soon the first national weather service was set up. The first weather map showing current conditions based on telegraphed information was published in England in 1851, and the first telegraph system for forecasting severe weather was established in France in 1854.

The United States published its first official weather forecast in 1870. Early weather forecasts were highly inaccurate because they were based on conditions on the ground and not on air masses and fronts.

Figure 18 This satellite photo shows an intense storm over the North Atlantic Ocean.
Observing What weather-related information can you see in the photo?

Weather Technology

Techniques for predicting weather have changed rapidly in recent years. Short-range forecasts—forecasts for up to five days—are now fairly reliable. Meteorologists can also make long-range predictions that were once impossible. **Changes in technology have occurred in two areas: gathering weather data and using computers to make forecasts.**

Weather Balloons and Satellites As you learned in Chapter 1, weather balloons carry instruments high into the troposphere and stratosphere. The instruments measure temperature, air pressure, and humidity.

The first weather satellite was launched in 1960. Cameras on weather satellites in the exosphere can photograph Earth's surface, clouds, storms, and ice and snow cover. These images are then transmitted to meteorologists on Earth, who interpret the information.

Computer Forecasts Computers are widely used to help forecast weather. *INTEGRATING TECHNOLOGY* Instruments can now gather thousands of bits of data about temperature, air pressure, wind speed, and other factors. Computers process large amounts of information quickly to help forecasters make predictions. To make a forecast, the computer starts with weather conditions reported from weather stations over a large area. Conditions reported include wind speed and direction, humidity, sunlight, temperature, and air pressure. Then the computer works through thousands of calculations and makes forecasts for 12 hours, 24 hours, 36 hours, and so on. Each forecast builds on the previous forecast. When new weather data come in, the computer revises its forecasts.

Weather Technology

Inquiry Challenge

ACTIVITY

Materials *globe, two small balls*
Time 10 minutes

Explain to students that there are two kinds of weather satellites. Geostationary satellites orbit Earth from west to east at a height of about 39,500 km. They always stay above the same spot on Earth's surface. Polar satellites orbit Earth from north to south at a height of about 850 km. They fly over both poles twice a day. Challenge small groups of students to use a globe and two balls, each ball representing one kind of weather satellite, to model how weather satellites orbit Earth. Then ask: **Which type of satellite do you think gets clearer pictures of clouds and other weather factors? Why?** *(Polar satellites, because they orbit at a lower altitude)* **Which type of satellite do you think gets a broader picture of clouds and other weather factors? Why?** *(Geostationary satellites, because they orbit at a higher altitude)* **learning modality: logical/mathematical**

Integrating Technology

Help students appreciate the role computers play in weather forecasting. Inform students that meteorologists divide the troposphere into about 3,000 grids, and weather data for each grid arrives at the National Weather Service twice a day. Managing all that data to track and forecast the weather requires billions of calculations. The computer used by the National Weather Service can perform over two billion calculations per second. If that work had to be done by hand, it would require more than 123,000 people. Ask: **What is the major role played by computers in weather forecasting?** *(Analyzing huge amounts of information quickly)* **learning modality: verbal**

Ongoing Assessment

Oral Presentation Call on various students to explain in their own words how advances in technology have led to more accurate weather forecasts.

Media and Technology

Exploring Earth Science Videodisc
Unit 4, Side 2, "Never Put Up the Umbrella Until It Starts to Rain"
Chapter 2

Answers to Self-Assessment

Checkpoint
Meteorologists get weather information from local weather observers, instruments carried by balloons, satellites, and weather stations around the world.

Caption Question
Figure 18 You can see temperature, cloud cover, and the location of a storm.

El Niño

Building Inquiry Skills: Communicating

Tell students that weather prediction has become more accurate now that scientists understand how global winds and ocean currents influence weather. Explain that periodic changes in highs and lows over the southern Pacific Ocean modify the trade winds, and changes in the trade winds, in turn, influence ocean currents, leading to an increase in the temperature of the water off the coast of South America. The warm ocean water causes unusually rainy weather along the coast of South America and also, by influencing other ocean currents, indirectly causes unusual weather conditions all over the world. Check students' understanding of the wide-spread influence of El Niño by asking: **How does understanding El Niño help meteorologists predict the weather?** *(Meteorologists can look for changes in ocean currents and, if they occur, anticipate certain unusual weather conditions over a wide area.)* **learning modality: verbal**

Reading Weather Maps

Sharpen your Skills

Interpreting Data

ACTIVITY

Time 10 minutes
Tips Make sure students understand how to read the symbol for wind direction. Explain that when the flag points down the wind is from the south, when it points left the wind is from the west, and so on.
Expected Outcome Temperature 30°F, wind speed 26–31 mph, wind blowing from the south, air pressure 1016 millibars, 70–80 percent of the sky covered by clouds, snow falling
Extend Ask: **How would you show the same station with a temperature of 34°F, wind direction from the southeast, and sleet falling?** *(Replace 30 with 34, point the flag halfway between down and right, and replace the star with a triangle containing a solid circle.)* **learning modality: logical/mathematical**

El Niño

Some long-term weather patterns may be caused by changes in ocean currents and global winds. Periodically, a warm-water event known as **El Niño** occurs in the tropical Pacific Ocean. During an El Niño event, winds shift and push warm surface water toward the west coast of South America. The warm water replaces the cold water that usually rises from the deep ocean near the coast.

El Niño events occur once every two to seven years. They can cause dramatic climate changes around the Pacific Ocean and in other places. In the winter of 1997 and 1998, a strong El Niño current caused droughts in Asia and Brazil, heavy rains and floods in California and Peru, and tornadoes in Florida and other parts of the southeastern United States.

Scientists have looked for clues and warnings to help predict the return of El Niño. One signal is rising surface temperatures in the tropical part of the Pacific Ocean. Using data gathered during past El Niño events, scientists were able to predict many of the results of the 1997–1998 El Niño.

☑ *Checkpoint* ***What evidence do scientists use to predict an El Niño?***

Sharpen your Skills

Interpreting Data

ACTIVITY

Use the key to Figure 19 to help you answer the questions about this weather station data.

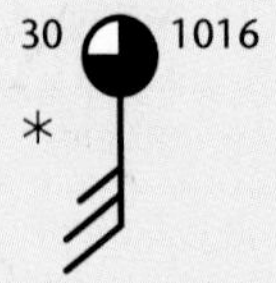

1. What is the temperature at this station?
2. What is the wind speed?
3. Which way is the wind blowing?
4. What is the air pressure?
5. What percent of the sky is covered by clouds?
6. What type of precipitation, if any, is falling?

Reading Weather Maps

A weather map is a "snapshot" of conditions at a particular time over a large area. There are many different types of weather maps. Television forecasters often present maps generated by computers from radar information.

Weather Service Maps Data from more than 300 local weather stations all over the country are assembled into weather maps at the National Weather Service. The information collected by a typical reporting station is summarized in the key to Figure 19. The weather map, which has been simplified, includes most of the weather station data shown in the key.

On some weather maps, you see curved lines. These lines connect places where certain conditions—temperature or air pressure—are the same. **Isobars** are lines joining places on the map that have the same air pressure. (*Iso* means "equal" and *bar* means "pressure.") The numbers on the isobars are the pressure readings. Air pressure readings may be given in inches of mercury or in millibars or both. Figure 19 has isobars.

Isotherms are lines joining places that have the same temperature. The isotherm may be labeled with the temperature in degrees Fahrenheit, degrees Celsius, or both.

Background

Facts and Figures There are three different methods of forecasting weather: the analog, numeric, and synoptic methods. The analog method, also called statistical forecasting, uses mathematical equations based on past weather patterns to forecast future weather. The numeric method uses mathematical equations based on the laws of physics, especially fluid dynamics, to forecast weather. The synoptic method uses a synopsis, or summary, of the total weather picture right now to predict what the weather will be like in the future. Using the synoptic method, the movement of weather systems is shown on a series of weather maps, like the one in Figure 19, which are called synoptic charts. The synoptic method is the most commonly used method of weather forecasting, by both professional and amateur meteorologists.

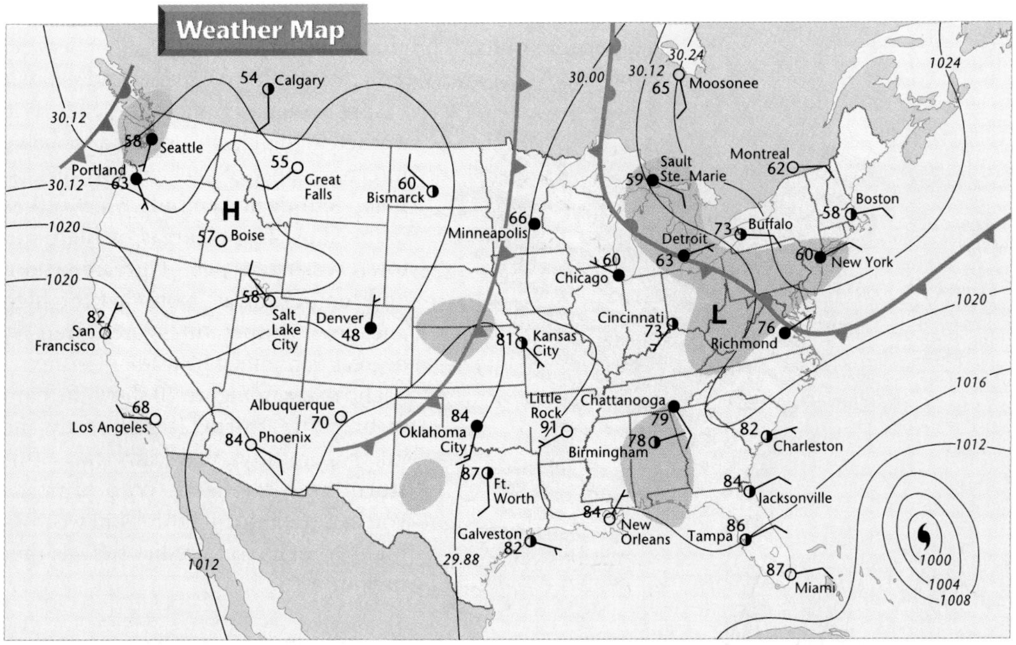

EXPLANATION OF FRONTS

Cold Front *Boundary between a cold air mass and a warm air mass. Brings brief storms and cooler weather.*

Warm Front *Boundary between a warm air mass and a cold air mass. Usually accompanied by precipitation.*

Stationary Front *Boundary between a warm air mass and a cold air mass when no movement occurs. Brings long periods of precipitation.*

Occluded Front *Boundary on which a warm front has been overtaken by a cold front. Brings precipitation.*

Weather	Symbol
Drizzle	
Fog	≡
Hail	△
Haze	∞
Rain	•
Shower	▽
Sleet	
Smoke	
Snow	✱
Thunderstorm	
Hurricane	

Wind Speed (mph)	Symbol
1–2	
3–8	
9–14	
15–20	
21–25	
26–31	
32–37	
38–43	
44–49	
50–54	
55–60	
61–66	
67–71	
72–77	

Cloud Cover (%)	Symbol
0	○
10	
20–30	
40	
50	◑
60	
70–80	
90	
100	●

How Symbols Are Used on a Weather Map

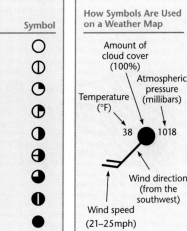

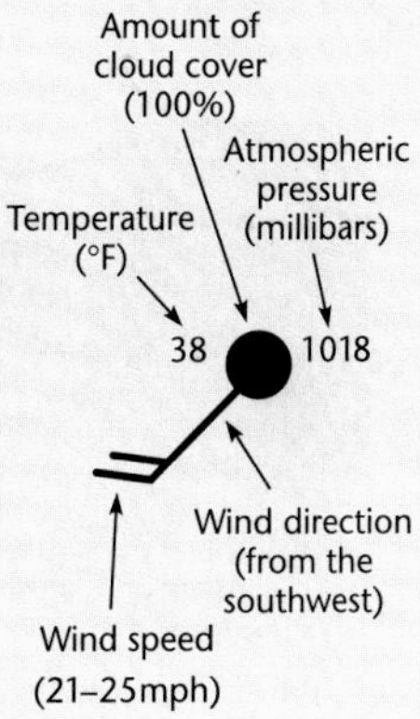

Figure 19 This weather map shows data collected from weather stations all over the country. Below the map is an explanation of what the symbols at each city mean.

Using the Visuals: Figure 19

Have students choose partners and quiz each other on the conditions represented by the symbols at several different weather stations shown in the figure. For example, a student might ask his or her partner from which direction the wind is blowing in Miami *(east)*, how much cloud cover there is in Seattle *(100%)*, or how fast the wind is blowing in Los Angeles *(9–14 mph)*. **cooperative learning**

Real-Life Learning

Challenge students to use the symbols in Figure 19 to summarize actual weather conditions in their location. You may either provide students with the relevant data on temperature, wind direction, and other weather factors for your local area or have students read the data from instruments. Ask: **What, if any, weather factors are not included in the key?** *(relative humidity, dew point, and cloud type)* **How could you represent them on a weather map?** *(Students may say that relative humidity and dew point could be represented by numbers placed near the weather station and cloud type by a symbol placed near the weather station.)* **learning modality: visual**

Building Inquiry Skills: Predicting

Call students' attention to the map in Figure 19 and challenge them to locate the longest cold front. Ask: **Where do you think the cold front will be in a few days?** *(Most likely it will have moved east.)* **As the cold front travels across the country, how do you think it will change the weather?** *(The cold front is likely to bring cloudy, wet, or even stormy weather.)* **learning modality: logical/mathematical**

Program Resources

Science Explorer Series *Earth's Waters*, Chapter 4, has more information about El Niño.

◆ **Integrated Science Laboratory Manual** I-3, "Investigating Weather Maps"

Media and Technology

Transparencies "Weather Map," Transparency 15

Answers to Self-Assessment

Checkpoint

To predict an El Niño, scientists look for evidence of rising surface temperatures in the tropical part of the Pacific Ocean.

Ongoing Assessment

Skills Check Have students interpret data in Figure 19 to find the following weather information: the air pressure in Tampa, Florida *(1016 millibars)*; a cyclone, or low pressure system *(between Ohio and West Virginia)*; a stationary front *(from Wisconsin to Virginia)*; a hurricane *(east of Florida)*.

Reading Weather Maps, continued

Using the Visuals: Figure 20

Make sure students understand how the three maps in the figure are related, then ask: **If you had a weather map for Day 4, how do you predict it would differ from the map for Day 3?** *(Chances are the weather systems would be farther east by Day 4.)* **learning modality: logical/mathematical**

Real-Life Learning

Time 20 minutes

ACTIVITY

Point out that even very detailed weather maps cannot give the precise weather conditions for every location because there are many factors that can modify local conditions. For example, the south side of a hill is likely to be warmer than the north side and an open area is likely to be windier than a wooded area. Ask: **What factors do you think might influence local weather conditions at our school?** *(Factors might include large buildings, open grassy areas, forests, hills or mountains, rivers or lakes.)* **learning modality: visual**

The Butterfly Effect

Building Inquiry Skills: Calculating

Materials *calculator*
Time 5 minutes

ACTIVITY

Help students appreciate how the butterfly effect works with this simple activity. Have students add three numbers, divide the sum by a fourth number, multiply the quotient by a fifth number, and then square the result. Give half the class five numbers written out to three decimal places and give the other half the same numbers rounded to the nearest whole number. Have students compare their results. They will find that answers based on the different sets of numbers diverge more and more with each step in the calculations. Ask: **How does this demonstrate the butterfly effect?** *(Tiny differences in the numbers accumulate into larger differences.)* **learning modality: logical/mathematical**

Newspaper Weather Maps Maps in newspapers are simplified versions of maps produced by the National Weather Service. *Exploring Newspaper Weather Maps* shows a typical newspaper weather map. From what you have learned in this chapter, you can probably interpret most of the symbols on this map. **Standard symbols on weather maps show fronts, areas of high and low pressure, types of precipitation, and temperatures.** Note that the high and low temperatures are given in degrees Fahrenheit instead of Celsius.

The maps in Figure 20 show the path of a winter storm. If you study the maps carefully, you can track this storm and its effects. With practice, you can use information from weather maps to help you predict the weather in your area.

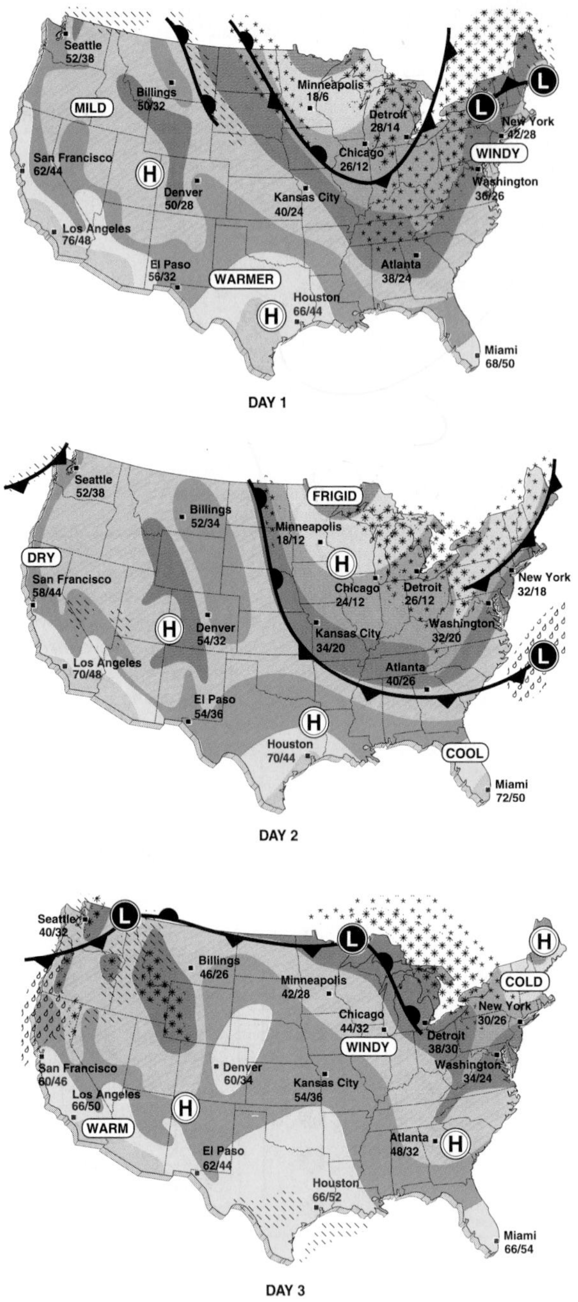

Figure 20 These weather maps show a storm moving from west to east over a three-day period.
Interpreting Diagrams What were the high and low temperatures in Chicago on Day 2? On Day 3?

The Butterfly Effect

Even with current technology, weather forecasting is tricky. The main reason is that weather patterns do not follow an orderly, step-by-step process.

A forecast for the weather six days from now is based on forecasts for all the days between now and then. A small change in the weather today can mean a larger change in the weather a week later! This is the so-called "butterfly effect." The name refers to a scientist's suggestion that even the flapping of a butterfly's wings causes a tiny disturbance in the atmosphere. This tiny event might cause a larger disturbance that could—eventually—grow into a hurricane.

Background

History of Science The butterfly effect was discovered by a theoretical meteorologist at the Massachusetts Institute of Technology named Edward Lorenz. One day in 1961, Lorenz decided to rerun a computer program for weather forecasting that he had been working on. Rather than enter all the numbers to six decimal places, he took a shortcut and entered the numbers to just three decimal places. After many computer calculations, Lorenz was surprised to discover that the results were very different from the results he had obtained earlier using numbers to six decimal places. This showed Lorenz that weather systems and other complex systems are very sensitive to tiny changes in initial conditions. Lorenz's work was the beginning of the mathematical theory of chaos, which is now important in most sciences, in addition to meteorology.

EXPLORING Newspaper Weather Maps

Weather maps in newspapers use symbols to show fronts, high and low pressure areas, and precipitation. Color bands indicate different temperatures.

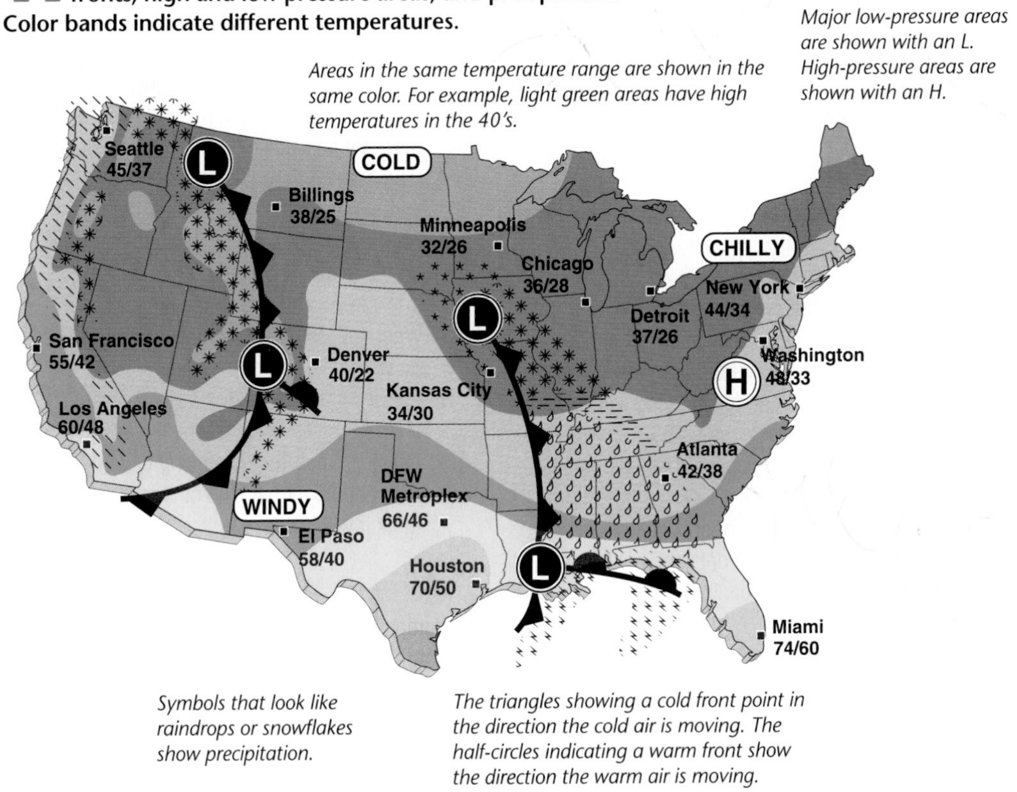

Areas in the same temperature range are shown in the same color. For example, light green areas have high temperatures in the 40's.
Major low-pressure areas are shown with an L. High-pressure areas are shown with an H.
Seattle 45/37
COLD
Billings 38/25
Minneapolis 32/26
Chicago 36/28
CHILLY
New York 44/34
Detroit 37/26
San Francisco 55/42
Denver 40/22
Washington 48/33
Kansas City 34/30
Los Angeles 60/48
Atlanta 42/38
DFW Metroplex 66/46
WINDY
El Paso 58/40
Houston 70/50
Miami 74/60
Symbols that look like raindrops or snowflakes show precipitation.
The triangles showing a cold front point in the direction the cold air is moving. The half-circles indicating a warm front show the direction the warm air is moving.

Section 4 Review

1. What kinds of technology do meteorologists use to help predict the weather?
2. Name at least three types of information you could get from a weather map of your area.
3. What lines on a weather map connect points that have the same temperature?
4. **Thinking Critically Predicting** If you observe that air pressure is rising, what kind of weather do you think is coming?

Check Your Progress

CHAPTER PROJECT 3

After a week of predicting the weather, you are ready to compare your predictions to the actual weather that occurred. Then compare your predictions with those made by professional meteorologists. How accurate were your predictions? How accurate were the predictions made by professional meteorologists?

Program Resources

◆ **Teaching Resources** 3-4 Review and Reinforce, p. 87; 3-4 Enrich, p. 88

Media and Technology

Transparencies "Newspaper Weather Map," Transparency 16

Interactive Student Tutorial CD-ROM I-3

Answers to Self-Assessment

Caption Question

Figure 20 The high temperature in Chicago on Day 2 was 24°F; low was 12°F. On Day 3 the high was 44°F; the low was 32°F.

EXPLORING Newspaper Weather Maps

ACTIVITY

Materials *poster board, colored markers*
Time 30 minutes

Challenge pairs of students to produce a brief national television weather report based on the weather map shown in the feature. Each pair should interpret the symbols on the map, write a script, and create graphics. Invite pairs to present their reports to the class. **cooperative learning**

3 Assess

Section 4 Review Answers

1. Meteorologists use weather balloons, weather satellites, and computers.
2. Temperature, air pressure, wind speed, wind direction, percent cloud cover, and type of precipitation.
3. isotherms
4. fair weather

Check Your Progress

CHAPTER PROJECT 3

To compare their predictions with the weather that occurs at each of their three locations, student should compare their own weather maps with the newspaper weather maps showing actual weather conditions for the same days. Most newspaper weather reports also give weather predictions that students can use to compare their own predictions with those made by professional meteorologists.

Performance Assessment

Skills Check Have students interpret the weather map in the Exploring feature on this page to find out weather conditions in Seattle. Then have them describe Seattle's weather using the symbols in the key to Figure 19.

Skills Lab

Interpreting Data

Reading a Weather Map

Preparing for Inquiry

Key Concept The symbols on weather maps communicate information about weather factors and systems.

Skills Objectives Students will be able to
- interpret data on a weather map;
- draw conclusions about the type of weather affecting different places.

Time 30 minutes

Advance Planning Make an overhead transparency of the map in the lab to use in class.

Alternative Materials You can use an actual weather map from a newspaper.

Guiding Inquiry

Troubleshooting the Experiment
- Make sure students realize how the front changes as it goes across the top of the map.
- Explain why two temperatures are given for each city on the map.

Expected Outcome

Students should use the map on page 105 to interpret the map in the lab. In Step 3, the symbols that look like snowflakes represent snow and those that look like raindrops represent rain. In Step 4, half-circles indicate warm fronts and triangles represent cold fronts. In Step 5, H is the symbol for high pressure and L is the symbol for low pressure.

Analyze and Conclude

1. Orange represents the highest temperatures and light purple represents the lowest temperatures.
2. Miami the highest, Billings the lowest
3. It is raining in California and snowing in parts of the Northwest.
4. Three—warm front, cold front, stationary front
5. Two areas of low pressure and two areas of high pressure
6. It is probably winter. The temperatures are fairly low.
7. A cold front; clouds and snow followed by cold, dry weather

Skills Lab

Interpreting Data

Reading a Weather Map

In this lab, you will interpret data from a weather map to describe weather conditions in various places.

Problem

How does a weather map communicate data?

Procedure

1. Examine the symbols on the weather map below. For more information about the symbols used on the map, refer to Figure 19 on page 103 and to *Exploring Newspaper Weather Maps* on page 105.
2. Observe the different colors on the weather map.
3. Find the symbols for snow and rain.
4. Locate the warm fronts and cold fronts.
5. Locate the symbols for high and low pressure.

Analyze and Conclude

1. What color represents the highest temperatures? What color represents the lowest temperatures?
2. What city has the highest temperature? What city has the lowest temperature?
3. Where on the map is it raining? Where on the map is it snowing?
4. How many different kinds of fronts are shown on the map?
5. How many areas of low pressure are shown on the map? How many areas of high pressure are shown on the map?
6. What season does this map represent? How do you know?
7. **Think About It** The triangles and semicircles on the front lines show which way the front is moving. What front is moving toward Minneapolis? What kind of weather do you think it will bring?

More to Explore

Compare this weather map with the weather map shown in a television news report. Which symbols on these maps are similar? Which symbols are different?

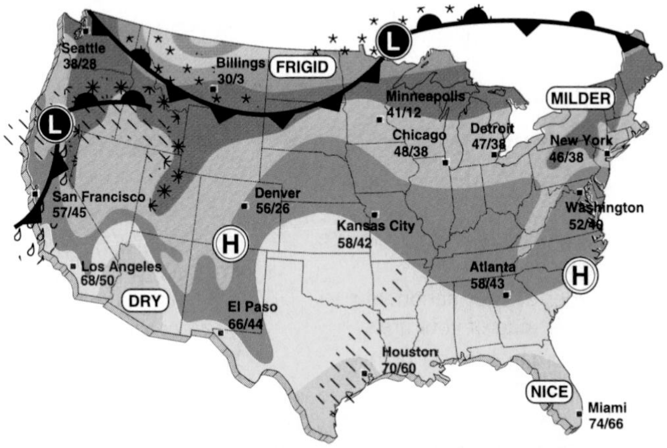

Extending the Inquiry

More to Explore Television weather maps use somewhat different symbols, but students should be able to interpret them with their knowledge of newspaper weather maps.

Program Resources

- **Teaching Resources** Skills Lab blackline masters, pp. 92–93

Section 1 Air Masses and Fronts

Key Ideas

- Four major types of air masses influence the weather in North America: maritime tropical, continental tropical, maritime polar, and continental polar.
- When air masses collide, they form four types of fronts: cold fronts, warm fronts, stationary fronts, and occluded fronts.
- Cyclones and decreasing air pressure are associated with storms and precipitation. Anticyclones bring high pressure and dry weather.

Key Terms

air mass	maritime	occluded
tropical	continental	cyclone
polar	front	anticyclone

Section 2 Storms

Key Ideas

- Thunderstorms and tornadoes form within large cumulonimbus clouds. During thunderstorms, avoid touching metal objects because they can conduct lightning into your body.
- The safest place to be during a tornado is in the basement of a well-built building.
- A hurricane begins over warm water as a low-pressure area. If you hear a hurricane warning and are told to evacuate, leave the area immediately.
- Snow falls when humid air cools below 0°C. If you are caught in a snowstorm, try to find shelter from the wind.

Key Terms

storm	tornado	storm surge
lightning	hurricane	evacuate

Section 3 Floods

INTEGRATING HEALTH AND SAFETY

Key Ideas

- Floods occur when so much water pours into a stream or river that it overflows its banks and covers the land on either side of the channel.
- The first rule of flood safety: Move to higher ground and stay away from flood waters.

Key Term

flash flood

Section 4 Predicting the Weather

Key Ideas

- Meteorologists interpret weather information from local weather observers, instruments carried by balloons, satellites, and weather stations around the world.
- Changes in weather technology have occurred in two areas: gathering weather data and using computers to make forecasts.
- Standard symbols on weather maps show fronts, areas of high and low pressure, types of precipitation, and temperatures.

Key Terms

meteorologist	isobar
El Niño	isotherm

ACTIVITY

USING THE INTERNET

www.science-explorer.phschool.com

Program Resources

- **Teaching Resources** Chapter 3 Project Scoring Rubric, p. 72; Chapter 3 Performance Assessment, pp. 148–150; Chapter 3 Test, pp. 151–154

Media and Technology

Interactive Student Tutorial CD-ROM I-3

Computer Test Bank Chapter 3 Test

CHAPTER 3 REVIEW

Reviewing Content

Multiple Choice

1. c **2.** b **3.** d **4.** a **5.** b

True or False

6. continental tropical **7.** stationary front **8.** true **9.** true **10.** isotherms

Checking Concepts

11. temperature and humidity
12. The prevailing westerlies generally push air masses from west to east in North America.
13. A cold front forms when a cold air mass moves underneath a warm air mass, forcing the warm air to rise.
14. Answers may vary. In addition to the dangers of high water to lives and property, floods can knock down electrical poles and cut off power supplies, cause landslides or mudslides, block or wash away roads, pollute drinking water and food.
15. Sources of information that meteorologists use to predict the weather include local weather observers, instruments carried by balloons, satellites, and weather stations around the world.
16. Writing to Learn Students' descriptions should show that they are familiar with the characteristics of hurricanes, including the heavy rains and high winds that swirl around the calm eye at the center of the hurricane. Their descriptions also should show that they know hurricanes may cover hundreds of kilometers.

Thinking Visually

17. Titles may vary. A suitable title would be "Comparing Hurricanes and Tornadoes." **a.** In cumulonimbus clouds **b.** Around 600 kilometers **c.** 15 minutes or less **d.** Summer, early fall **e.** Move to the basement of a well-built building

Applying Skills

18. The map shows a cyclone. You can tell because the air pressure at the center is low.
19. The winds are spinning in a counterclockwise direction. The low pressure area at the center indicates the winds are spinning inward toward the center.
20. Students' drawings should show a high pressure area surrounded by winds flowing outward from the center in a clockwise direction.
21. If you saw a pressure center like the one depicted on the map on a weather map, you would predict stormy, wet weather. To make a better prediction, you would need to ask about the direction and rate of movement of the pressure center.

CHAPTER 3 REVIEW

Reviewing Content

For more review of key concepts, see the Interactive Student Tutorial CD-ROM.

Multiple Choice

Choose the letter of the answer that best completes each statement.

1. An air mass that forms over an ocean is called
a. tropical.
b. continental.
c. maritime.
d. polar.

2. Cool, clear weather is usually brought by a
a. warm front.
b. cold front.
c. stationary front.
d. occluded front.

3. Winds spiraling inward toward a center of low pressure form a(n)
a. anticyclone.
b. front.
c. isobar.
d. cyclone.

4. Very large tropical storms with high winds are called
a. hurricanes.
b. tornadoes.
c. thunderstorms.
d. blizzards.

5. Most flash floods are caused by
a. hailstorms.
b. heavy rainfall.
c. high winds.
d. melting snow.

True or False

If the statement is true, write true. If it is false, change the underlined word or words to make it true.

6. Summers in the Southwest are hot and dry because of maritime tropical air masses.
7. A cold front over an area will bring many days of cloudy weather.
8. Foggy, rainy, or humid weather usually follows the passage of a warm front through an area.
9. Low cumulonimbus clouds may bring both thunderstorms and tornadoes.
10. On a weather map, isobars join places on the map with the same temperature.

Checking Concepts

11. What are the basic characteristics used to describe air masses?
12. Describe how wind patterns affect the movement of air masses in North America.
13. How does a cold front form?
14. Describe three hazards associated with floods.
15. What are some of the sources of information that meteorologists use to predict the weather?
16. Writing to Learn Imagine you are a meteorologist. Your assignment is to investigate a hurricane by flying into it with a large plane. Describe your experiences in a journal entry. Be sure to include descriptive words. How did it look? Sound? Feel?

Thinking Visually

17. Compare/Contrast Table Copy the compare/contrast table about hurricanes and tornadoes onto a separate sheet of paper. Then fill in the empty spaces and add a title. (For more on compare/contrast tables, see the Skills Handbook.)

Type of Storm	Hurricane	Tornado
Where storm forms	Over warm ocean water	a. __?__
Size of storm	b. __?__	Several hundred meters
How long storm lasts	A week or more	c. __?__
Time of year	d. __?__	Spring, early summer
Safety rules	Evacuate or move to the interior of a well-built building	e. __?__

Thinking Critically

22. Warm air masses that influence weather in the United States include maritime tropical air masses from the Gulf of Mexico and the Pacific Ocean and continental tropical air masses from the Southwest. Cold air masses that influence weather in the United States include maritime polar air masses from the Atlantic and Pacific Oceans and continental polar air masses from central and northern Canada. Air masses that form over the water include maritime polar and maritime tropical air masses. Air masses

Applying Skills

Use the map to answer Questions 18–21.

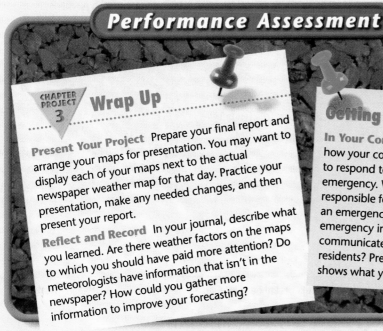

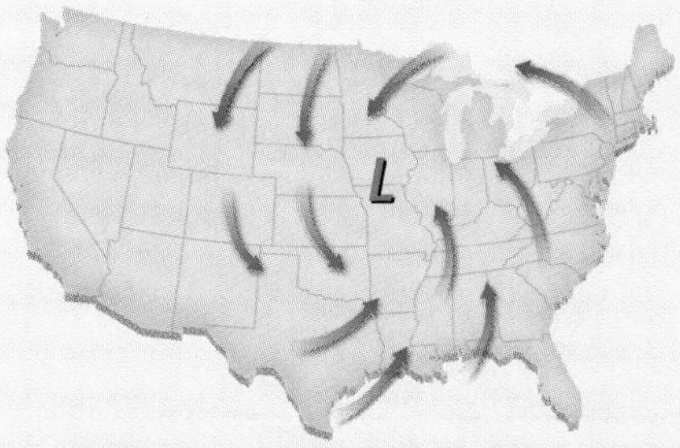

18. Interpreting Maps Does the map show a cyclone or an anticyclone? How can you tell?

19. Interpreting Data What do the arrows show about the movement of the winds in this pressure center? What else indicates wind direction?

20. Making Models Using this diagram as an example, draw a similar diagram to illustrate a high pressure area. Remember to indicate wind direction in your diagram.

21. Posing Questions If you saw a pressure center like this on a weather map, what prediction could you make about the weather? What questions would you need to ask in order to make a better prediction?

Thinking Critically

22. Classifying Classify the major types of air masses that influence weather in the United States in two ways: by temperature and by where they form.

23. Applying Concepts Would you expect hurricanes to form over the oceans off the northeast and northwest coasts of the United States? Explain.

24. Relating Cause and Effect How do differences in air density influence the movement of cold and warm fronts?

25. Making Judgments What do you think is the most important thing people should do to reduce the dangers of storms?

CHAPTER 3 REVIEW

Performance Assessment

CHAPTER PROJECT 3

Wrap Up

Present Your Project Prepare your final report and arrange your maps for presentation. You may want to display each of your maps next to the actual newspaper weather map for that day. Practice your presentation, make any needed changes, and then present your report.

Reflect and Record In your journal, describe what you learned. Are there weather factors on the maps to which you should have paid more attention? Do meteorologists have information that isn't in the newspaper? How could you gather more information to improve your forecasting?

Getting Involved

In Your Community Find out how your community is prepared to respond to a weather emergency. What agency is responsible for determining that an emergency exists? How would emergency information be communicated to the local residents? Prepare a poster that shows what you learned.

that form over land include continental polar and continental tropical air masses.

23. You would not expect hurricanes to form over the oceans off the northeast and northwest coasts of the United States because the temperature of the water is too cold to provide energy for a hurricane.

24. Warm air is less dense than cold air. When a cold front moves through, it flows underneath warm air. When a warm front moves through, it rises up over cold air.

25. Answers may vary. Many students will state the importance of staying informed about conditions during storms by listening to weather reports on radio or television.

Program Resources

- **Inquiry Skills Activity Book** Provides teaching and review of all inquiry skills

Performance Assessment

CHAPTER PROJECT 3

Wrap Up

Presenting Your Project Encourage students to use a variety of formats for presenting their projects, such as television weather reports and bulletin board displays. Advise students to be prepared to explain the patterns they observed in the weather and how they made their predictions.

Reflect and Record Students may find that they should have paid more attention to the movement of air masses and fronts. They probably learned that it is difficult to predict weather accurately. Meteorologists have a great deal more information than what appears in newspapers, including information from weather radar. To improve their forecasting accuracy, students might consider gathering information from local and national television weather reports. These reports may show weather radar images and other information not found in newspapers.

Getting Involved

In Your Community For more information, suggest to students that they contact local television stations as well as their local emergency management agency. Have students find out how a weather emergency is defined and what restrictions are placed on travel and other activities during weather emergencies. Radio and television probably are used to communicate emergency weather information to local residents, but students should be aware that there may be other ways as well, such as sirens to warn residents of tornadoes. Students' posters should show how to respond to the type of weather emergencies that are likely in their local area, as well as where to find out more about weather conditions during weather emergencies.

CHAPTER 4 Climate and Climate Change

Sections	Time	Student Edition Activities	ACTIVITY Other Activities
CHAPTER PROJECT 4 **Investigating Microclimates** p. 111	Ongoing (3 weeks)	Check Your Progress, p. 119 Check Your Progress, p. 138 Wrap Up, p. 145	
1 What Causes Climate? pp. 112–121 ◆ Identify the factors that influence temperature and precipitation. ◆ Explain what causes the seasons.	4–5 periods/ 2–2$\frac{1}{2}$ blocks	**Discover** How Does Earth's Shape Affect Climate Zones?, p. 112 **Sharpen Your Skills** Inferring, p. 115 **Skills Lab: Controlling Variables** Sunny Rays and Angles, pp. 120–121	**TE** Demonstration, p. 114 **TE** Inquiry Challenge, p. 114 **TE** Building Inquiry Skills: Observing, p. 115 **TE** Including All Students, p. 116 **TE** Building Inquiry Skills: Inferring, p. 116 **TE** Including All Students, p. 117 **TE** Exploring the Seasons, p. 118
2 Climate Regions pp. 122–133 ◆ Identify factors used to define climates. ◆ Name the five main climate regions.	4–5 periods/ 2–2$\frac{1}{2}$ blocks	**Discover** What Are Different Climate Types?, p. 122 **Try This** Modeling a Humid Climate, p. 127 **Sharpen Your Skills** Classifying, p. 129 **Science at Home,** p. 131 **Real-World Lab: Careers** Cool Climate Graphs, pp. 132–133	**TE** Real-Life Learning, p. 125 **TE** Inquiry Challenge, p. 127 **TE** Including All Students, p. 130 **ISLM** I-4, "Investigating Differences in Climate"
3 Long-Term Changes in Climate pp. 134–138 ◆ Identify the sources of information that can be used to study ancient climates. ◆ Describe how Earth's surface changes during an ice age. ◆ List the theories that have been proposed to explain natural climate change.	2 periods/ 1 block	**Discover** What Story Can Tree Rings Tell?, p. 134	**TE** Including All Students, p. 136 **TE** Demonstration, p. 137 **TE** Including All Students, p. 138
4 *Integrating Environmental Science* **Global Changes in the Atmosphere** pp. 139–142 ◆ Explain how human activities might be affecting the temperature of Earth's atmosphere. ◆ Describe how human activities have affected the ozone layer.	2 periods/ 1 block	**Discover** What Is the Greenhouse Effect?, p. 139 **Try This** It's Your Skin!, p. 141 **Science at Home,** p. 142	**TE** Demonstration, p. 140
Study Guide/Chapter Review pp. 143–145	1 period/ $\frac{1}{2}$ block		**ISAB** Provides teaching and review of all inquiry skills

For Standard or Block Schedule The Resource Pro® CD-ROM gives you maximum flexibility for planning your instruction for any type of schedule. Resource Pro® contains Planning Express®, an advanced scheduling program, as well as the entire contents of the Teaching Resources and the Computer Test Bank.

CHAPTER PLANNING GUIDE

Program Resources	Assessment Strategies	Media and Technology
TR Chapter 4 Project Teacher Notes, pp. 94–95 **TR** Chapter 4 Project Overview and Worksheets, pp. 96–99 **TR** Chapter 4 Project Scoring Rubric, p. 100	**SE** Performance Assessment: Chapter 4 Project Wrap Up, p. 145 **TE** Check Your Progress, pp. 119, 138 **TR** Chapter 4 Project Scoring Rubric, p. 100	Science Explorer Internet Site
TR 4-1 Lesson Plan, p. 101 **TR** 4-1 Section Summary, p. 102 **TR** 4-1 Review and Reinforce, p. 103 **TR** 4-1 Enrich, p. 104 **TR** Skills Lab blackline masters, pp. 117–119 **SES** Book H, *Earth's Water,* Chapters 1 and 4 **SES** Book J, *Astronomy,* Chapter 1	**SE** Section 1 Review, p. 119 **SE** Analyze and Conclude, pp. 120–121 **TE** Ongoing Assessment, pp. 113, 115, 117 **TE** Performance Assessment, p. 119 **TR** 4-1 Review and Reinforce, p. 103	Exploring Earth Science Videodisc, Unit 1 Side 1, "Sunny Days" Audiotapes: English-Spanish Summary 4-1 Transparency 17, "The Seasons" Interactive Student Tutorial CD-ROM, I-4
TR 4-2 Lesson Plan, p. 105 **TR** 4-2 Section Summary, p. 106 **TR** 4-2 Review and Reinforce, p. 107 **TR** 4-2 Enrich, p. 108 **TR** Real-World Lab blackline masters, pp. 120–121 **SES** Book A, *From Bacteria to Plants,* Chapter 5 **SES** Book B, *Animals,* Chapter 4 **SES** Book G, *Earth's Changing Surface,* Appendix B	**SE** Section 2 Review, p. 131 **SE** Analyze and Conclude, p. 133 **TE** Ongoing Assessment, pp. 123, 125, 127, 129 **TE** Performance Assessment, p. 131 **TR** 4-2 Review and Reinforce, p. 107	Exploring Earth Science Videodisc, Unit 4 Side 2, "Climate in the U.S." Audiotapes: English-Spanish Summary 4-2 Transparencies 18, "World Climate Regions"; 19, "Climate Graph for Washington, D.C." Interactive Student Tutorial CD-ROM, I-4
TR 4-3 Lesson Plan, p. 109 **TR** 4-3 Section Summary, p. 110 **TR** 4-3 Review and Reinforce, p. 111 **TR** 4-3 Enrich, p. 112 **SES** Book G, *Earth's Changing Surface,* Chapter 4 **SES** Book J, *Astronomy,* Chapter 2	**SE** Section 3 Review, p. 138 **TE** Ongoing Assessment, pp. 135, 137 **TE** Performance Assessment, p. 138 **TR** 4-3 Review and Reinforce, p. 111	Exploring Earth Science Videodisc, Unit 5 Side 1, "Geologic Time" Exploring Earth Science Videodisc, Unit 4 Side 2, "Changes in Climate" Audiotapes: English-Spanish Summary 4-3 Transparency 20, "Extent of Northern Hemisphere Glaciation" Interactive Student Tutorial CD-ROM, I-4
TR 4-4 Lesson Plan, p. 113 **TR** 4-4 Section Summary, p. 114 **TR** 4-4 Review and Reinforce, p. 115 **TR** 4-4 Enrich, p. 116	**SE** Section 4 Review, p. 142 **TE** Ongoing Assessment, p. 141 **TE** Performance Assessment, p. 143 **TR** 4-4 Review and Reinforce, p. 115	Exploring Earth Science Videodisc, Unit 4 Side 2, "The Greenhouse Effect" Exploring Earth Science Videodisc, Unit 6 Side 2, "Our Passion for Driving" Audiotapes: English-Spanish Summary 4-4 Interactive Student Tutorial CD-ROM, I-4
TR Chapter 4 Performance Assessment, pp. 155–157 **TR** Chapter 4 Test, pp. 158–161	**SE** Chapter 4 Review, pp. 143–145 **TR** Chapter 4 Performance Assessment, pp. 155–157 **TR** Chapter 4 Test, pp. 158–161 **CTB** I–4 Test	Interactive Student Tutorial CD-ROM, I-4 Computer Test Bank, I–4 Test

Key: **SE** Student Edition
CTB Computer Test Bank
ISAB Inquiry Skills Activity Book
TE Teacher's Edition
SES Science Explorer Series Text
PTA Product Testing Activities by *Consumer Reports*
TR Teaching Resources
ISLM Integrated Science Laboratory Manual
IES Interdisciplinary Explorations Series

Meeting the National Science Education Standards and AAAS Benchmarks

National Science Education Standards	Benchmarks for Science Literacy	Unifying Themes
Science As Inquiry (Content Standard A) ◆ **Design and conduct a scientific investigation** Students investigate how the angle of a light source affects the rate of temperature change on a surface. *(Skills Lab)* ◆ **Use appropriate tools and techniques to gather, analyze, and interpret data** Students investigate microclimates. Students analyze climate graphs. *(Chapter Project; Real-World Lab)* **Life Science** (Content Standard C) ◆ **Populations and ecosystems** There are five main climate regions, each with typical plants and animals. *(Section 2)* **Earth and Space Science** (Content Standard D) ◆ **Structure of the Earth system** The climate of a region is determined mainly by temperature and precipitation. *(Sections 1, 2)* ◆ **Earth's history** Scientists study fossils, tree rings, and pollen records to learn about ancient climates. *(Section 3)* ◆ **Earth in the solar system** The seasons are caused by the tilt of Earth's axis. *(Section 1)* **Science in Personal and Social Perspectives** (Content Standard F) ◆ **Science and technology in society** Human activities are affecting Earth's climate and atmosphere. *(Section 4)*	**1B Scientific Inquiry** Students investigate microclimates. Students examine how the angle of a light source affects the rate of temperature change of a surface. *(Chapter Project; Skills Lab)* **3C Issues in Technology** Two important worldwide issues are global warming and thinning of the ozone layer. *(Section 4)* **4B The Earth** The seasons are caused by the tilt of Earth's axis. Scientists classify climates according to temperature and precipitation. Throughout Earth's history, climates have gradually changed. *(Sections 1, 2, 4)* **4C Processes That Shape the Earth** Human activities have had an effect on Earth's climate and atmosphere. *(Section 4)* **5D Interdependence of Life** There are five main climate regions, each with its own particular plants and animals. *(Section 2)* **9B Symbolic Relationships** Students compare climate data for four cities. *(Real-World Lab)* **12D Communication Skills** Students present data on the microclimates they studied. *(Chapter Project)*	◆ **Energy** Latitude, altitude, distance from large bodies of water, and ocean currents influence temperature. Students investigate how the angle of a light source affects the rate of temperature change. Global warming is a gradual increase in the temperature of Earth's atmosphere. *(Sections 1, 4; Skills Lab)* ◆ **Scale and Structure** A small area with its own climate is a microclimate. Earth has three main temperature zones. Earth has five main climate regions. *(Chapter Project; Sections 1, 2)* ◆ **Stability** Climate regions are determined on the basis of average temperature and precipitation. Although weather can vary from day to day, climates change more slowly. *(Sections 2, 3)* ◆ **Systems and Interactions** Students relate microclimates to the plants and animals found there. The seasons are caused by the tilt of Earth's axis. Students investigate how the angle of the sun's rays affects the amount of energy absorbed by different parts of Earth's surface. Human activities have had an effect on Earth's climate and atmosphere. *(Chapter Project; Sections 1, 4; Skills Lab)* ◆ **Unity and Diversity** Each hemisphere has a polar zone, temperate zone, and tropical zone. Each climate region has a characteristic average temperature and precipitation. Students compare climate data for four cities. *(Sections 1, 2; Real-World Lab)*

Media and Technology

Exploring Earth Science Videodiscs

◆ **Section 1** "Sunny Days" describes the sun as the ultimate energy source.

◆ **Section 2** "Climate in the U.S." illustrates the different climates found in the United States.

◆ **Section 3** "Geologic Time" illustrates Earth's geologic history. "Changes in Climate" describes the impact of natural factors and human activities on climate.

◆ **Section 4** "The Greenhouse Effect" models how trapped heat from the sun creates global warming. "Our Passion for Driving" examines the impact of the automobile.

Interactive Student Tutorial CD-ROM

◆ **Chapter Review** Interactive questions help students to self-assess their mastery of key chapter concepts.

Student Edition Connection Strategies

◆ **Section 1** **Math Toolbox**, p. 118
Integrating Space Science, p. 118

◆ **Section 3** **Social Studies Connection**, p. 137
Integrating Space Science, p. 137

◆ **Section 4** **Integrating Environmental Science**, pp. 139–142

ACTIVITY

USING THE INTERNET

www.science-explorer.phschool.com

Visit the Science Explorer Internet site to find an up-to-date activity for Chapter 4 of *Weather and Climate.*

ACTIVITY	Time (minutes)	Materials *Quantities for one work group*	Skills
Section 1			
Discover, p. 112	15	**Consumable** cash register or adding machine paper, clear tape, empty toilet paper roll **Nonconsumable** globe, pencil, flashlight, metric ruler	Observing
Sharpen Your Skills, p. 115	10	No special materials required.	Inferring
Skills Lab, pp. 120–121	40	**Consumable** black construction paper, clear tape, graph paper **Nonconsumable** scissors, ruler, 3 thermometers, protractor, books, 100-W incandescent lamp, watch or clock, pencil	Controlling Variables, Collecting Data, Graphing, Inferring
Section 2			
Discover, p. 122	15	**Consumable** newspapers or magazines **Nonconsumable** scissors	Forming Operational Definitions
Try This, p. 127	10, 5	**Consumable** water, clear plastic wrap **Nonconsumable** 2 small plastic bowls, 2 rubber bands	Inferring
Sharpen Your Skills, p. 129	10	No special materials required.	Classifying
Science at Home, p. 131	home	No special materials required.	Classifying
Real-World Lab, pp. 132–133	40	**Consumable** 3 pieces of graph paper **Nonconsumable** calculator, ruler, black pencil, blue pencil, red pencil, green pencil, climate map on pages 124–125, U.S. map with city names and latitude lines	Graphing, Interpreting Data, Drawing Conclusions
Section 3			
Discover, p. 134	10	**Nonconsumable** Figure 16 on page 135, magnifying lens	Inferring
Section 4			
Discover, p. 139	15, 5	**Consumable** 2 pieces of black construction paper, 2 shoe boxes, clear plastic wrap, masking tape **Nonconsumable** 2 thermometers, lamp	Inferring
Try This, p. 141	15	**Consumable** ultraviolet-sensitive paper, 3 plastic sandwich bags, 2 sunscreens with different SPF numbers **Nonconsumable** black marking pen	Drawing Conclusions
Science at Home, p. 142	home	**Nonconsumable** calculator	Comparing and Contrasting

A list of all materials required for the Student Edition activities can be found on pages T14–T15. You can order Materials Kits by calling 1-800-828-7777 or by accessing the Science Explorer Internet site at **www.science-explorer.phschool.com.**

CHAPTER 4

Climate and Climate Change

WHAT'S AHEAD

SECTION 1 What Causes Climate?
- Discover **How Does Earth's Shape Affect Climate Zones?**
- Skills Lab **Sunny Rays and Angles**
- Sharpen Your Skills **Inferring**

SECTION 2 Climate Regions
- Discover **What Are Different Climate Types?**
- Try This **Modeling a Humid Climate**
- Sharpen Your Skills **Classifying**
- Real-World Lab **Cool Climate Graphs**

SECTION 3 Long-Term Changes in Climate
- Discover **What Story Can Tree Rings Tell?**

110 ◆ I

CHAPTER PROJECT 4 Investigating Microclimates

All students notice daily weather conditions, but many are not aware that these daily patterns determine the climate in which they live. Even more subtle are the various microclimates located in an area. These microclimates support different organisms based on slightly different daily weather conditions.

Purpose In this project, students will gather weather data and observe the organisms living in three different areas to determine their microclimates. In doing so, they will be able to conclude that climates in very small areas can be different from each other, even though these areas are located near each other.

Skills Focus After completing the Chapter 4 Project, students will be able to
- ◆ develop hypotheses about how microclimates in three areas will differ;
- ◆ create data tables for weather data and environmental factors;
- ◆ graph weather data and analyze the data for patterns;
- ◆ relate each microclimate to the plants and animals found there;
- ◆ communicate the project results in a class presentation.

Project Time Line The entire project will require about three weeks. Begin by distributing Chapter 4 Project Student Materials and Scoring Rubric on pages 96–100 in Teaching Resources. See Chapter 4 Project Teacher Notes on pages 94–95 in Teaching Resources for more information.

Divide the class into groups and allow time for them to choose their three microclimates. For convenience, these areas should be relatively close to the school. Make sure each group chooses areas that have different environmental conditions.

At this point, students can use Worksheet 1 to help them organize their group logbook. Review how to use various weather instruments, if necessary. Students can use Worksheet 2 to practice analyzing weather data. Then students will be ready to gather data in each area for two weeks. Students should collect data from the same location at the same time each day for consistent results. Students will also need time to prepare graphs for their class presentations.

Suggested Shortcuts You can simplify this project by asking each student group to collect data from only one microclimate. The entire class can compare and contrast the data collected by each group. Students could also collect data for only one week instead of two.

Possible Materials Students will need instruments that measure weather data such as thermometers, anemometers, wind vanes, wet and dry bulb thermometers, rain gauges, and light meters. If you don't have class sets of these instruments, schedule their use for each group throughout the day, or students can use the weather instruments they have made for activities in Chapter 2. Students will also need hand lenses to observe organisms and field guides to identify them, a logbook, and graph paper.

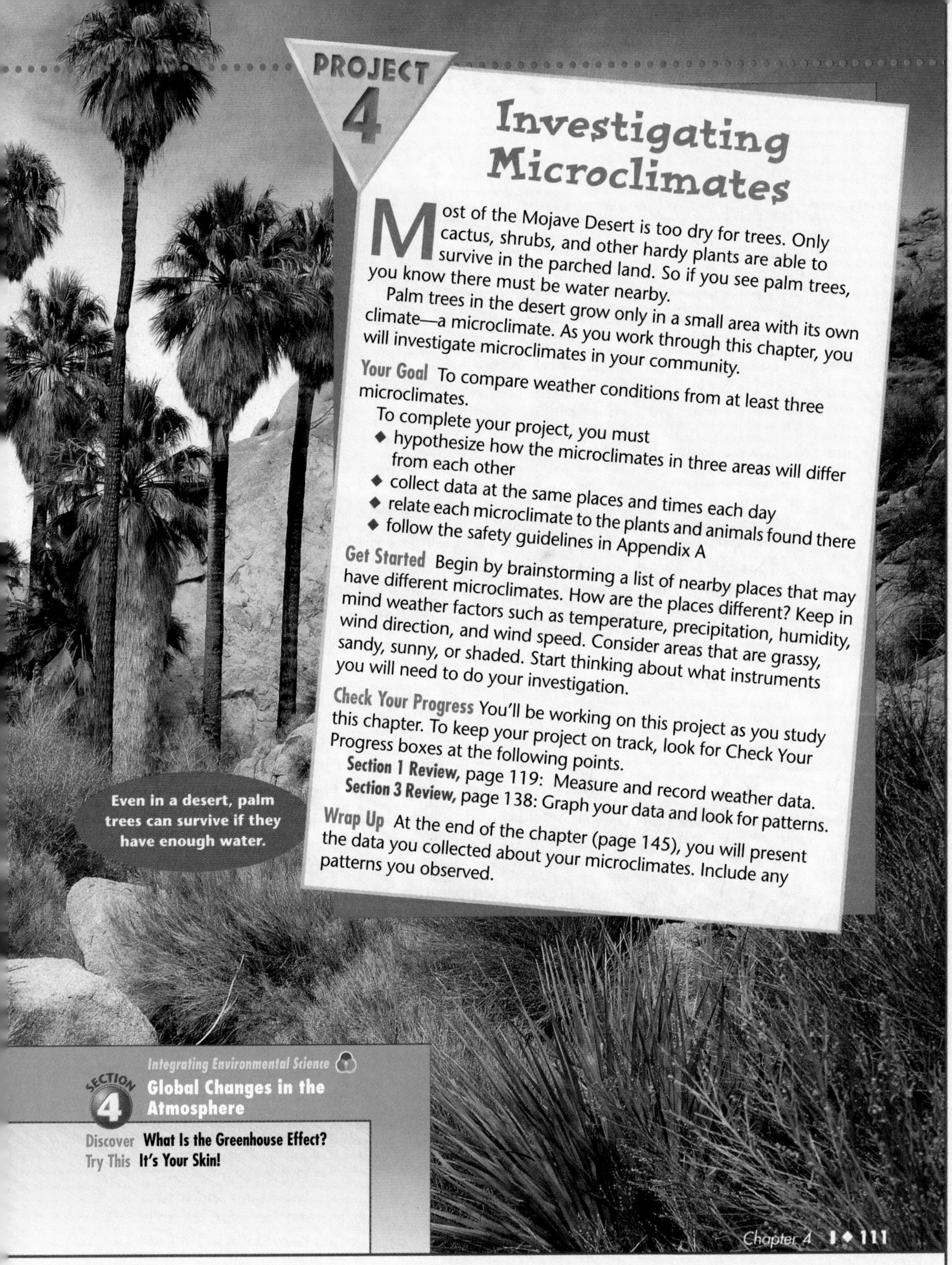

PROJECT 4

Investigating Microclimates

Most of the Mojave Desert is too dry for trees. Only cactus, shrubs, and other hardy plants are able to survive in the parched land. So if you see palm trees, you know there must be water nearby.

Palm trees in the desert grow only in a small area with its own climate—a microclimate. As you work through this chapter, you will investigate microclimates in your community.

Your Goal To compare weather conditions from at least three microclimates.

To complete your project, you must
- hypothesize how the microclimates in three areas will differ from each other
- collect data at the same places and times each day
- relate each microclimate to the plants and animals found there
- follow the safety guidelines in Appendix A

Get Started Begin by brainstorming a list of nearby places that may have different microclimates. How are the places different? Keep in mind weather factors such as temperature, precipitation, humidity, wind direction, and wind speed. Consider areas that are grassy, sandy, sunny, or shaded. Start thinking about what instruments you will need to do your investigation.

Check Your Progress You'll be working on this project as you study this chapter. To keep your project on track, look for Check Your Progress boxes at the following points.

Section 1 Review, page 119: Measure and record weather data.
Section 3 Review, page 138: Graph your data and look for patterns.

Wrap Up At the end of the chapter (page 145), you will present the data you collected about your microclimates. Include any patterns you observed.

Even in a desert, palm trees can survive if they have enough water.

Integrating Environmental Science

SECTION 4 **Global Changes in the Atmosphere**

Discover **What Is the Greenhouse Effect?**
Try This **It's Your Skin!**

Program Resources

- **Teaching Resources** Chapter 4 Project Teacher Notes, pp. 94–95; Chapter 4 Project Overview and Worksheets, pp. 96–99; Chapter 4 Project Scoring Rubric, p. 100

Launching the Project To introduce this project, take the class on a walk around the school grounds or neighborhood. Call students' attention to the plants and animals found in specific places. Focus on the environmental conditions these organisms need to survive. For example, moss grows only in moist areas. Encourage students to offer comments and to ask questions about the organisms and the environmental conditions that they observe.

Give students time to read the description of the Chapter 4 Project in their text and in the Chapter 4 Project Overview on pages 96–97 in Teaching Resources. Encourage students to begin thinking of nearby places with different microclimates and the conditions that make each place different.

Performance Assessment

The Chapter 4 Project Scoring Rubric on page 100 of Teaching Resources will help you evaluate how well students complete the Chapter 4 Project. Students will be assessed on
- how completely and accurately they collect data from their microclimate areas,
- how neat, thorough, and accurate their logbooks are,
- how thorough and interesting their class presentations are,
- how well they worked together in their groups.

By sharing the Chapter 4 Project Scoring Rubric with students at the beginning of the project, you will make it clear to them what they are expected to do.

SECTION 1 What Causes Climate?

Objectives

After completing the lesson, students will be able to
- ◆ identify the factors that influence temperature and precipitation;
- ◆ explain what causes the seasons.

Key Terms climate, tropical zone, polar zone, temperate zone, marine climate, continental climate, windward, leeward, microclimate

1 Engage/Explore

Activating Prior Knowledge

Ask students: **What is the weather like today?** Then ask: **Is today's weather typical of the weather we usually have at this time of year?** *(Accept all answers without comment.)* Explain that the average, year-after-year weather conditions is climate.

DISCOVER ACTIVITY

Skills Focus observing
Materials *globe, cash register or adding machine paper, clear tape, pencil, flashlight, empty toilet paper roll, metric ruler*
Time 15 minutes
Advance Preparation Cut the cash register paper into lengths that are slightly longer than the distance between the equator and the North Pole on the globe.
Tips Have students label the paper before they tape it to the globe. One student should hold the flashlight the same distance from the globe, but move it up in a straight line perpendicular to the globe for each drawing.
Expected Outcome The shapes will change from a perfect circle at the equator to an elongated oval at the North Pole.
Think It Over The shape is a perfect circle at the equator, an oval at the mid-latitudes, and an elongated, faded oval at the poles. The sun's rays heat Earth unevenly because the light rays from the sun hit Earth's surface at different angles.

SECTION 1 What Causes Climate?

DISCOVER ACTIVITY

How Does Earth's Shape Affect Climate Zones?

1. On a globe, tape a strip of cash register paper from the equator to the North Pole. Divide the tape into three equal parts. Label the section near the North Pole *poles,* the section near the equator *equator,* and the middle section *mid-latitudes.*
2. Tape the end of an empty toilet paper roll to the end of a flashlight. Hold the flashlight about 30 cm from the equator. Turn on the flashlight to represent the sun. On the paper strip, have a partner draw the shape of the area the light shines on.
3. Move the flashlight up slightly to aim at the section of the paper marked "mid-latitudes." Keep the flashlight horizontal and at the same distance from the globe. Again have a partner draw the shape of the area that the light shines on.

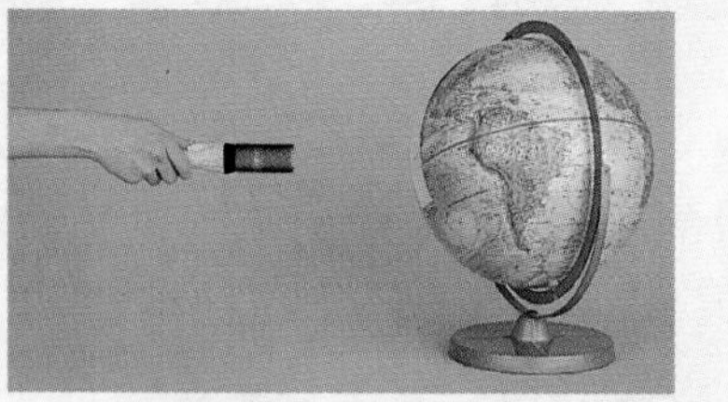

4. Move the flashlight up again to shine on the section of the paper marked "poles." Keep the flashlight horizontal and at the same distance from the globe. Draw the shape of the area that the light shines on.

Think It Over
Observing How does the shape of the area that is illuminated change? Do you think the sun's rays heat Earth's surface evenly?

GUIDE FOR READING

- ◆ **What are the factors that influence temperature and precipitation?**
- ◆ **What causes the seasons?**

Reading Tip **As you read, use the headings to make an outline of the factors that affect climate.**

If you telephone a friend in another state and ask, "What's the weather there today?" she might answer: "It's gray, cool, and rainy. It's usually like that this time of year." Your friend has told you something about both weather and climate.

Weather is day-to-day events. The weather may be cloudy and rainy one day and clear and sunny the next. Weather refers to the condition of the atmosphere at a particular place and time. **Climate,** on the other hand, refers to the average, year-after-year conditions of temperature, precipitation, winds, and clouds in an area. How would you describe the climate where you live?

Two main factors—temperature and precipitation—determine the climate of a region. A climate region is a large area with similar climate conditions throughout. For example, the climate in the southeastern United States is humid, with moderate temperatures.

◀ **These polar bears—two males and their mother—are taking it easy in the polar zone.**

READING STRATEGIES

Reading Tip Suggest to students that they skim the section first before making their outlines. Students should use the section title as the title for their outlines. They should use the main heads of the section as the main headings in their outlines and the section subheads as the subheadings. Students can fill in details under outline headings as they read the section. Students can use their outlines as study aids.

Vocabulary To help students remember the meanings of the terms *windward* and *leeward,* explain that *lee* means "shelter," and *leeward* refers to the side of the mountain that is sheltered from the wind. *Windward* refers to the side of the mountain that is hit by the wind. Students can diagram a mountain showing the wind direction and the windward and leeward sides.

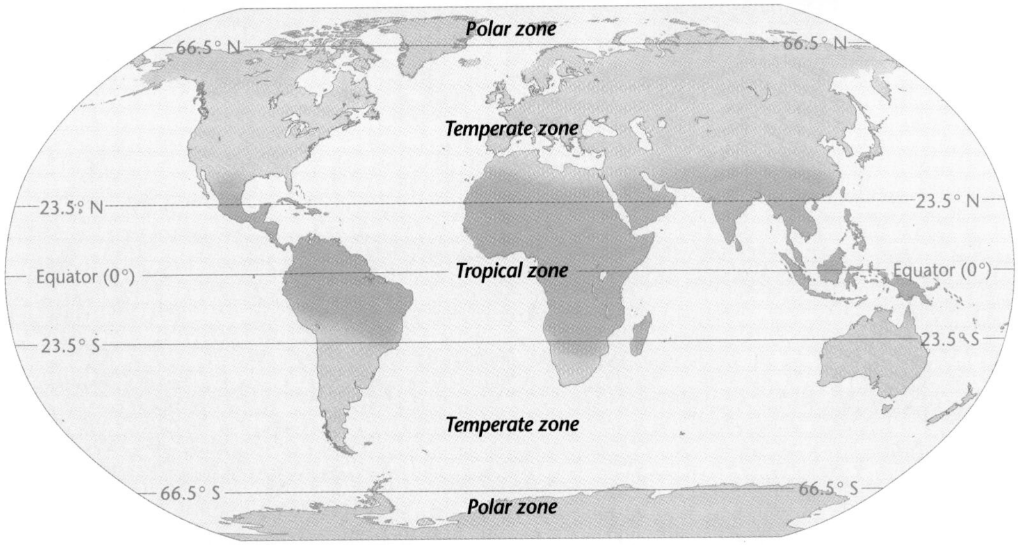

Figure 1 Earth has three main temperature zones. *Interpreting Maps In which temperature zone is most of the United States located?*

Factors Affecting Temperature

Tropical countries, such as Panama, are usually hot. Northern countries, such as Finland, are usually cold. Why are some places warm and others cold? **The main factors that influence temperature are latitude, altitude, distance from large bodies of water, and ocean currents.**

Latitude In general, climates of locations farther from the equator are cooler than climates of areas closer to the equator. Why is this? As you found out if you tried the Discover activity, the sun's rays hit Earth's surface most directly at the equator. At the poles, the same amount of solar radiation is spread out over a larger area, and therefore brings less warmth.

Recall that latitude is the distance from the equator, measured in degrees. Based on latitude, Earth's surface can be divided into the three temperature zones shown in Figure 1. The **tropical zone** is the area near the equator, between about 23.5° north latitude and 23.5° south latitude. The tropical zone receives direct or nearly direct sunlight all year round, making climates there warm.

In contrast, the sun's rays always strike at a lower angle near the North and South poles. As a result, the areas near both poles have cold climates. These **polar zones** extend from about 66.5° to 90° north and 66.5° to 90° south latitudes.

The **temperate zones** are between the tropical and the polar zones—from about 23.5° to 66.5° north and 23.5° to 66.5° south latitudes. In summer, the sun's rays strike the temperate zones more directly. In winter, the sun's rays strike at a lower angle. As a result, the weather in the temperate zones ranges from warm or hot in summer to cool or cold in winter.

2 Facilitate

Factors Affecting Temperature

Using the Visuals: Figure 1

Review latitude with students. Ask: **What does latitude measure?** *(The distance from the equator)* Instruct students to find the equator in Figure 1. Then ask: **At what degree of latitude is the North Pole?** *(90° north latitude)* Draw a circle on the board and show students that 360° is a full circle and 180° is a half circle. Ask: **How many degrees are equal to one-fourth of a circle?** *(90°)* Relate these measurements of a circle to degrees of latitude. **learning modality: logical/ mathematical**

Cultural Diversity

Students can learn how climate affects the culture of a group of people by comparing and contrasting types of clothing, housing, and customs of people living in different temperature zones. Encourage groups of students to choose a group of people to study. Groups may choose native cultures or modern cultures from around the world or from different areas of the United States. Monitor the groups' choices so that each is studying a different culture. Groups should divide the research tasks and the preparation for a class presentation. Challenge students to find creative ways to present the culture of the people they studied. **cooperative learning**

Media and Technology

Audiotapes English-Spanish Summary 4-1

Exploring Earth Science Videodisc Unit 1, Side 1, "Sunny Days"
Chapter 6

Answers to Self-Assessment

Caption Question

Figure 1 the temperate zone

Program Resources

◆ **Teaching Resources** 4-1 Lesson Plan, p. 101; 4-1 Section Summary, p. 102

Ongoing Assessment

Drawing Instruct students to make a diagram that shows the different angles at which the sun's rays strike Earth in each temperature zone.

Portfolio Students can save their diagrams in their portfolios.

Factors Affecting Temperature, continued

Demonstration

Materials *small black mat, desk lamp with high intensity bulb, 2 thermometers, 2 ring stands with clamps for thermometers*
Time 15–20 minutes

ACTIVITY

To demonstrate why air temperature is colder at higher altitudes, shine the light directly on the black mat for 10 minutes. During this time, set up the ring stands so that one holds the bulb of one thermometer 5 cm above the mat and the other holds the thermometer 20 cm above the mat. When you turn out the light, place the thermometers over the black mat. Read the thermometers right away, then every minute until the temperature stops rising. Encourage students to infer why the lower thermometer had a higher temperature reading than the higher thermometer. *(The black mat absorbed the light energy from the light as heat, then radiated the heat into the air above it.)*
learning modality: visual

Inquiry Challenge

ACTIVITY

With the knowledge that large bodies of water greatly moderate the temperatures of nearby land, challenge small groups of students to devise a plan that would help them cool off on a hot summer day. After checking each group's plan, help them gather the materials they will need to implement it. *(One possible plan: set up a fan so that it blows across ice water.)*
cooperative learning

Figure 2 Mount Kilimanjaro in Tanzania, Africa, is near the equator. *Applying Concepts Why is there snow on top of the mountain?*

Altitude The peak of Mount Kilimanjaro towers high above the African plains. At nearly 6 kilometers above sea level, Kilimanjaro is covered in snow all year round. Yet it is located near the equator, at 3° south latitude. Why is Mount Kilimanjaro so cold?

In the case of high mountains, altitude is a more important climate factor than latitude. Recall from Chapter 1 that the temperature of the troposphere decreases about 6.5 Celsius degrees for every 1-kilometer increase in altitude. As a result, highland areas everywhere have cool climates, no matter what their latitude. At nearly 6 kilometers, the air at the top of Mount Kilimanjaro is about 39 Celsius degrees colder than the air at sea level at the same latitude.

Distance From Large Bodies of Water Oceans or large lakes can also affect temperatures. Oceans greatly moderate, or make less extreme, the temperatures of nearby land. Water heats up more slowly than land; it also cools down more slowly. Therefore, winds from the ocean keep coastal regions from reaching extremes of hot and cold. Much of the west coasts of North America, South America, and Europe have mild **marine climates,** with relatively warm winters and cool summers.

The centers of North America and Asia are too far inland to be warmed or cooled by the oceans. Most of Canada and Russia, as well as the central United States, have **continental climates.** Continental climates have more extreme temperatures than marine climates. Winters are cold, while summers are warm or hot.

Background

Facts and Figures Like altitude, large bodies of water and ocean currents can be as important in influencing the temperature of a location as latitude. For example, Bergen, Norway, is a coastal city located over 2,000 km north of Omaha, Nebraska. Based only on latitude, one would assume that Bergen would have a colder climate. However, the average January temperature in Bergen is higher than that of Omaha, and on average, Bergen is cooler than Omaha in July.

The seasonal temperatures in Bergen are directly influenced by its proximity to the ocean and the North Atlantic drift. The ocean acts as a huge reservoir of heat energy due to its great depth and volume, and its ability to absorb large amounts of solar radiation.

Ocean Currents Many marine climates are influenced by ocean currents, streams of water within the oceans that move in regular patterns. In general, warm ocean currents carry warm water from the tropics toward the poles. Cold currents bring cold water from the polar zones toward the equator. The surface of the water warms or cools the air above it. The warmed or cooled air then moves over the nearby land. So a warm current brings warm air to the land it touches. A cold current brings cool air.

As you read about the following currents, trace their paths on the map in Figure 3. The best-known warm-water current is the Gulf Stream. The Gulf Stream begins in the Gulf of Mexico, then flows north along the east coast of the United States. When it crosses the North Atlantic, it becomes the North Atlantic Drift. This warm current gives Ireland and southern England a mild, wet climate despite their relatively high latitude.

In contrast, the cool California Current flows from Alaska southward down the West Coast. The California Current makes climates of places along the West Coast cooler than you would expect at their latitudes.

☑ *Checkpoint* ***What effect do oceans have on the temperatures of nearby land areas?***

Sharpen your Skills

Inferring

ACTIVITY

Look at the currents in the South Pacific, South Atlantic, and Indian oceans. What pattern can you observe? Now compare currents in the South Atlantic to those in the North Atlantic. What might be responsible for differences in the current patterns?

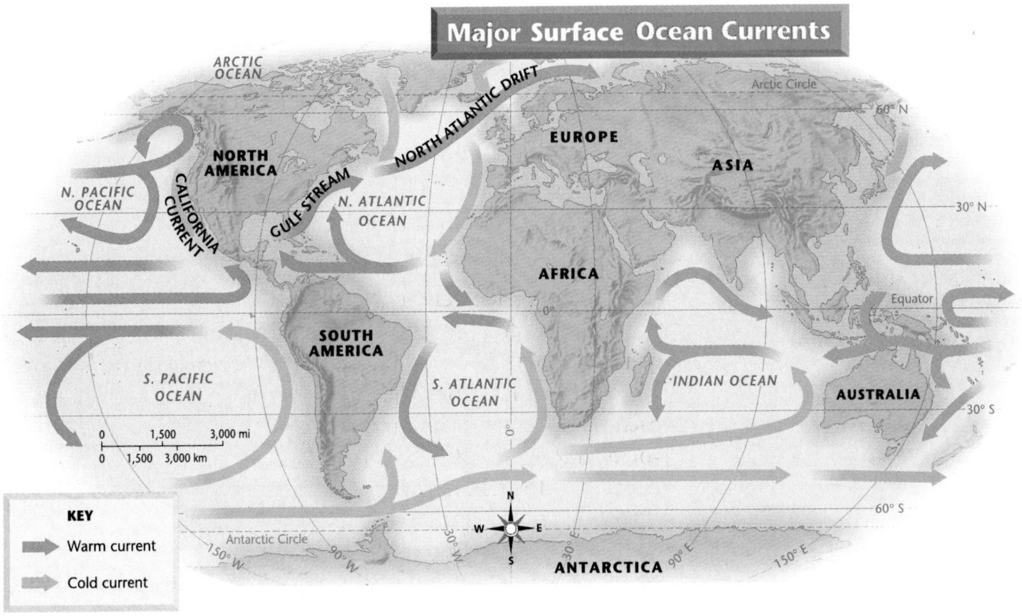

Figure 3 On this map, warm currents are shown in red and cold currents in blue.

Program Resources

Science Explorer Series *Earth's Waters,* Chapter 4, has more information about ocean currents and climate.

Answers to Self-Assessment

Caption Question

Figure 2 The top of the mountain is at a higher altitude, so the air there is much cooler than the air at the bottom.

☑ *Checkpoint*

The surface of the water warms or cools the air above it. The warmed or cooled air then moves over nearby land, affecting the temperatures there.

Building Inquiry Skills: Observing

ACTIVITY

Materials *heat-resistant pan, water, ice, bricks, bunsen burner or candle, food coloring*
Time 15 minutes

Have students observe how differences in water temperature cause currents. First, they should fill a shallow pan with water and place ice cubes in the center of the pan. Then they should elevate the pan with bricks so that a bunsen burner or candle will fit under the pan. They should heat one side of the pan and place a few drops of food coloring in the water. Students should observe the movement of the colored water in the pan. Ask: **What is causing the water to move?** *(As the water warms, it becomes less dense and rises. The cold water, which is denser, sinks and pushes the warmer water out of the way.)* Encourage students to relate their observations to the movement of ocean currents. **learning modality: kinesthetic**

Sharpen your Skills

Inferring

ACTIVITY

Time 10 minutes

Students should observe that the currents in the South Pacific, South Atlantic, and Indian oceans move south toward Antarctica. Students should infer that movement of cold water from the poles toward the equator pushes warm water at the equator toward the poles. The direction of the wind and the location of land also affect the direction of currents.

Extend El Niño is an ocean current located off the coast of Peru that forms when winds blowing off the coast of South America weaken, allowing warm water from the western Pacific Ocean to flow eastward. Challenge students to trace the changes in Figure 3 when an El Niño occurs. **learning modality:**

Ongoing Assessment

Writing Instruct students to write a description of how the temperature of a climate is affected by altitude, distance from large bodies of water, and ocean currents.

Factors Affecting Precipitation

Including All Students

Materials *2 sponges, water*
Time 10 minutes

ACTIVITY

Students can use sponges to model prevailing winds that blow inland from oceans and those that blow from over land. Allow students to completely saturate a sponge with water. Have them describe what type of prevailing wind it represents. *(Humid wind blowing inland from an ocean)* Then instruct them to compare the saturated sponge with a dry sponge. Ask: **Which sponge can absorb more water?** *(the dry sponge)* **Which sponge represents wind blowing from over land?** *(the dry sponge)* **Which sponge represents the kind of wind that blows over the Sahara?** *(the dry sponge)* **learning modality: kinesthetic**

Building Inquiry Skills: Inferring

Materials *physical map of the United States, map of global wind patterns*
Time 20 minutes

ACTIVITY

Challenge students to work together in small groups to make inferences about the amount of precipitation in different regions of the United States. Groups can compare wind patterns with topography. Invite groups to share their inferences with the rest of the class. You might wish to record each group's inferences and revisit them as you study climate regions in the next section. Help students determine why they might have inferred incorrectly. **cooperative learning**

Factors Affecting Precipitation

The amount of rain and snow that falls in an area each year determines how wet or dry its climate is. But what determines how much precipitation an area gets? **The main factors that affect precipitation are prevailing winds and the presence of mountains.**

Prevailing Winds As you know, weather patterns depend on the movement of huge air masses. Air masses are moved from place to place by prevailing winds, the directional winds that usually blow in a region. Air masses can be warm or cool, dry or humid. The amount of water vapor in the air mass influences how much rain or snow will fall.

Warm air can carry more water vapor than cold air can. When warm air rises and cools, water comes out of the air as precipitation. For example, surface air near the equator is generally hot and humid. As the air rises and cools, heavy rains fall, nourishing thick tropical forests. In contrast, sinking cold air is usually dry. Because the air becomes warmer as it sinks, it can hold more water vapor. The water vapor stays in the air and little or no rain falls. The result may be a desert.

The amount of water vapor in prevailing winds also depends on where the winds come from. Winds that blow inland from oceans carry more water vapor than winds that blow from over land. For example, the Sahara in Africa is near both the Atlantic Ocean and the Mediterranean Sea. Yet the Sahara is very dry. This is because few winds blow from the oceans toward this area. Instead, the prevailing winds are the dry northeast trade winds. The source of these winds is cool, sinking air from southwest Asia.

Figure 4 The prevailing winds that blow across the Sahara begin far inland. Since the air is dry, the Sahara gets very little rain.

Background

Facts and Figures The dry prevailing winds that blow across the Sahara absorb any water that is present on land, rather than bring rain. Because of this, these winds are sometimes called evaporating winds.

An evaporating wind in northwestern United States, called a chinook, is a westerly wind that blows down the eastern slope of the Rocky Mountains. This wind is made up of warm Pacific air that has lost its water vapor on the western slope of the Rockies. It is so warm and dry that it melts snow in the valleys during winter.

Mountain Ranges A mountain range in the path of prevailing winds can also influence where precipitation falls. As you have learned, when humid winds blow from the ocean toward coastal mountains, they are forced to rise up to pass over the mountains. The rising warm air cools and its water vapor condenses, forming clouds. Rain or snow falls on the **windward** side of the mountains, the side the oncoming wind hits.

By the time the air reaches the other side of the mountains, it has lost much of its water vapor, so it is cool and dry. The land on the **leeward** side of the mountains—downwind—is in a rain shadow.

The Owens Valley in California, shown in Figure 5, is in the rain shadow of the Sierra Nevada, about 80 kilometers west of Death Valley. Humid winds blow eastward from the Pacific Ocean. In the photo, you can see that this humid air has left snow on top of the mountains. Then the air flowed down the leeward side of the mountains. As it moved downward, the air became warmer. The desert in the Owens Valley, on the eastern side of the Sierra Nevada, was formed by this hot, dry air.

☑ *Checkpoint* *Why does precipitation fall mainly on the windward sides of mountains?*

Figure 5 The Sierra Nevada runs through eastern California, parallel to the Pacific coast. To the east of the Sierras is the Owens Valley, shown above. *Inferring Is the Owens Valley on the windward or leeward side of the mountains?*

Microclimates

Have you ever noticed that it is cooler and more humid in a grove of trees than in an open field? The same factors that affect large climate regions also affect smaller areas. A small area with specific climate conditions may have its own **microclimate.** Inland mountains, lakes, forests, and other natural features can influence climate nearby, resulting in a microclimate.

You might find a microclimate in a downtown area with clusters of tall buildings, or on a windy peninsula jutting out into the ocean. Even a small park, if it is usually sunnier or windier than nearby areas, may have its own microclimate. The grass on a lawn can be covered in dew and produce conditions like a rain forest, while the pavement in the parking lot is dry, like a desert.

Including All Students

ACTIVITY

Allow students to make shadows on the wall with a flashlight in the darkened classroom or outside on a sunny day. Then ask: **What is a shadow?** *(An area that doesn't receive light because something is blocking the light)* Relate this idea to a rain shadow by explaining that a rain shadow is an area that doesn't receive rain because a mountain range is blocking the rain. Ask: **Which side of a mountain is in a rain shadow?** *(the leeward side)* **limited English proficiency**

Microclimates

Real-Life Learning

Challenge students to identify the locations of microclimates around the school grounds. Lead them to identify microclimates as small as the north side of the school building compared to the south side. They should compare the climates of the microclimates they identify. Ask: **What climate factors cause the microclimates to exist?** *(Students should explain how the amount of precipitation and the temperature are affected in the microclimates.)* **learning modality: logical/mathematical**

Program Resources

Science Explorer Series *Earth's Waters,* Chapter 1, has more information about the water cycle.

Answers to Self-Assessment

Caption Question

Figure 5 the leeward side

☑ *Checkpoint*

Winds are forced to rise up and over mountains. As the air rises it cools, and the water vapor condenses and falls as rain or snow. When the air drops down the leeward side, it's dry because it lost most of its water vapor.

Ongoing Assessment

Oral Presentation Have several students describe the factors that affect the amount of precipitation in an area, and challenge others to relate temperature and precipitation to microclimates.

The Seasons

Integrating Space Science

Draw on the chalkboard Earth's orbit around the sun. Draw Earth so that its poles are perpendicular to its orbit. Ask students: **How long does it take Earth to revolve around the sun?** *(365 days, or one year)* Remind students that Earth spins on its axis, or rotates, once every 24 hours. Explain that the hours of daylight would equal the hours of nighttime if Earth had a straight axis. Then draw Earth with a tilted axis. Ask: **How does the tilted axis affect the length of day and night on Earth?** *(The tilt causes the length of day and night to be different, depending on where Earth is in its orbit.)* **How does the tilted axis affect how the sun's rays strike different parts of Earth?** *(The tilt causes the sun's rays to strike one hemisphere more directly at the equator than the other at different times of the year.)* **learning modality: visual**

Math TOOLBOX

Time 10 minutes
Tips Have students set up the fraction by writing 23.5/90. When students divide the numbers, they should find that Earth's tilt is about 0.26, or just over one quarter, of a right angle. **learning modality: logical/mathematical**

EXPLORING the Seasons

Materials *flashlight, balloon, marker*
Time 10 minutes

ACTIVITY

Challenge students to use a flashlight and a balloon to observe the effect of Earth's tilted axis on the seasons. One student should hold a round balloon at a tilt similar to Earth's axis while another student shines a flashlight on it. A third student can use a permanent marker to outline the darkened area of the balloon and label the dark side, the light side, the North Pole, the South Pole, and the equator. Then have students compare their balloons to the diagram in *Exploring the Seasons.* **learning modality: kinesthetic**

Math TOOLBOX

Angles

Light from the sun strikes Earth's surface at different angles. An angle is made up of two lines that meet at a point. Angles are measured in degrees. A full circle has 360 degrees.

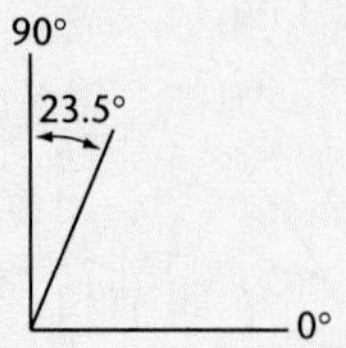

When the sun is directly overhead near the equator, it is at an angle of 90° to Earth's surface. A 90° angle is called a right angle. It is one fourth of a circle.

When the sun is near the horizon, it is at an angle of close to 0° to Earth's surface.

Earth's axis is tilted at an angle of 23.5°. About what fraction of a right angle is this?

The Seasons

INTEGRATING SPACE SCIENCE Although you can describe the average weather conditions of a climate region, these conditions are not constant all year long. Instead, most places on Earth outside the tropics have four seasons: winter, spring, summer, and autumn.

You might think that Earth is closer to the sun during the summer and farther away during winter. If this were true, every place on Earth would have summer at the same time. Actually, when it is summer in the Northern Hemisphere it is winter in the Southern Hemisphere. So the seasons are *not* a result of changes in the distance between Earth and the sun.

Tilted Axis *Exploring the Seasons* on page 119 shows how Earth's axis is tilted in relation to the sun. **The seasons are caused by the tilt of Earth's axis as Earth travels around the sun.** The axis is an imaginary line through Earth's center that passes through both poles. Earth turns, or rotates, around this axis once each day. Earth's axis is not straight up and down, but is tilted at an angle of 23.5°. The axis always points in the same direction—toward the North Star. As Earth travels around the sun, the north end of the axis is pointed away from the sun for part of the year and toward the sun for part of the year.

Winter or Summer Look at *Exploring the Seasons* on the next page. Which way is the north end of Earth's axis tilted in June? Notice that the Northern Hemisphere receives more direct rays from the sun. Also, in June the days in the Northern Hemisphere are longer than the nights. The combination of more direct rays and longer days makes Earth's surface warmer in the Northern Hemisphere than at any other time of the year. It is summer.

In June, when the north end of Earth's axis is tilted toward the sun, the south end of the axis is tilted away from the sun. The Southern Hemisphere receives fewer direct rays from the sun. The days are shorter than the nights. As a result, the Southern Hemisphere is experiencing winter.

Now look at the situation in December, six months later. Which way is the north end of Earth's axis tilted now? The Northern Hemisphere receives fewer direct rays from the sun and has shorter days. It is winter in the Northern Hemisphere and summer in the Southern Hemisphere.

Twice during the year, in March and September, neither end of Earth's axis is tilted toward the sun. At both of these times, one hemisphere has spring while the other has autumn.

Background

Facts and Figures The equator does not have the same seasonal changes as other latitudes because the length of day at the equator changes very little through the year and the sun's rays always hit the equator almost directly. Because of this, the equator receives about the same amount of energy from the sun all year long. At higher latitudes, the length of day changes because of Earth's tilted axis. This is seen in the extreme at the poles, where six months of continuous daylight are followed by six months of continuous darkness. Even during continuous daylight, temperatures at the poles are very cold because the poles do not receive much of the sun's energy. The sun's energy that reaches the poles is spread over a larger area than at the equator, and much of that sunlight is reflected off the ice and snow near the poles.

EXPLORING the Seasons

The seasons are a result of Earth's tilted axis. The seasons change as the amount of energy each hemisphere receives from the sun changes.

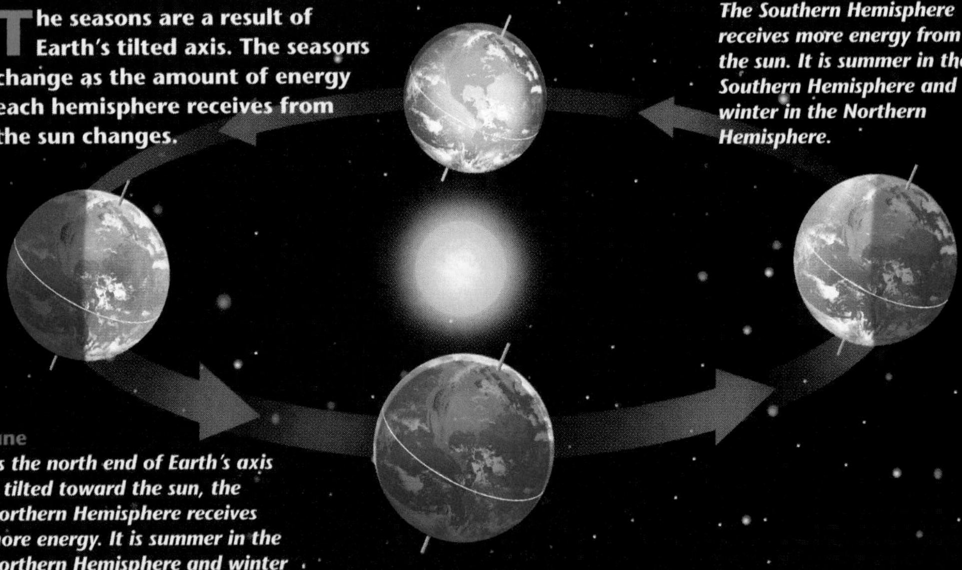

December
The south end of Earth's axis is tilted toward the sun. The Southern Hemisphere receives more energy from the sun. It is summer in the Southern Hemisphere and winter in the Northern Hemisphere.

June
As the north end of Earth's axis is tilted toward the sun, the Northern Hemisphere receives more energy. It is summer in the Northern Hemisphere and winter in the Southern Hemisphere.

March and September
Neither end of Earth's axis is tilted toward the sun. Both hemispheres receive the same amounts of energy.

Section 1 Review

1. Name the four main factors that influence the temperature of an area.
2. How do prevailing winds affect the amount of precipitation an area receives?
3. On which side of mountains—leeward or windward—does precipitation fall?
4. How does the tilt of Earth's axis cause the seasons?
5. **Thinking Critically** **Developing Hypotheses** How might Earth's climates be different if Earth were not tilted on its axis?

Check Your Progress (CHAPTER PROJECT 4)

Have you chosen your microclimate study sites? If your sites are on private property, get permission. Set up a logbook so that you can record your data. How do you think the conditions in these sites will differ? Write down your hypotheses. Now you are ready to measure daily weather conditions for your microclimates. (*Hint:* Be sure to take your measurements at the same time each day.)

Program Resources

◆ **Teaching Resources** 4-1 Review and Reinforce, p. 103; 4-1 Enrich, p. 104

Science Explorer Series *Astronomy,* Chapter 1, gives more information about Earth's position in space.

Media and Technology

Transparencies "The Seasons," Transparency 17

Interactive Student Tutorial CD-ROM I-4

3 Assess

Section 1 Review Answers

1. Latitude, altitude, distance from large bodies of water, and ocean currents
2. Prevailing winds that carry more water vapor will cause more precipitation in an area. Prevailing winds that carry warmer air will also cause more precipitation than winds carrying cooler air.
3. windward
4. As Earth travels around the sun, the north end of the axis points toward the sun for part of the year and away from the sun for part of the year. When the north end points toward the sun, the Northern Hemisphere receives more energy than the Southern Hemisphere receives. The seasons change as the amount of energy each hemisphere receives from the sun changes.
5. There would not be seasons, so there would not be the seasonal changes in the climate that many parts of Earth experience now.

Check Your Progress (CHAPTER PROJECT 4)

Meet with each group and review their chosen study sites. If they have chosen a site located on private property, make sure they have permission from the property owners. Review their logbooks. Find out when they plan to measure the daily weather conditions at their study sites. Remind them to take measurements at the same time each day. Invite students to demonstrate how to operate the weather instruments they plan to use. Correct their techniques if necessary.

Performance Assessment

Drawing Challenge students to draw a diagram or map that shows how the factors that affect climate affect your local climate. Students should include all the factors that affect temperature and precipitation that are appropriate for your area. Students should also diagram why or why not your area has seasons.

Skills Lab

Controlling Variables

Sunny Rays and Angles

Preparing for Inquiry

Key Concept The angle at which the sun's rays hit Earth affects the amount of energy absorbed by Earth's surface.

Skills Objectives Students will be able to

- control variables to determine the effect of the angle of light rays on temperature;
- collect temperature data by reading thermometers;
- graph temperature data that they collected;
- infer which thermometer represents certain regions of Earth's surface.

Time 40 minutes

Alternative Materials If you wish to save time, you can make the construction paper pockets for students ahead of time.

Guided Inquiry

Invitation Remind students of their results from the Discover activity. Ask: **On what part of Earth's surface do the sun's rays hit straight on?** *(at the equator)* **Where do the sun's rays hit Earth at the lowest angle?** *(at the poles)* Challenge students to explain how the angle at which the sun's rays hit Earth affects the temperature of each climate zone.

Introducing the Procedure

- Have students read the entire procedure. Then ask: **What part of the experimental setup represents the sun?** *(the lamp)* **What represents Earth's surface?** *(the paper pockets)*
- Point out in the photo how the books are used to hold the thermometers at a 45° and a 90° angle. Demonstrate how to use the protractor.

Skills Lab

Controlling Variables

Sunny Rays and Angles

In this lab, you will investigate how the angle of the sun's rays affects the amount of energy absorbed by different parts of Earth's surface.

Problem

How does the angle of a light source affect the rate of temperature change of a surface?

Materials

books, graph paper, pencil, scissors, ruler, clear tape, watch or clock, 3 thermometers, protractor, 100-W incandescent lamp, black construction paper

Procedure

1. Cut a strip of black construction paper 5 cm by 10 cm. Fold the paper in half and tape two sides to form a pocket.
2. Repeat Step 1 to make two more pockets.
3. Place the bulb of a thermometer inside each pocket.
4. Place the pockets with thermometers close together, as shown in the photo. Place one thermometer in a vertical position (90° angle), one at a 45° angle, and the third one in a horizontal position (0° angle). Use a protractor to measure the angles. Support the thermometers with books.
5. Position the lamp so that it is 30 cm from each of the thermometer bulbs. Make sure the lamp will not move during the activity.
6. Copy a data table like the one below into your notebook.
7. In your data table, record the temperature on all three thermometers. (All three temperatures should be the same.)
8. Switch on the lamp. In your data table, record the temperature on each thermometer every minute for 15 minutes. **CAUTION:** *Be careful not to touch the hot lampshade.*
9. After 15 minutes, switch off the lamp.

Analyze and Conclude

1. In this experiment, what was the manipulated variable? What was the responding variable? How do you know which is which?
2. Graph your data. Label the horizontal axis and vertical axis of your graph as shown on the sample graph. Use solid, dashed, and dotted lines to show the results from each thermometer, as shown in the key.
3. Based on your data, at which angle did the temperature increase the most?
4. At which angle did the temperature increase the least?

DATA TABLE

	Temperature (°C)		
Time (min.)	0° Angle	45° Angle	90° Angle
Start			
1			
2			
3			
4			
5			

Troubleshooting the Experiment

- Show students one completed thermometer pocket to help them construct the pockets properly.
- Make sure students place all three of the thermometer bulbs near each other so that each one is the same distance from the lamp.
- Remind students to record the temperature from each thermometer before they turn on the lamp.

Expected Outcome

The thermometer at the 0° angle will show the highest increase in temperature. The thermometer at the 90° angle will show the lowest increase in temperature. The thermometer at the 45° angle will show a moderate temperature increase.

5. What part of Earth's surface does each thermometer represent?
6. Why is air at the North Pole still very cold in the summer even though the Northern Hemisphere is tilted toward the sun?
7. **Think About It** In this experiment, what variables were held constant?

Design an Experiment

Design an experiment to find out how the results of this investigation would change if the lamp were placed farther from the thermometers. Then design another experiment to find out what would happen if the lamp were placed closer to the thermometers.

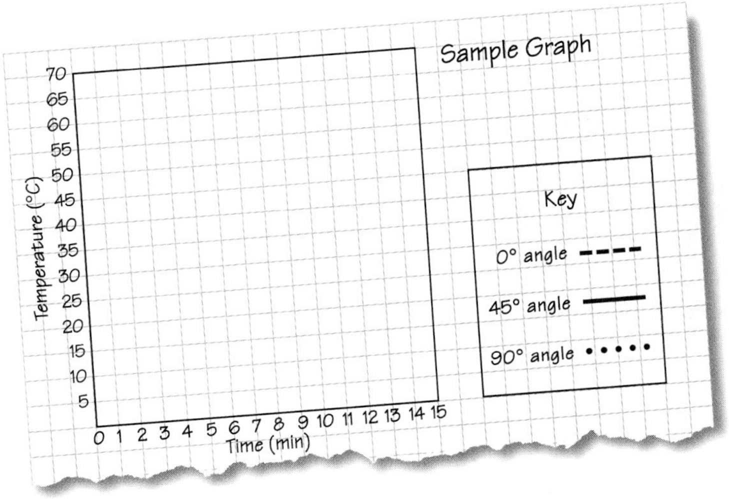

Analyze and Conclude

1. The manipulated variable is the angle of the thermometer. The responding variable is the rate of temperature change. The responding variable is affected by the changes in the manipulated variable.
2. All three lines of the graph should show an increase in temperature over time. However, the line for the thermometer at 0° should show a greater temperature increase than the thermometer at 45°, which should show a greater temperature increase than the thermometer at 90°.
3. at the 0° angle
4. at the 90° angle
5. The thermometer at 0° represents the tropical zone, the thermometer at 45° represents the temperate zone, and the thermometer at 90° represents the polar zone.
6. Because the angle at which the sun's rays strike the North Pole in summer is still very low
7. Variables that were held constant include the thermometers, the heat source, the distance of the heat source from the thermometer bulbs, and the type of heat-absorbing material that enclosed the thermometer bulbs.

Extending the Inquiry

Design an Experiment Students should use the same procedure, except they should change the distances between the thermometers and the lamp.

Program Resources

◆ **Teaching Resources** Skills Lab blackline masters, pp. 117–119

Safety

Caution students to be careful when handling the lamp, because the lightbulb and the lampshade get hot. Review the safety guidelines in Appendix A.

Section 2 Climate Regions

Objectives

After completing the lesson, students will be able to
- ◆ identify factors used to define climates;
- ◆ name the five main climate regions.

Key Terms rain forest, savanna, desert, steppe, humid subtropical, subarctic, tundra, permafrost

1 Engage/Explore

Activating Prior Knowledge

Invite students to describe places to which they have traveled, read about, or seen in movies. Elicit details about the weather and the kinds of plants and animals that live there. Challenge students to compare the climate and the plants and animals of these places and their home. Ask: **What climate factors cause the climate at home to be different from the places you visited or learned about?** *(Any of the climate factors from Section 1 will cause places to have different climates and organisms.)*

Discover Activity

Skills Focus forming operational definitions
Materials *magazines or newspapers, scissors*
Time 15 minutes
Tips To save class time, assign students to collect magazine pictures for homework, or you could provide the pictures. Before students look at the pictures, encourage them to list some characteristics of various climates.
Expected Outcome Students should sort the pictures into categories such as desert, forest, mountain, and prairie. However, students might sort the pictures based on other climate factors.
Think It Over Accept all answers that are based on some logical classification system. Some students might use actual climate names to describe their pictures.

Section 2 Climate Regions

Discover Activity

What Are Different Climate Types?

1. Collect pictures from magazines and newspapers of a variety of land areas around the world.
2. Sort the pictures into categories according to common weather characteristics.

Think It Over
Forming Operational Definitions Choose several words that describe the typical weather for each of your categories. What words would you use to describe the typical weather where you live?

Guide for Reading

- ◆ What factors are used to define climates?
- ◆ What are the five main climate regions?

Reading Tip Before you read, preview *Exploring Climate Regions.* Write a list of any questions you have about climate regions.

When the Spanish settlers came to California in the 1700s, they brought with them plants from home. The padres, or priests, who established missions planted vineyards and orchards. They found that grapes, figs, and olives grew as well in California as they had in Spain. What do Spain and California have in common? They have similar climates.

Classifying Climates

The Spanish padres traveled a long distance but found a familiar climate. Suppose you traveled from your home to a place where the weather, the sunlight, and even the plants and trees were very different from what you are used to. Would you know what caused those differences?

Scientists classify climates according to two major factors: temperature and precipitation. They use a system developed around 1900 by Wladimir Köppen (KEP un). This system identifies broad climate regions, each of which has smaller subdivisions.

There are five main climate regions: tropical rainy, dry, temperate marine, temperate continental, and polar. Note that there is only one category of dry climates, whether hot or cold. These climate regions are shown in *Exploring Climate Regions* on pages 124–125.

◀ Olive trees

Reading Strategies

Reading Tip Encourage students to use what they learned in the first section as a basis for writing questions about climate regions. Some questions that students might ask: **How are climate regions defined?** *(By temperature and precipitation)* **How many climate regions are there?** *(Five in the Köppen system, six including highlands)* **Do certain plants and animals live in certain climate regions?** *(Yes, climate regions have very different plants and animals that are especially adapted to living there.)*

Vocabulary Show students that in the word *permafrost,* the prefix *perma* is short for *permanent.* Explain that permafrost is soil that is permanently frozen.

Exploring Climate Regions also shows a sixth type of climate: highlands. Recall that temperatures are cooler at the tops of mountains than in the surrounding areas. So a highland climate can occur within any of the other zones.

Maps show boundaries between the climate regions. In the real world, of course, no clear boundaries mark where one climate region ends and another begins. Each region blends gradually into the next.

☑ *Checkpoint* *What are the five main climate regions?*

Tropical Rainy Climates

The tropics have two types of rainy climates: tropical wet and tropical wet-and-dry. Trace the equator on *Exploring Climate Regions* with your finger. Tropical wet climates are found in low-lying lands near the equator. If you look north and south of tropical wet climates on the map, you can see two bands of tropical wet-and-dry climates.

Tropical Wet In areas that have a tropical wet climate, many days are rainy, often with afternoon thunderstorms. With year-round heat and heavy rainfall, vegetation grows lush and green. Dense rain forests grow in these rainy climates. **Rain forests** are forests in which plenty of rain falls all year-round. Tall trees such as teak and mahogany form the top layer, or canopy, while smaller bushes and vines grow near the ground. There are also many animals in the rain forest, including colorful parrots and toucans, bats, insects, frogs, and snakes.

In the United States, only the windward sides of the Hawaiian islands have a tropical wet climate. Rainfall is very heavy—over 10 meters per year on the windward side of the Hawaiian island of Kauai. The rain forests in Hawaii have a large variety of plants, including ferns, orchids, and many types of vines and trees.

Figure 6 Lush tropical rain forests grow in the tropical wet climate. *Relating Cause and Effect What climate factors encourage this growth?*

2 Facilitate

Classifying Climates

Addressing Naive Conceptions

Question students to find out what ideas they have about climates in other parts of the world. Ask: **Do you think that other parts of the world have similar climates to areas of the United States?** *(Some students may not think so.)* To make sure students understand that many parts of the world have similar climates, direct them to study the map in *Exploring Climate Regions*. Challenge them to find different countries that share similar climates. Ask: **What factors cause these different regions of the world to have similar climates?** *(These regions share similar factors that affect temperature and precipitation.)* **learning modality: visual**

Tropical Rainy Climates

Using the Visuals: Figure 6

Direct students to study the plants in the photo and ask: **How do you know this photo shows a tropical wet climate?** *(the lush vegetation)* **How would you describe the temperature of this climate region** *(warm all year long)* **The precipitation?** *(a large amount of precipitation)* Challenge students to identify the climate factors that affect precipitation and temperature in a tropical wet climate. *(Low altitude, near the equator, windward side of mountains, warm and moist prevailing winds)* **learning modality: visual**

Program Resources

◆ **Teaching Resources** 4-2 Lesson Plan, p. 105; 4-2 Section Summary, p. 106

Media and Technology

Audiotapes English-Spanish Summary 4-2

Answers to Self-Assessment

☑ *Checkpoint*

Tropical rainy, dry, temperate marine, temperate continental, and polar

Caption Question

Figure 6 Large amounts of rain and warm temperatures

Ongoing Assessment

Writing Instruct students to list the six climate regions. Then have them write a description of a tropical wet climate that includes temperature and precipitation.

Tropical Rainy Climates, continued

EXPLORING

Climate Regions

Instruct student pairs to read aloud the map key and the descriptions of the climate regions to each other. Encourage them to talk about how the climate region definitions on the map are similar to and different from the Köppen system. *(Highland region added and more detailed divisions of the five climate regions)* Then have pairs identify the climate region they live in and the climate region in which their family originated, if they know where. Challenge them to find other places that have the same climates. **learning modality: verbal**

Including All Students

Have students make a flip book of the climate regions using index cards held together with string or a binder ring. This activity will be especially helpful to students with limited English proficiency. Instruct students to write the name of each climate region on one index card. Then have students write a brief description of each region. These descriptions should include precipitation and temperature information. Encourage students with limited English to add illustrations or words from their native language to help them understand the terms. **limited English proficiency**

Portfolio Students can save their flip books in their portfolios.

EXPLORING *Climate Regions*

Climate regions are classified according to a combination of temperature and precipitation. Climates in highland regions change rapidly as altitude changes.

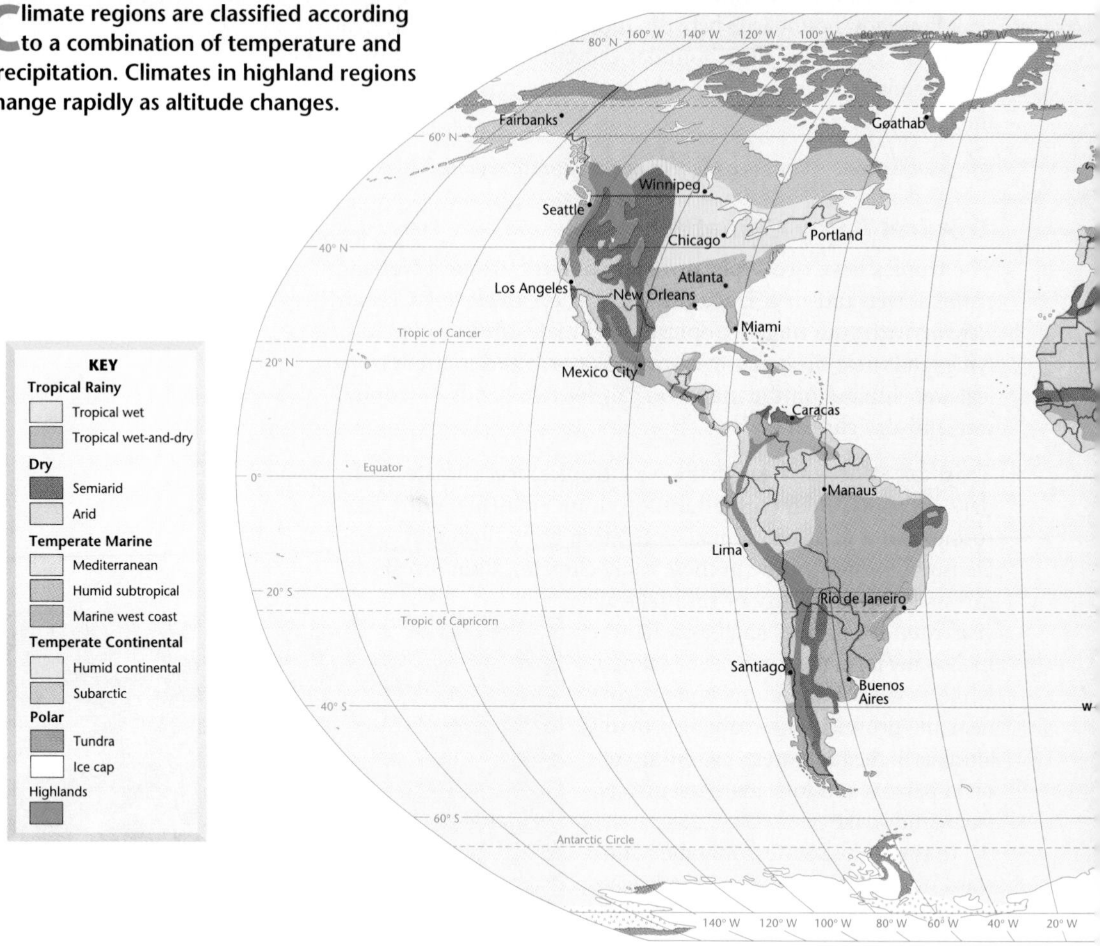

Tropical Rainy
Temperature always 18°C or above.

Tropical wet *Always hot and humid, with heavy rainfall (at least 6 centimeters a month) all year round.*
Tropical wet-and-dry *Always hot, with alternating wet and dry seasons; heavy rainfall in the wet season.*

Dry
Occurs wherever potential evaporation is greater than precipitation. May be hot or cold.

Arid *Desert, with little precipitation, usually less than 25 centimeters a year.*
Semiarid *Dry but receives about 25 to 50 centimeters of precipitation a year.*

Temperate Marine
Average temperature 10°C or above in the warmest month, between –3° and 18°C in the coldest month.

Mediterranean *Warm, dry summers and rainy winters.*
Humid subtropical *Hot summers and cool winters.*
Marine west coast *Mild winters and cool summers, with moderate precipitation year round.*

124 ◆ I

Background

Integrating Science Plant growth is influenced by genetics and the environment. All plants have different requirements for growth, based on their genetic makeup. Environmental requirements include sunlight, climate, and soil condition. Some plants grow best in sun, others in shade. Plants also differ in the amount of light and water they require for growth.

Wladimir Peter Köppen became interested in the influence of climate on plants while he was a student. He recognized that plants required more rainfall at higher temperatures. From these observations of plants and his knowledge as a meteorologist, Köppen introduced a system to classify climates based on rainfall and temperature. He used monthly rainfall amounts and average monthly temperatures to define the five major climate regions.

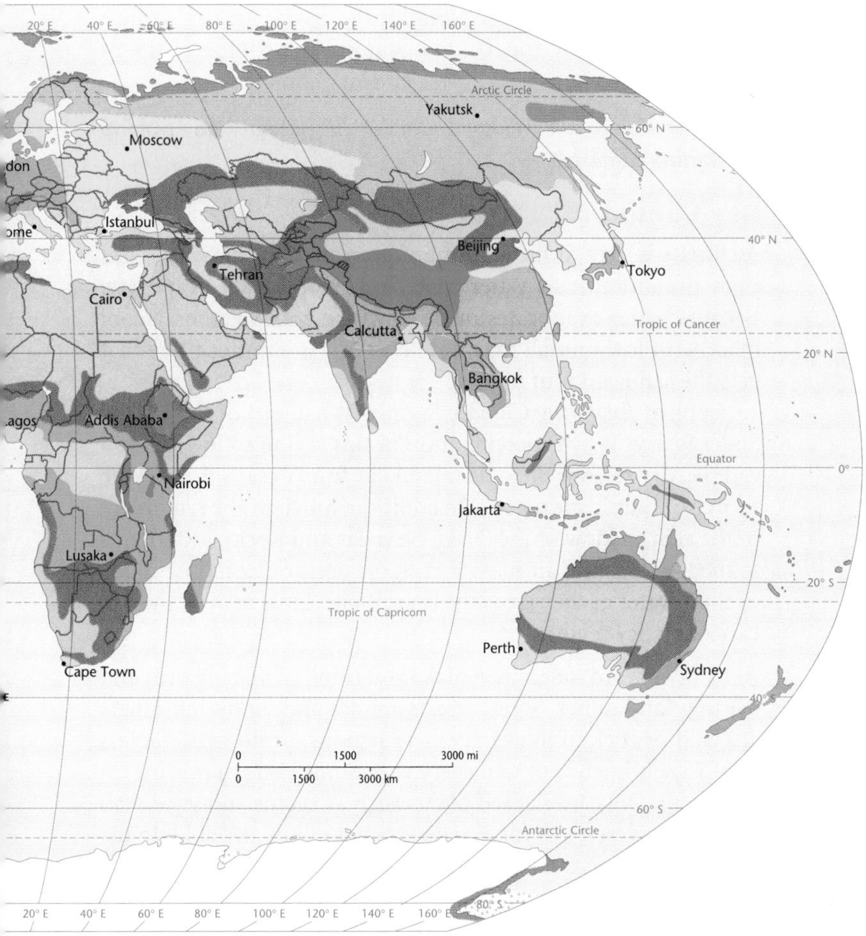

Temperate Continental
Average temperature 10°C or above in the warmest month, –3°C or below in the coldest month.

Humid continental *Hot, humid summers and cold winters, with moderate precipitation year round.*
Subarctic *Short, cool summers and long, cold winters. Light precipitation, mainly in summer.*

Polar
Average temperature below 10°C in the warmest month.

Tundra *Always cold with a short, cool summer—warmest temperature about 10°C.*
Ice cap *Always cold, average temperature at or below 0°C.*

Highlands
Generally cooler and wetter than nearby lowlands, temperature decreasing with altitude.

Real-Life Learning

ACTIVITY

Challenge small student groups to assume the role of a travel agency. Groups should choose one destination and use the climate regions map to identify its climate. Then have groups assemble a travel brochure that describes the destination, its climate, and what travelers would expect to see there. Display actual travel brochures to give students ideas about what to include in their own brochures. Invite groups to share their brochures with the class. You might wish to use the brochures for a bulletin board display. **cooperative learning**

Building Inquiry Skills: Creating Data Tables

As students continue this section, they will learn more about the different climate regions. To help them organize this information, instruct students to create a data table or chart in which they record the characteristics of each climate region. Encourage students to identify climate factors that they will use to organize their tables. Explain that these factors will help them classify each climate region. Students can use the information in *Exploring Climate Regions* to help them organize their tables. **learning modality: logical/mathematical**

Portfolio Students can save their data tables in their portfolios.

Program Resources

- **Integrated Science Laboratory Manual I-4,** "Investigating Differences in Climate"

Media and Technology

Transparencies "World Climate Regions," Transparency 18

Exploring Earth Science Videodisc Unit 4, Side 2, "Climate in the U.S."

Chapter 7

Ongoing Assessment

Writing Challenge students to write an outline about the climate regions. In the outline, they should include the temperature and precipitation factors that are used to classify each climate region.

Tropical Rainy Climates, continued

Using the Visuals: Figure 7

Instruct students to compare the photo in Figure 7 with the one in Figure 6. Ask: **What climate factor do both climate regions have in common?** *(hot temperatures)* **What climate factor differs in these climate regions?** *(the amount and frequency of precipitation)* Challenge students to infer how the difference in the amounts of precipitation can have such a visible affect on a climate. *(Plants with different water requirements live in each climate region. A rain forest plant would not survive in a savanna because there is not enough precipitation.)* **learning modality: visual**

Dry Climates

Including All Students

To help students with the vocabulary terms, invite them to write each of the words, *rain forest, savanna, steppe,* and *desert* on separate index cards. Suggest that students write the definitions of the words on the cards and any other words, phrases, or illustrations that will help them to remember the meanings of the words. Some students might also find it helpful to write the phonetic pronunciation of the words. Students can add their cards to their flip books. **limited English proficiency**

Figure 7 A reticulated giraffe gazes across the grasses and shrubby trees of the African savanna. Savannas are found in tropical wet-and-dry climates.

Tropical Wet-and-Dry Tropical wet-and-dry climates get slightly less rain than tropical climates and have distinct dry and rainy seasons. Instead of rain forests, there are tropical grasslands called **savannas**. Scattered clumps of trees that can survive the dry season dot the coarse grasses. Only a small part of the United States—the southern tip of Florida—has a tropical wet-and-dry climate.

☑ *Checkpoint* ***What parts of the United States have tropical rainy climates?***

Dry Climates

A climate is "dry" if the amount of precipitation that falls is less than the amount of water that could potentially evaporate. Because water evaporates more slowly in cool weather, a cool place with low rainfall may not be as dry as a hotter place that gets the same amount of rain.

Look at *Exploring Climate Regions.* What part of the United States is dry? Why is precipitation in this region so low? As you can see, dry regions often lie inland, far from oceans that are the source of humid air masses. In addition, much of the region lies in the rain shadow of the Sierra Nevadas and Rocky Mountains to the west. Humid air masses from the Pacific Ocean lose much of their water as they cross the mountains. Little rain or snow is carried to dry regions.

Arid The word *desert* may make you think of blazing heat and drifting sand dunes. Some deserts are hot and sandy, but others are cold or rocky. On average, arid regions, or **deserts,** get less than 25 centimeters of rain every year. Some years may bring no rain at all. Only specialized plants such as cactus and yucca can survive the desert's dryness and extremes of hot and cold. In the United States there are arid climates in portions of California, the Great Basin, and the southwest.

Figure 8 Dry-land wheat farming is common in the steppe region of the Great Plains. *Comparing and Contrasting How are steppes similar to savannas, shown in Figure 7? How are they different?*

Background

Integrating Science Plants adapted to living in dry climates have special ways to collect and store water. Desert plants are spread apart so that they don't compete for the small amount of water available. Many cactus plants have roots that spread over a large area just below the surface to capture as much rainwater as possible. The mesquite tree has very deep roots that get water from sources deep below the surface.

Plants also store water in their roots, stems, and leaves. A barrel cactus swells after a rainfall because of the water it stores in its stem. Jade plants store water in their leaves. Plants also lose water through their leaves. To survive, many desert plants either lose their leaves during dry periods or have evolved spines.

Semiarid Locate the semiarid regions on *Exploring Climate Regions.* As you can see, large semiarid areas are usually located on the edges of deserts. A steppe is dry but gets enough rainfall for short grasses and low bushes to grow. For this reason, a **steppe** may also be called a prairie or grassland.

The Great Plains are the steppe region of the United States. Many kinds of short grasses and wildflowers grow here, along with scattered forests. Livestock grazing is an important part of the economy of the Great Plains. Beef cattle, sheep, and goats graze on the short grasses of the region. Farm crops include grains, such as wheat and oats, and sunflowers.

Temperate Marine Climates

Look at *Exploring Climate Regions,* along the coasts of continents in the temperate zones. You will find the third main climate region, temperate marine. There are three kinds of temperate marine climates. Because of the moderating influence of oceans, all three are humid and have mild winters.

Marine West Coast The coolest temperate marine climates are found on the west coasts of continents north of 40° north latitude and south of 40° south latitude. Humid ocean air brings cool, rainy summers and mild, rainy winters.

In North America, the marine west coast climate extends from northern California to southern Alaska. In the Pacific Northwest of the United States, humid air from the Pacific Ocean rises as it hits the western slopes of the Coastal Ranges. As the air cools, large amounts of rain or snow fall on the western slopes.

Because of the heavy precipitation, thick forests of tall trees grow in this region, including coniferous, or cone-bearing, trees such as Sitka spruce, Douglas fir, redwoods, and Western red cedar. One of the main industries of this region is harvesting and processing wood for lumber, paper, and furniture.

TRY THIS

Modeling a Humid Climate

ACTIVITY

Here's how you can create humidity.

1. Put the same amount of water in each of two small plastic bowls.
2. Place a sheet of transparent plastic wrap over each bowl. Secure each sheet with a rubber band.
3. Place one bowl on a warm, sunny windowsill or near a radiator. Put the other bowl in a cool location.
4. Wait a day and then look at the two bowls. What do you see on the plastic wrap over each bowl?

Inferring Would you expect to find more water vapor in the air in a warm climate or in a cool one? Why? Explain your results in terms of solar energy.

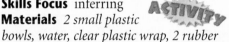

Figure 9 Seattle, Washington, is in the marine west coast climate region. Here the summers are cool and rainy, and winters are wet and mild.

Inquiry Challenge

ACTIVITY

Materials *cactus plant, jade plant, various grasses, magnifying lens, forceps*
Time 20 minutes

Challenge students to identify the adaptations that enable these plants to live in a desert or steppe. Encourage students to use a magnifying lens to examine all parts of the plants, including the roots, stems, and leaves. You can use a scalpel or razor blade to slice some cross-sections of leaves, stems, and roots for students to examine. Then have students explain how such adaptations allow the plants to survive in their climates. **learning modality: logical/mathematical**

Temperate Marine Climates

TRY THIS

ACTIVITY

Skills Focus inferring
Materials *2 small plastic bowls, water, clear plastic wrap, 2 rubber bands*
Time 10 minutes for set up, 5 minutes for later observation
Tips Have students find their own locations to place the bowls. Or, to save time, choose the locations yourself.
Expected Outcome Students will observe more water drops on the plastic wrap of the warm bowl than on the plastic wrap of the cool bowl.

More water vapor is present in the air of warm climates because solar energy warms water, causing it to evaporate into the air.

Extend Instruct students to keep the bowls in the same places, but remove the plastic wrap. Have them check the bowls everyday for one week to find out which bowl has less water at the end of the week. **learning modality: visual**

Program Resources

Science Explorer Series *From Bacteria to Plants,* Chapter 5, has more information about plants.

Answers to Self-Assessment

Checkpoint

The windward sides of the Hawaiian Islands and the southern tip of Florida have tropical rainy climates.

Caption Question

Figure 8 Both steppes and savannas are flat regions where grasses grow. Savannas have clumps of trees while steppes do not.

Ongoing Assessment

Writing Have students describe an air mass in a dry climate and one in a temperate marine climate. *(Air masses in dry climates have little water vapor and air masses in temperate marine climates have a lot of water vapor.)*

Temperate Marine Climates, continued

Including All Students

Give each student a blank map of the United States that has the state borders indicated. Instruct students to shade in the climate regions using a different colored pencil for each climate region. Also have students make a map key. **learning modality: kinesthetic**

Portfolio Students can save their maps in their portfolios.

Real-Life Learning

Help students relate the economy of a region to its climate by asking: **How does the climate of each temperate marine climate affect the industry of that region?** *(The climate enables certain plants to grow that have either an agricultural use or are used for lumber, paper, or furniture.)* Challenge students to infer how these industries are affected in a year when the weather is extreme. *(Farmers may lose money because the weather doesn't permit the usual crops to grow, or the crops are damaged.)* **learning modality: logical/mathematical**

Building Inquiry Skills: Comparing and Contrasting

Reinforce that the marine west coast climate, the Mediterranean climate, and the humid subtropical climate are three kinds of temperate marine climates. Have students compare and contrast the three kinds of temperate marine climates. Then challenge students to devise a means of presenting this information. Students might create a table, a map, a diagram, or even a poem. Encourage students to be creative. Invite them to present their comparisons to the class. **learning modality: logical/mathematical**

Figure 10 **A.** Much of Italy has a Mediterranean climate, with warm, dry summers and cool, rainy winters. **B.** Rice is a major food crop in places with a humid subtropical climate, as in parts of China. *Comparing and Contrasting How are Mediterranean and humid subtropical climates similar? How do they differ?*

Mediterranean A coastal climate that is drier and warmer than west coast marine is known as Mediterranean. Find the Mediterranean climates in *Exploring Climate Regions.* In the United States, the southern coast of California has a Mediterranean climate. This climate is mild, with two seasons. In winter, marine air masses bring cool, rainy weather. Summers are somewhat warmer, with little rain.

Mediterranean climates have two main vegetation types. One is made up of dense shrubs and small trees, called chaparral (chap uh RAL). The other vegetation type includes grasses with a few oak trees.

Agriculture is an important part of the economy of California's Mediterranean climate region. Some crops, including olives and grapes, were originally introduced by Spanish settlers. With the help of irrigation, farmers grow many different crops, including rice, oranges, and many vegetables, fruits, and nuts.

Humid Subtropical The warmest temperate marine climates are on the edges of the tropics. **Humid subtropical** climates are wet and warm, but not as constantly hot as the tropics. Locate the humid subtropical climates in *Exploring Climate Regions.*

The southeastern United States has a humid subtropical climate. Summers are hot, with much more rainfall than in winter. Maritime tropical air masses move inland, bringing tropical weather conditions, including thunderstorms and occasional hurricanes, to southern cities such as Houston, New Orleans, and Atlanta. Winters are cool to mild, with more rain than snow. However, polar air masses moving in from the north can bring freezing temperatures and severe frosts.

Mixed forests of oak, ash, hickory, and pines grow in the humid subtropical region of the United States. Cotton was once the most important crop grown in this region. Other crops, including oranges, grapefruits, peaches, peanuts, sugar cane, and rice, are now more important to the economy.

☑ *Checkpoint* ***What is the main difference between a humid subtropical climate and a tropical climate?***

Background

Facts and Figures The chaparral biome, or plant and animal community, is very typical of Mediterranean climates. The chaparral is characterized by dense growth of evergreen shrubs and small trees. Chaparral plants have small, thick, waxy leaves. These plants are dormant in the hot, dry summer and spring to life with the first rainfall in winter.

The chaparral is a fire-dependent biome. Fires wipe out dead plant material, recycle nutrients, thin old growth, and stimulate new growth from seeds and sprouts. Chaparral plants have adapted to fire by producing seeds early in their life cycles that are either resistant to fire or require fire for germination. Many chaparral plants also produce volatile oils that are highly flammable.

Temperate Continental Climates

Temperate continental climates are found on continents in the Northern Hemisphere. Because they are not influenced very much by oceans, temperate continental climates have extremes of temperature. Why do continental climates occur only in the Northern Hemisphere? The parts of continents in the Southern Hemisphere south of 40° south latitude are not far enough from oceans for dry continental air masses to form.

Humid Continental Shifting tropical and polar air masses bring constantly changing weather to humid continental climates. In winter, continental polar air masses move south, bringing bitterly cold weather. In summer, tropical air masses move north, bringing heat and high humidity. Humid continental climates receive moderate amounts of rain in the summer. Smaller amounts of rain or snow fall in winter.

What parts of the United States have a humid continental climate? The eastern part of the region—the Northeast—has a range of forest types, from mixed forests in the south to coniferous forests in the north. Much of the western part of this region—the Midwest—was once tall grasslands, but is now farmland. Farmers in the Midwest grow wheat, corn, other grains, and soybeans. These crops are used as food for people and for hogs, poultry, and beef cattle.

Subarctic The **subarctic** climates lie north of the humid continental climates. The world's largest subarctic regions are in Russia, Canada, and Alaska. Summers in the subarctic are short and cool. Winters are long and bitterly cold.

In North America, coniferous trees such as spruce and fir make up a huge northern forest that stretches from Alaska to Canada's east coast. Many large mammals, including bears, wolves, and moose, live in the forest. Small mammals such as beavers, porcupines, and red squirrels, and birds such as grouse and owls also live in the forest. Wood products from the northern forest are an important part of the economy.

Sharpen your Skills

Classifying ACTIVITY

The table shows some climate data for three cities.

	City A	City B	City C
Average January Temperature (°C)	12.8	18.9	–5.6
Average July Temperature (°C)	21.1	27.2	20
Annual Precipitation (cm)	33	152	109

Describe the climate you would expect each city to have. Identify which city is Miami, which is Los Angeles, and which is Portland, Maine. Use *Exploring Climate Regions* on pages 124–125 to help identify each city's climate.

Figure 11 Subarctic climates have cool summers and cold winters. Parts of this region are called "spruce-moose belts."

Temperate Continental Climates

Building Inquiry Skills: Applying Concepts

Invite students to compare and contrast the characteristics of humid continental and subarctic climates. List their similarities and differences on the board. Then ask: **What factor or factors affecting climate causes the differences between subarctic and humid continental climates?** *(primarily latitude)* **What climate factor or factors causes the similarities between these two climates?** *(Distance from large bodies of water and prevailing winds)* **learning modality: logical/mathematical**

Sharpen your Skills

Classifying ACTIVITY

Time 10 minutes

Expected Outcome City A is Los Angeles. Its warm and dry climate is a Mediterranean climate. City B is Miami. Its hot and humid climate is a tropical wet-and-dry climate. City C is Portland, Maine. With hot summers and cool winters, it is a humid continental climate.

Extend Challenge students to classify the climates of Seattle, Atlanta, and Chicago. Ask: **Which of these cities has climates similar to City A, City B, or City C?** *(Chicago is like City C, Portland, Maine.)* **Which do not?** *(Seattle has a marine west coast climate, and Atlanta has a humid subtropical climate.)* **learning modality: logical/mathematical**

Program Resources

Science Explorer Series *Animals,* Chapter 4, gives more information about mammals and their adaptations.

Answers to Self-Assessment

Caption Question

Figure 10 Both climates are humid with hot summers and mild winters. The Mediterranean climate has dry summers and the humid subtropical climate has wet summers.

Checkpoint

A humid subtropical climate is not as constantly hot as a tropical climate.

Ongoing Assessment

Writing Have students summarize the differences between a temperate continental climate and a temperate marine climate.

Polar Climates

Cultural Diversity

The Inuit and the Pueblo are two Native American groups that lived in extreme climates. Show students pictures of the climates these groups lived in. Help students locate where these groups lived on the map in *Exploring Climate Regions* on pages 124–125. Then challenge student groups to learn how these two groups have adapted to their environments. You might assign groups to study one aspect of their cultures, such as housing, food, dress, customs, social structure, communication, and art. Have groups present their findings to the class. **cooperative learning**

Highlands

Including All Students

ACTIVITY

Students can make models of a highland climate using salt dough or papier-mâché. They may base their models on the description of the Rocky Mountains in the text, or they can choose a different mountain range. Their models should show how the climate changes as altitude increases. Encourage students to be creative. Not only could they color-code the various climate regions on the mountain, but they could also add models of the plants and animals that live there. **learning modality: kinesthetic**

Figure 12 Emperor penguins live on the ice cap of Antarctica.

Polar Climates

The polar climate is the coldest climate region. Ice cap and tundra climates are found only in the far north and south, near the North and South poles.

Ice Cap As you can see in *Exploring Climate Regions*, ice cap climates are found mainly on Greenland and in Antarctica. With average temperatures always at or below freezing, the land in ice cap climate regions is covered with ice and snow. Intense cold makes the air dry. Lichens and a few low plants may grow on the rocks.

Tundra The **tundra** climate region stretches across northern Alaska, Canada, and Russia. Short, cool summers follow bitterly cold winters. Because of the cold, some layers of the tundra soil are always frozen. This permanently frozen tundra soil is called **permafrost.** Because of the permafrost, water cannot drain away, so the soil is wet and boggy in summer.

It is too cold on the tundra for trees to grow. Despite the harsh climate, during the short summers the tundra is filled with life. Mosquitoes and other insects hatch in the ponds and marshes above the frozen permafrost. Mosses, grasses, lichens, wildflowers, and shrubs grow quickly during the short summers. Herds of caribou and musk oxen eat the vegetation and are in turn preyed upon by wolves. Some birds, such as the white-tailed ptarmigan, live on the tundra year-round. Others, such as the arctic tern and many waterfowl, spend only the summer there.

☑ *Checkpoint* ***What type of vegetation is found on the tundra?***

Figure 13 The tundra is often very cold, but still many plants and animals live there. *Observing How are these musk oxen adapted to the cold climate?*

Background

Facts and Figures The alpine tundra, which is the tundra found in a highland climate, is somewhat different from the arctic tundra of a polar climate. The main differences are that the alpine tundra does not have permafrost and receives much more precipitation. Most alpine tundra has well-drained soil. However, bare rock-covered ground is also very common. Low-growing plants, mosses, and lichens characterize both the arctic and the alpine tundras. The alpine tundra plants include more mat-growing plants that are adapted to the gusty winds, heavy snowfalls, and fluctuating temperatures found at mountaintops. Common alpine tundra animals include mountain goats, big-horned sheep, pikas, and marmots. Butterflies, beetles, and grasshoppers are also common, whereas flies and mosquitoes are more rare.

Highlands

Why are highlands a distinct climate region? Remember that temperature falls as altitude increases, so highland regions are colder than the regions that surround them. Increasing altitude produces climate changes similar to the climate changes you would expect with increasing latitude. In the tropics, highlands are like cold islands overlooking the warm lowlands.

The climate on the lower slopes of a mountain range is like that of the surrounding countryside. The foothills of the Rocky Mountains, for instance, share the semiarid climate of the Great Plains. But as you go higher up into the mountains, temperatures become lower. Climbing 1,000 meters up in elevation is like traveling 1,200 kilometers north. The climate higher in the mountains is like that of the subarctic: cool with coniferous trees. Animals typical of the subarctic zone—such as moose and porcupines—live in the mountain forest.

Above a certain elevation—the tree line—no trees can grow. The climate above the tree line is like that of the tundra. Only low plants, mosses, and lichens can grow there.

Figure 14 The top of this mountain is too cold and windy for trees to grow. *Classifying What climate zone does this mountaintop resemble?*

Section 2 Review

1. What two factors are used to classify climates?
2. Briefly describe each of the five main climate types.
3. Give three examples of how the climate of a region affects what plants and animals can live there.
4. **Thinking Critically Applying Concepts** Which of these two places has more severe winters—central Russia or the west coast of France? Why?
5. **Thinking Critically Classifying** Classify the main climate regions according to whether or not trees usually grow in each one.

Science at Home

Describe to your family the characteristics of each of the climate regions found in the United States. Which climate region does your family live in? What plants and animals live in your climate region? What characteristics do these plants and animals have that make them well-adapted to living in your climate region?

3 Assess

Section 2 Review Answers

1. Temperature and precipitation
2. Tropical: hot and rainy; dry: little precipitation; temperate marine: humid with mild winters; temperate continental: warm or cool summers and cold winters, moderate precipitation; polar: cool summers and very cold winters, little precipitation
3. Answers may vary. Students should give examples that show how the climate affects what plants or animals live in a region or what types of farming, ranching, or forestry are important.
4. Central Russia has more severe winters because it is at a higher latitude than France in the center of the continent and has a continental climate; the climate of the coast of France is west coast marine and is more moderate.
5. Trees: tropical rainy, temperate marine, temperate continental, highlands; no trees: dry, polar

Science at Home

ACTIVITY

To ensure students identify their climate correctly, encourage volunteers to identify your climate region and explain what climate factors your community has. Help students identify the special factors of your climate to which plants and animals must adapt. For example, in a temperate continental climate, animals need some kind of adaptation to survive the change of seasons. Encourage students to interview family members about other climate regions they have visited.

Program Resources

◆ **Teaching Resources** 4-2 Review and Reinforce, p. 107; 4-2 Enrich, p. 108

Media and Technology

Interactive Student Tutorial CD-ROM I-4

Answers to Self-Assessment

Caption Question

Figure 13 They have thick, long coats.
Figure 14 tundra

Checkpoint

Mosses, grasses, lichens, wildflowers, and shrubs

Performance Assessment

Organizing Information Instruct students to make a table in which they list the climate factors and types of living things for each of the six climate regions they studied. Students should also include in their tables information about the subtypes of climate regions, such as ice cap and tundra climates.

Real-World Lab

Careers in Science

Cool Climate Graphs

Preparing for Inquiry

Key Concept Factors in addition to latitude, such as the proximity of large bodies of water, altitude, and the presence of mountains, also help to determine the climate of a region.
Skills Objectives Students will be able to
- graph the monthly average precipitation, high temperature, and low temperature for three different cities;
- interpret data to determine which city matches which climate graph;
- draw conclusions about which city has the best climate for different types of recreational facilities.

Time 40 minutes
Advance Planning Depending on the level of your students, you may want to distribute copies of graphs with the axes already marked. An overhead transparency of a climate graph will help instruct students on making their own.

Guided Inquiry

Invitation To help students relate to the lab, ask: **How does climate affect your life?** *(Students should explain how they have to change their lifestyle based on the yearly weather changes.)* Discuss what kinds of activities students can or cannot do because of the climate.

Introducing the Procedure
Instruct students to look over the climate graph shown in their text. Discuss what kinds of information are being graphed. Ask: **Why is this type of graph useful?** *(A visual picture of monthly temperatures and precipitation makes it easier to compare the climates among different cities.)*

Real-World Lab

Careers in Science

Cool Climate Graphs

You are a land-use planner who has been hired by a company that builds recreational facilities. Your company is considering buying land near at least one of four cities, all at about the same latitude. Your job is to decide which of the cities would be the best place to build a water park and which is the best place to build a ski-touring center.

Problem

Based on climate data, which city is the best place for each type of recreational facility?

Skills Focus

graphing, interpreting data, drawing conclusions

Materials

calculator
ruler
3 pieces of graph paper
black, blue, red, and green pencils
climate map on pages 124–125
U.S. map with city names and latitude lines

Procedure

1. Work in groups of three. Each person should graph the data for a different city, A, B, or C.
2. On graph paper, use a black pencil to label the axes as on the climate graph below. Title your climate graph City A, City B, or City C.
3. Use your green pencil to make a bar graph of the monthly average amount of precipitation. Place a star below the name of each month that has more than a trace of snow.
4. Use a red pencil to plot the average monthly maximum temperature. Make a dot for the temperature in the middle of each space for the month. When you have plotted data for all 12 months, connect the points into a smooth curved line.
5. Use a blue pencil to plot the average monthly minimum temperature for your city. Use the same procedure as in Step 4.
6. Calculate the total average annual precipitation for this city and include it in your observations. Do this by adding the average precipitation for each month and dividing by 12.

Washington, D.C., Climate Averages

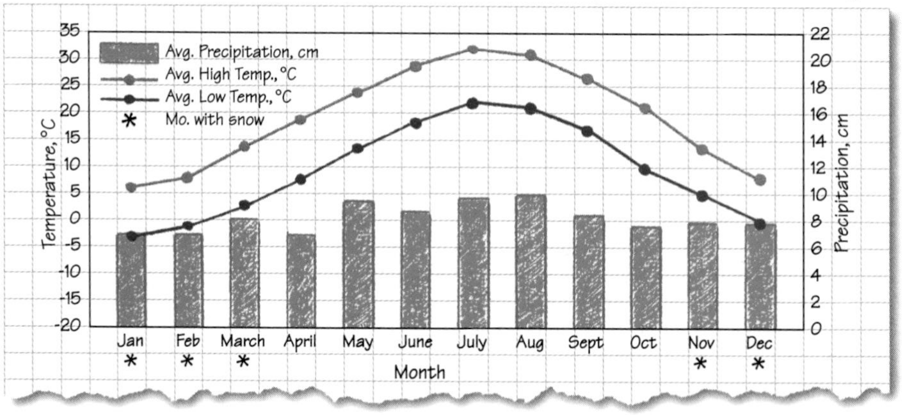

Troubleshooting the Experiment
- If necessary, review with students the factors that affect climate from Section 1.
- Walk around the room as students are graphing to help with any problems they might be having.
- Using maps that show the names of cities and the physical geography will help students match their climate graphs with the proper cities.
- Encourage students to list the climate criteria for a water-slide park and a cross-country ski touring center.

Expected Outcome
Students should determine the climate type of each city and the identity of each city based on their climate graphs and their U.S. maps.

Climate Data												
Washington, D.C.	Jan	Feb	Mar	April	May	June	July	Aug	Sept	Oct	Nov	Dec
Average High Temp. (°C)	6	8	14	19	24	29	32	31	27	21	14	8
Average Low Temp. (°C)	-3	-2	3	8	14	19	22	21	17	10	5	0
Average Precipitation (cm)	6.9	6.9	8.1	6.9	9.4	8.6	9.7	9.9	8.4	7.6	7.9	7.9
Months With Snow	*	*	*	trace	—	—	—	—	—	trace	*	*
City A	Jan	Feb	Mar	Apr	May	Jun	July	Aug	Sept	Oct	Nov	Dec
Average High Temp. (°C)	13	16	16	17	17	18	18	19	21	21	17	13
Average Low Temp. (°C)	8	9	9	10	11	12	12	13	13	13	11	8
Average Precipitation (cm)	10.4	7.6	7.9	3.3	0.8	0.5	0.3	0.3	0.8	3.3	8.1	7.9
Months With Snow	trace	trace	trace	—	—	—	—	—	—	—	—	trace
City B	Jan	Feb	Mar	Apr	May	Jun	July	Aug	Sept	Oct	Nov	Dec
Average High Temp. (°C)	5	7	10	16	21	26	29	27	23	18	11	6
Average Low Temp. (°C)	−9	−7	−4	1	6	11	14	13	8	2	−4	−8
Average Precipitation (cm)	0.8	1.0	2.3	3.0	5.6	5.8	7.4	7.6	3.3	2.0	1.3	1.3
Months With Snow	*	*	*	*	*	—	—	—	trace	*	*	*
City C	Jan	Feb	Mar	Apr	May	Jun	July	Aug	Sept	Oct	Nov	Dec
Average High Temp. (°C)	7	11	13	18	23	28	33	32	27	21	12	8
Average Low Temp. (°C)	−6	−4	−2	1	4	8	11	10	5	1	−3	−7
Average Precipitation (cm)	2.5	2.3	1.8	1.3	1.8	1	0.8	0.5	0.8	1	2	2.5
Months With Snow	*	*	*	*	*	trace	—	—	trace	trace	*	*

Analyze and Conclude

Compare your climate graphs and observations. Use all three climate graphs, plus the graph for Washington, D.C., to answer these questions.

1. Which of the four cities has the least change in average temperatures during the year?
2. In which climate region is each city located?
3. Which of the cities listed below matches each climate graph?

Colorado Springs, Colorado	latitude 39° N
San Francisco, California	latitude 38° N
Reno, Nevada	latitude 40° N
Washington, D.C.	latitude 39° N

4. Even though these cities are at approximately the same latitude, why are their climate graphs so different?
5. **Apply** Which city would be the best location for a water slide park? For a cross-country ski touring center? What other factors should you consider when deciding where to build each type of recreational facility? Explain.

More to Explore

What type of climate does the area where you live have? Find out what outdoor recreational facilities your community has. How is each one particularly suited to the climate of *your* area?

Analyze and Conclude

1. City A
2. Washington, D.C.: humid subtropical; City A: Mediterranean; City B: semiarid; City C: arid
3. Colorado Springs: City B; San Francisco: City A; Reno: City C
4. Other climate factors, such as distance from large bodies of water, altitude, and mountain ranges, affect the climate of these cities.
5. Washington, D.C., would be the best choice for a water-slide park because it has fewer months with snow and very warm summertime temperatures, even though it has relatively high amounts of precipitation. Colorado Springs would be the best choice for a cross-country ski touring center because it has the most months with enough snow. Other factors to consider include water supply, local economy, building sites, numbers of tourists, roads, and the amount of taxes. These factors will affect the cost of building and maintaining the facility and whether there are enough people to use the facility so that it will make money.

Extending the Inquiry

More to Explore Help students identify and list the recreational facilities in and around your community. Some facilities in your community might include parks, ice skating rinks, pools, amusement parks, water slide parks, ski hills, golf courses, and toboggan runs. Students should describe how the climate requirements of the recreation facilities match the climate factors in your community.

Program Resources

◆ **Teaching Resources** Real-World Lab blackline masters, pp. 120–121

Science Explorer Series *Earth's Changing Surface,* Appendix B, is a Physical Map of the United States

Media and Technology

Transparencies "Climate Graph for Washington, D.C.," Transparency 19

Section 3 Long-Term Changes in Climate

Objectives

After completing the lesson, students will be able to

- state the principle that scientists follow in studying ancient climates;
- describe how Earth's surface changes during an ice age;
- list the theories that have been proposed to explain natural climate change.

Key Terms ice age, sunspot

1 Engage/Explore

Activating Prior Knowledge

To find out what students know about ancient climates ask: **What do you know about climate changes in Earth's past?** *(Some students might mention past ice ages or climate changes that might have caused the extinction of dinosaurs.)* **How do you think these climate changes might have affected plants and animals?** *(Students might mention that plants and animals would die out if they couldn't move or adapt to the climate changes. Accept all answers without comment.)*

Discover Activity

Skills Focus inferring
Materials *Figure 16 from student text, magnifying lens*
Time 10 minutes
Tips Make a photocopy of Figure 16 and enlarge the photo of the tree rings. Students can label on the photocopy thick and thin tree rings. If possible, provide students with cross-sections of tree trunks to examine.
Expected Outcome Students should observe that tree rings are not all the same thickness. Students might infer that temperature and precipitation affect the thickness of tree rings.
Think It Over Students should infer that the relative thickness of tree rings tells about weather conditions in the past.

Section 3 Long-Term Changes in Climate

Discover Activity

What Story Can Tree Rings Tell?

1. Look at the photo of tree rings on page 135. Tree rings are the layers of new wood that form as a tree grows each year.
2. Look closely at the tree rings. Note whether they are all the same thickness.
3. What weather conditions might cause a tree to form thicker or thinner tree rings?

Think It Over

Inferring How could you use tree rings to tell you about weather in the past?

Guide for Reading

- What principle do scientists follow in studying ancient climates?
- What changes occur on Earth's surface during an ice age?
- What theories have been proposed to explain natural climate change?

Reading Tip **Before you read, preview the art and photos and read the captions to predict how Earth's climate has changed through time.**

One of the greatest Native American cultures in the American Southwest was the Ancestral Pueblos. These farming people built great pueblos, or "apartment houses," of stone and sun-baked clay, with hundreds of rooms. By about the year 1000, the Ancestral Pueblos were flourishing. They grew crops of corn, beans, and squash and traded extensively with other groups of people. But in the late 1200s, the climate became drier, reducing the size of their crops. After a long period of drought, the Ancestral Pueblos migrated to other areas.

Although weather can vary from day to day, climates usually change more slowly. But climates do change, both in small areas and throughout the world. Although climate change is usually slow, its consequences are great. Climate changes have affected many civilizations, including the Ancestral Pueblos.

Figure 15 The Ancestral Pueblos lived in these buildings, now in Mesa Verde National Park in southwestern Colorado, about 1,000 years ago.

Reading Strategies

Study and Comprehension Encourage students to look over the section before they read it to identify the main topics. Suggest that they use the topic heads from the section to organize an outline. Then students can use their completed outlines as a study guide.

Studying Climate Change

In studying ancient climates, scientists follow an important principle: If plants or animals today need certain conditions to live, then similar plants and animals in the past also required those conditions. For example, today magnolia and palm trees grow only in warm, moist climates. Scientists assume that the ancestors of these trees required similar conditions. Thus, 80-million-year-old fossils of these trees in Greenland are good evidence that the climate of Greenland was warm and moist 80 million years ago.

Tree rings can also be used to learn about ancient climates. Every summer, a tree grows a new layer of wood under its bark. These layers form rings when seen in a cross section, as shown in Figure 16. In cool climates, the amount the tree grows—the thickness of a ring—depends on the length of the warm growing season. In dry climates, the thickness of each ring depends on the amount of rainfall. By looking at cross sections of trees, scientists can count backward from the outer ring to see whether previous years were warm or cool, wet or dry. A thin ring indicates that the year was cool or dry. A thick ring indicates that the year was warm or wet.

A third source of information about ancient climates is pollen records. Each type of plant has a particular type of pollen. The bottoms of some lakes are covered with thick layers of mud and plant material, including pollen, that fell to the bottom of the lake over thousands of years. Scientists can drill down into these layers and bring up cores to examine. By looking at the pollen present in each layer, scientists can tell what types of plants lived in the area. The scientists can then infer that the climate that existed when the pollen was deposited was similar to the climate where the same plants grow today.

Figure 16 Scientists have learned about past climates by studying tree rings. They can learn much from giant sequoias, some of which may be 3,000–4,000 years old.

2 Facilitate

Studying Climate Change

Including All Students

Help students organize the information in the text by asking: **What three sources of information do scientists use in studying ancient climates?** *(Fossil evidence, tree rings, pollen records)* **What important principle do scientists follow while studying ancient climates?** *(Ancient plants and animals require the same living conditions as similar plants and animals living now.)* **learning modality: verbal**

Building Inquiry Skills: Drawing Conclusions

Explain to students that scientists have found fossils of brachiopods and trilobites in southeastern Wisconsin. These fossils are about 400 million years old. Encourage students to use encyclopedias to learn more about trilobites and brachiopods, or display pictures or fossils of these organisms and help students infer their habitats. Challenge students to use this information to draw a conclusion about the climate of southeastern Wisconsin about 400 million years ago. *(Brachiopods and trilobites are organisms that lived on the bottom of warm, shallow seas. The presence of these fossils in southeastern Wisconsin indicates that this area was covered by warm, shallow seas about 400 million years ago.)* **learning modality: logical/mathematical**

Program Resources

- **Teaching Resources** 4-3 Lesson Plan, p. 109, 4-3 Section Summary, p. 110
- **Audiotapes** English-Spanish Summary 4-3

Science Explorer Series *Earth's Changing Surface*, Chapter 4, gives more information about using fossils to identify geologic time.

Media and Technology

Exploring Earth Science Videodisc
Unit 5, Side 1, "Geologic Time"
Chapter 4

Ongoing Assessment

Oral Presentation Call on various students to describe the three sources of information that scientists use to study ancient climates.

Ice Ages

Using the Visuals: Figure 17

Invite students to use Figure 17 to determine whether your area was covered by glaciers 18,000 years ago. Ask: **What could you conclude if a fossil of a mammoth were found north of the mammoth steppe region shown on the map?** *(That the size of the glaciers changed over time, and the mammoth steppe region changed accordingly.)* Elicit suggestions about why woolly mammoths and scimitar-toothed cats are extinct. Discuss how the changing climate might have affected these animals. **learning modality: visual**

Building Inquiry Skills: Inferring

Challenge students to infer what your community might have looked like during the last ice age. Then have students draw a picture showing how the street on which they live might have looked about 18,000 years ago. **learning modality: visual**

Including All Students

Materials *shallow pan, damp sand, ice cubes or crushed ice, water, toothpicks*
Time 20 minutes, 5 minutes

ACTIVITY

Students can construct models to show why the ocean level rises as ice sheets melt. Instruct students to use the damp sand to mold a land mass in the shallow pan. Suggest that they include depressions, mountains, and coastal areas. Students should add water to the pan to simulate the ocean. Then they can pack the ice on the land masses to represent glaciers and ice sheets. Have students mark the water level at various places on their land masses with toothpicks. Ask students to predict what will happen to the ice sheets and oceans in their models. *(The ice sheets will melt, and the ocean level will rise.)* (Note: Keep pans in a cool, shady area overnight to minimize evaporation.) The next day, have students observe the changes in ice and water in their models. Discuss why oceans are lower during the ice ages than they are now. **learning modality: kinesthetic**

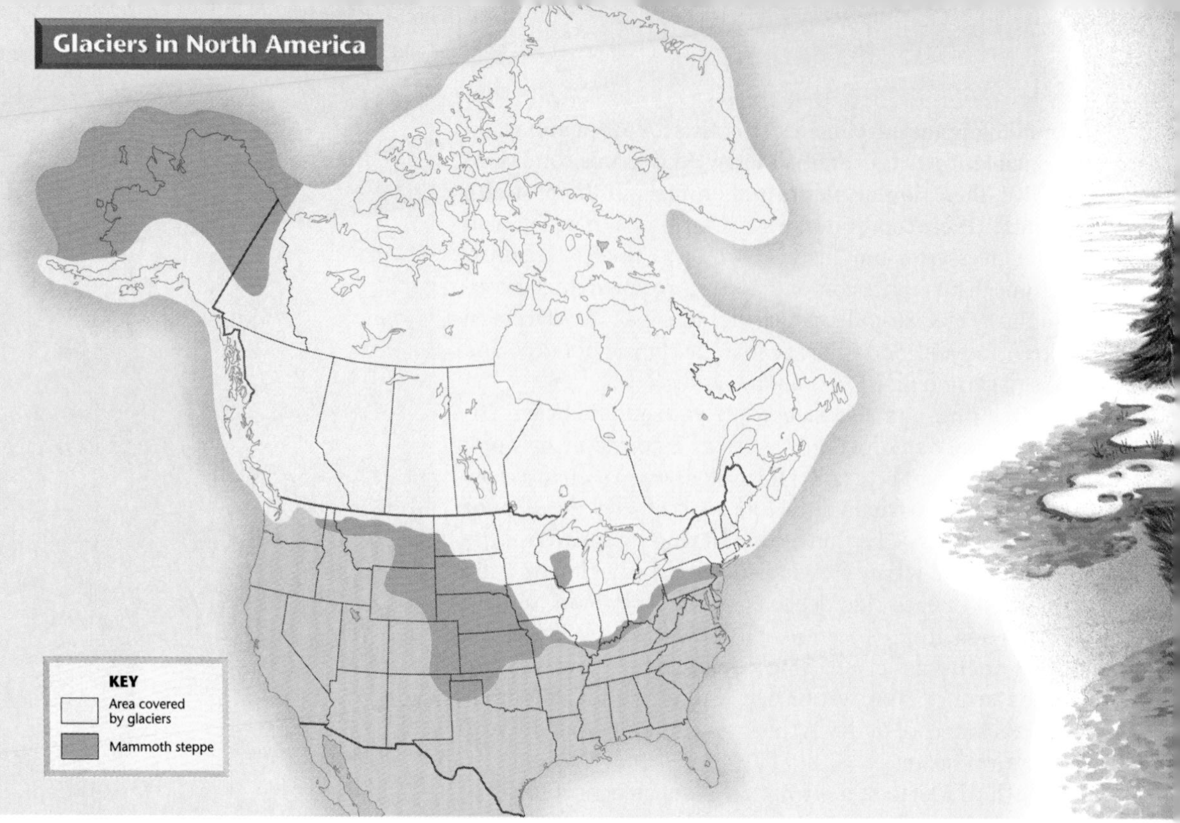

Figure 17 The map shows the parts of North America that were covered by glaciers 18,000 years ago. On the steppe near the glaciers lived many mammals that are now extinct, including woolly mammoths and scimitar-toothed cats.

Ice Ages

Throughout Earth's history, climates have gradually changed. Over millions of years, warm periods have alternated with cold periods known as **ice ages,** or glacial episodes. **During each ice age, huge sheets of ice called glaciers covered large parts of Earth's surface.**

From fossils and other evidence, scientists have concluded that in the past two million years there have been at least four major ice ages. Each one lasted 100,000 years or longer. Long, warmer periods known as interglacials occurred between the ice ages. Some scientists think that we are now in a warm period between ice ages.

The most recent major ice age ended only about 10,500 years ago. Ice sheets covered much of northern Europe and North America, reaching as far south as present-day Iowa and Nebraska. In some places, the ice was more than 3 kilometers thick. So much water was frozen in the ice sheets that the average sea level was much lower than it is today. When the ice sheets melted, the rising oceans flooded coastal areas. Inland, large lakes formed.

✓ *Checkpoint* *Why were the oceans lower during the ice ages than they are now?*

Background

Integrating Science All planets, including Earth, revolve around the sun in elliptical orbits. Because its orbit is not circular, Earth is not the same distance from the sun at all points in its orbit. About January 3, Earth is nearest the sun at a point called the perihelion. About July 4, Earth is farthest from the sun at the aphelion. Since planets move faster when they are closer to the sun, the time interval from the March equinox to the September equinox is longer than the interval between September and March. If Earth's orbit shifts so that its perihelion is in July, the winter season in the Northern Hemisphere will be longer because Earth will be moving more slowly between September and March. This could cause the climate to become cooler, setting the stage for an ice age.

Social Studies CONNECTION

To help students think about how their lives might change, ask: **How would a colder climate affect the plants and animals living in our environment?** *(Some plants might not survive. Animals that depend on them for food also might not survive. Some animals might migrate.)* Explain that the climate in an ice age would be similar to subarctic, tundra, or ice cap climates. Discuss how these climates are different from your current climate.

In Your Journal Provide time for students to make their lists. Encourage students to share their lists in a class discussion. **learning modality: verbal**

Causes of Climate Change

Why do climates change? Scientists have formed several hypotheses. **Possible explanations for major climate changes include variations in the position of Earth relative to the sun, changes in the sun's energy output, and the movement of continents.**

Earth's Position Changes in Earth's position relative to the sun may have affected climates. According to one hypothesis, as Earth revolves around the sun, the time of year when Earth is closest to the sun shifts from January to July and back again over a period of about 26,000 years.

The angle at which Earth's axis tilts and the shape of Earth's orbit around the sun also change slightly over long periods of time. The combined effects of these changes in Earth's movements may be the main cause of ice ages.

INTEGRATING SPACE SCIENCE **Solar Energy** Short-term changes in climate have been linked to changes in the number of **sunspots**—dark, cooler regions on the surface of the sun. Sunspots increase and decrease in regular 11-year cycles. Sunspot cycles could in turn be caused by changes in the sun's energy output.

Social Studies CONNECTION

Prehistoric people who lived during the last ice age faced a harsh environment. To endure the cold, they learned to make clothing from animal skins. They also used fires for warmth and cooking.

In Your Journal

Make a list of five ways your life would change if the climate suddenly became colder.

Media and Technology

Transparencies "Extent of Northern Hemisphere Glaciation," Transparency 20

Exploring Earth Science Videodisc Unit 4, Side 2, "Changes in Climate"

Chapter 6

Answers to Self-Assessment

Checkpoint

Much of the water on Earth was frozen in ice sheets that covered the land.

Program Resources

- **Explorer Science Series** *Astronomy,* Chapters 1 and 2, gives more information about the motion of Earth.

Ongoing Assessment

Writing Have students explain what an ice age is and how one might occur.

Causes of Climate Change, continued

Including All Students

ACTIVITY

Give students a photocopied map of the world. Tell them to cut out the continents and India, but leave Europe and Asia together as one continent. Then challenge them to fit the continents together to form Pangaea. **learning modality: kinesthetic**

3 Assess

Section 3 Review Answers

1. Fossil evidence, tree rings, and pollen records
2. The temperature was colder and huge sheets of ice covered large parts of Earth.
3. Earth's position relative to the sun, changes in the sun's energy output, and the movement of continents
4. A volcanic eruption would send ash and other particles into the air that would block the sun's energy from Earth's surface. The climate would become cool, but the change would not be permanent. Over time, the volcanic ash and dust would settle out of the air.

CHAPTER PROJECT 4

Check Your Progress

Groups should be finished collecting weather data and starting to graph the data. Encourage students to look critically at the data for any similarities and differences. Besides graphing their data, suggest that students construct tables or charts to help them compare and contrast their observations. Encourage students to think about which climate factors caused the weather data to be different in each microclimate.

Performance Assessment

Skills Check Have students make a cause and effect table showing causes for climate change and the effects.

225 million years ago

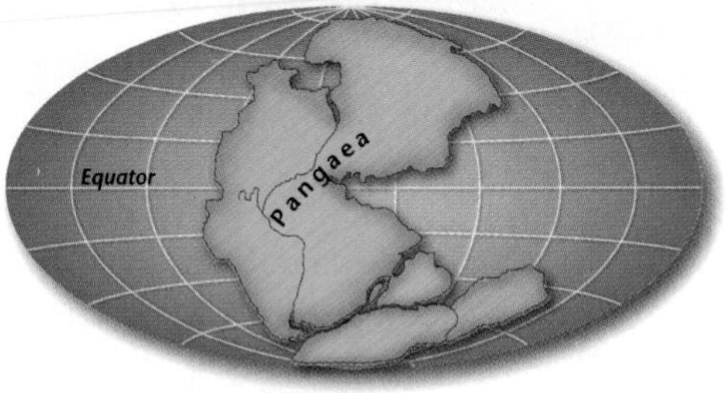

180–200 million years ago

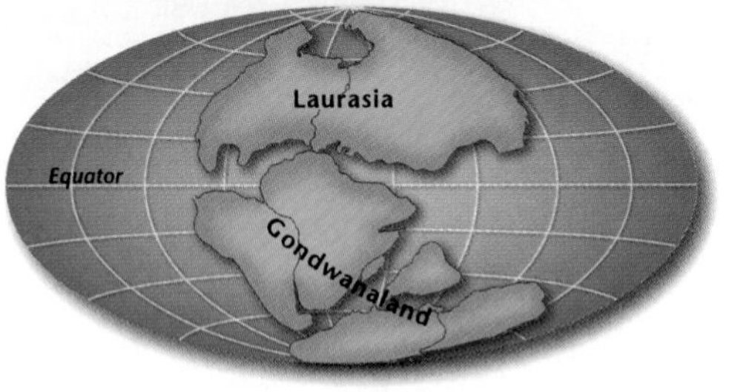

Figure 18 The continents have moved over millions of years. *Interpreting Maps Which present-day continents broke away from Gondwanaland? Which broke away from Laurasia?*

Recently, satellite measurements have shown that the amount of energy the sun produces increases and decreases slightly from year to year. These changes may cause Earth's temperature to increase and decrease. More observations are needed to test this hypothesis.

Movement of Continents Earth's continents have not always been located where they are now. About 225 million years ago, most of the land on Earth was part of a single continent called Pangaea (pan JEE uh).

As Figure 18 shows, most continents were far from their present positions. Continents that are now in the polar zones were once near the equator. This movement explains how tropical plants such as magnolias and palm trees could once have grown in Greenland.

Over millions of years, the continents broke away and gradually moved to their present positions. The movements of continents over time changed the locations of land and sea. These changes affected the global patterns of winds and ocean currents, which in turn slowly changed climates. And as the continents continue to move, climates will continue to change.

Section 3 Review

1. What types of evidence do scientists use to study changes in climate?
2. How was the climate during an ice age different from the climate today?
3. List three factors that could be responsible for changing Earth's climates.
4. **Thinking Critically** **Predicting** What kinds of climate changes might be caused by a volcanic eruption? Would these changes be permanent? Explain.

CHAPTER PROJECT 4

Check Your Progress

What types of weather conditions have you measured at each site? Have you been recording all the data in your logbook? You should now be ready to graph and analyze your data. Are the weather conditions at all of your test areas similar, or do you see differences? What do you think causes the different conditions? What organisms did you observe at your sites?

Answers to Self-Assessment

Caption Question

Figure 18 South America, Africa, Australia, and Antarctica broke away from Gondwanaland; North America, Europe, and Asia broke away from Laurasia.

Program Resources

- **Teaching Resources** 4-3 Review and Reinforce, p. 111; 4-3 Enrich, p. 112

Media and Technology

Interactive Student Tutorial CD-ROM I-4

SECTION 4 Global Changes in the Atmosphere

DISCOVER ········· ACTIVITY

What Is the Greenhouse Effect?

1. Cut two pieces of black construction paper to fit the bottoms of two shoe boxes.

2. Place a thermometer in one end of each box. Read the temperatures on the thermometers. (They should be the same.) Cover one box with plastic wrap.

3. Place the boxes together where sunlight or a light bulb can shine on them equally. Make sure the thermometers are shaded by the sides of the boxes.

4. What do think will happen to the temperatures on the thermometers? Wait 15 minutes and read the thermometers again. Record the temperatures.

Think It Over

Inferring How can you explain the temperature difference between the box with the plastic wrap and the open box? Why does the inside of a car left in direct sunlight get so warm?

Have you ever seen a headline like the one below? If you hate cold winters and love summer sports, you may wonder what would be wrong with a slightly warmer world. Some experts agree with you, but many scientists are worried about such climate change.

> ◆ ANYWHERE U.S.A. DAILY NEWS ◆
> **Earth's Average Temperature Expected to Increase by 3 Celsius Degrees**

Most changes in world climates are caused by natural factors. In the last hundred years, however, human activities have also had an effect on Earth's climate and atmosphere. Two of the most important worldwide issues are global warming and thinning of the ozone layer.

Global Warming

Over the last 120 years, the average temperature of the troposphere has risen by about 0.5 Celsius degree. Was this increase part of natural variations, or was it caused by human activities? What effects could higher temperatures have? Scientists have done a great deal of research to try to answer these questions.

GUIDE FOR READING

◆ How might human activities be affecting the temperature of Earth's atmosphere?

◆ How have human activities affected the ozone layer?

Reading Tip As you read, draw a concept map showing how human activities can cause changes in the atmosphere and climate.

Chapter 4 I ◆ 139

INTEGRATING ENVIRONMENTAL SCIENCE

SECTION 4 Global Changes in the Atmosphere

Objectives

After completing the lesson, students will be able to

◆ explain how human activities might be affecting the temperature of Earth's atmosphere;

◆ describe how human activities have affected the ozone layer.

Key Terms greenhouse gas, global warming, chlorofluorocarbon

1 Engage/Explore

Activating Prior Knowledge

Invite students to explain what they think of when they hear about global warming and the depletion of the ozone layer. Then elicit their ideas of how the actions of people might affect climate. Record students' remarks on the board. As they study this section, refer to these comments and encourage students to modify the remarks, if necessary.

········· DISCOVER ·········

Skills Focus inferring
Materials *2 pieces of black construction paper, 2 shoe boxes, 2 thermometers, plastic wrap, masking tape, source of sunlight or lamp*
Time 15 minutes, 5 minutes
Tips Tape the plastic wrap tightly to the box so that the box is air tight. The thermometers must be shaded. If not, they will give artificially high readings.
Expected Outcome The box covered with plastic wrap will be warmer.
Think It Over Light rays that enter both boxes radiate as heat from the box bottom. Heat is trapped inside the box with plastic wrap; heat escapes from the box without. The temperature inside a car increases as the heat from sunlight entering the car builds up and cannot escape.

READING STRATEGIES

Reading Tip Suggest that students look over the section before they read it so they can choose a title and the major concepts for their concept maps.
Vocabulary You can break apart the term *chlorofluorocarbon* for students. Explain that *chloro-* refers to the element chlorine, *-fluoro-* refers to fluorine, and *–carbon* refers to carbon. Chlorofluorocarbons are chemicals made up of these elements.

Program Resources

◆ **Teaching Resources** 4-4 Lesson Plan, p. 113; 4-4 Section Summary, p. 114

Media and Technology

 Audiotapes English-Spanish Summary 4-4

2 Facilitate

Global Warming

Using the Visuals: Figure 19

If students have done the Discover activity, encourage them to compare their plastic covered box with the greenhouse in Figure 19. Then help students understand the analogy of a greenhouse to the greenhouse effect. Ask: **What part of Earth's atmosphere acts like a greenhouse roof?** *(Certain gases in the atmosphere—water vapor, carbon dioxide, and methane)* **What affect do these gases have on Earth's atmosphere?** *(They trap energy in the atmosphere.)* **Why are some scientists concerned about greenhouse gases?** *(As these gases increase in the atmosphere, they may trap more energy and cause global temperatures to increase.)* **learning modality: verbal**

Sunlight
Infrared radiation cannot pass through greenhouse roof

Figure 19 Sunlight enters the greenhouse and is absorbed. The interior of the greenhouse radiates back energy in the form of infrared radiation, or heat. The heat is trapped and held inside the greenhouse, warming it. *Applying Concepts What gases in Earth's atmosphere can trap heat like a greenhouse?*

The Greenhouse Effect Recall that gases in Earth's atmosphere hold in heat from the sun, keeping the atmosphere at a comfortable temperature for living things. The process by which gases in Earth's atmosphere trap solar energy is called the greenhouse effect.

Gases in the atmosphere that trap solar energy are called **greenhouse gases.** Water vapor, carbon dioxide, and methane are some of the greenhouse gases. **Human activities that add greenhouse gases to the atmosphere may be warming Earth's atmosphere.** For example, the burning of wood, coal, oil, and natural gas adds carbon dioxide to the air. If the increased carbon dioxide traps more heat, the result could be **global warming,** a gradual increase in the temperature of Earth's atmosphere.

The amount of carbon dioxide in the atmosphere has been steadily increasing. Some scientists predict that if the level of carbon dioxide doubles by the year 2100, the average global temperature could go up by 1.5 to 3.5 Celsius degrees.

Another Hypothesis Not everyone agrees about the causes of global warming. Some scientists think that the 0.5 Celsius degree rise in global temperatures over the past 120 years may be part of natural variations in climate rather than a result of increases in carbon dioxide.

Background

Facts and Figures Much of the carbon dioxide produced by burning fossil fuels is absorbed instead of staying in the atmosphere. Plants absorb carbon dioxide from the air and use it to make food in the process of photosynthesis. Rain forests absorb large amounts of carbon dioxide from the atmosphere. Not only is the destruction of rain forests reducing the amount of carbon dioxide that can be absorbed from the atmosphere, but burning them also increases the amount of carbon dioxide added to it.

Earth's oceans also absorb much of the extra carbon dioxide in the atmosphere. Carbon dioxide from the air enters water by simple diffusion. As long as the concentration of carbon dioxide in ocean water is less than that of the air, carbon dioxide gas will diffuse into the water.

As you learned in Section 3, satellite measurements have shown that the amount of energy the sun produces increases and decreases from year to year. These changes in solar energy could be causing periods of warmer and cooler climates. Or climate change could be a result of changes in both carbon dioxide levels and amounts of solar energy.

Possible Effects Global warming has some potential advantages. Farmers in cool areas could plant two crops a year. Places that are too cold for farming today could become farmland. However, many effects of global warming are likely to be less positive. Higher temperatures would cause water to evaporate from exposed soil, such as plowed farmland. Dry soil blows away easily. Thus some fertile fields might become "dust bowls."

A rise in temperatures of even a few degrees could warm up water in the oceans. As ocean surface temperatures increased, the number of hurricanes might increase.

As the water warmed, it would expand, raising sea levels around the world. Glaciers and polar ice caps might partially melt, which would also increase sea levels. Sea levels have already risen by 10 to 20 centimeters over the last 100 years, and could rise another 25 to 80 centimeters by the year 2100. Even such a small rise in sea levels would flood low-lying coastal areas.

☑ *Checkpoint* ***What are three possible effects of global warming?***

Ozone Depletion

Another global change in the atmosphere involves the ozone layer, which you learned about in Chapter 1. Ozone in the stratosphere filters out much of the harmful ultraviolet radiation from the sun.

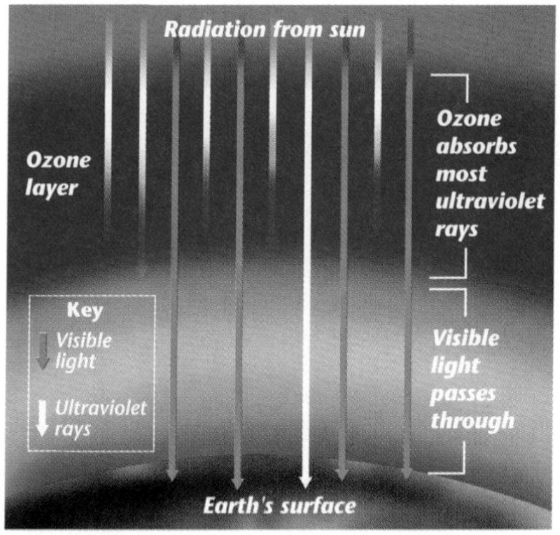

Figure 20 The ozone layer blocks much of the ultraviolet radiation coming from the sun. Visible light can pass through the ozone layer.

TRY THIS

It's Your Skin!

ACTIVITY

How well do sunscreens block out ultraviolet rays? Here's how to compare sunscreens.

1. Close the blinds or curtains in the room. Place one square of sun-sensitive paper inside each of three plastic sandwich bags.
2. Place three drops of one sunscreen on the outside of one bag. Spread the sunscreen as evenly as possible. Label this bag with the SPF number of the sunscreen.
3. On another bag, repeat Step 2 using a sunscreen with a different SPF. Wash your hands after spreading the sunscreen. Leave the third bag untreated as a control.
4. Place the bags outside in direct sunlight. Bring them back inside after 3 minutes or after one of the squares of paper has turned completely white.

Drawing Conclusions Did both of the sunscreens block ultraviolet radiation? Did one of the sunscreens block more ultraviolet radiation than the other one? Explain your results.

Real-Life Learning

Challenge student groups to make a plan for personally reducing carbon dioxide. Direct groups to first brainstorm a list of sources of carbon dioxide. (You might provide various resources to help groups identify these sources.) Then groups should identify the carbon-dioxide producing activities in which they are involved. Finally, groups should formulate a plan to reduce their carbon dioxide output. Encourage groups to present their plans to the class. **cooperative learning**

Ozone Depletion

TRY THIS

ACTIVITY

Skills Focus drawing conclusions
Materials *ultraviolet-sensitive paper, 3 plastic sandwich bags, 2 sunscreens with different SPF numbers, black marking pen*
Time 15 minutes
Tips Results will be more obvious if students use sunscreens with highly different SPF numbers. Obtain ultraviolet-sensitive paper from toy or craft stores (called "Sunprint Kit"). Save class time by precutting the paper.
Expected Outcome The paper without sunscreen will show the most color change, and the paper covered with the higher SPF sunscreen will show the least.
Answers Since the untreated paper showed the most color change, the sunscreens did block ultraviolet radiation. The sunscreen with the lower SPF number blocked less ultraviolet radiation because it showed more color change than the paper covered with the higher SPF sunscreen.
Extend Encourage students to return the bags with sunscreen to direct sunlight and monitor them to find out how long the sunscreen is effective. **learning modality: kinesthetic**

Media and Technology

Exploring Earth Science Videodisc
Unit 4, Side 2, "The Greenhouse Effect"
Chapter 5

Answers to Self-Assessment

Caption Question

Figure 19 Water vapor, carbon dioxide, methane

☑ *Checkpoint*

Areas too cold for farming today could become farmland, some fertile fields could become "dust bowls," the number of hurricanes could increase, and sea levels could rise and flood low-lying coastal areas.

Ongoing Assessment

Drawing Challenge students to draw their own diagrams showing how greenhouse gases trap heat energy from sunlight in Earth's atmosphere.
Portfolio Students can save their diagrams in their portfolios.

Ozone Depletion, continued

Addressing Naive Conceptions

Some students might be confused about why the depletion of the ozone layer is harmful when many metropolitan areas have Ozone Action Days to reduce air pollution. Ask: **Do you know why ozone is harmful to people?** *(Some students may not.)* Explain that ozone is part of smog. Ozone forms when sunlight irradiates the emissions from gasoline engines. Smog reduces visibility, irritates the respiratory system, causes eye irritations, and can damage plants. Point out that the ozone layer in the stratosphere would also not be a healthy place for people to live and breathe. However, it protects us from the ultraviolet radiation from the sun. **learning modality: verbal**

3 Assess

Section 4 Review Answers

1. The burning of wood, coal, oil, and natural gas
2. More carbon dioxide in the air traps more heat in the atmosphere, which causes a gradual increase in global temperatures.
3. chlorofluorocarbons
4. Depending on where they live, students might mention milder winters, longer growing seasons, coastal flooding, more hurricanes, and heat waves.

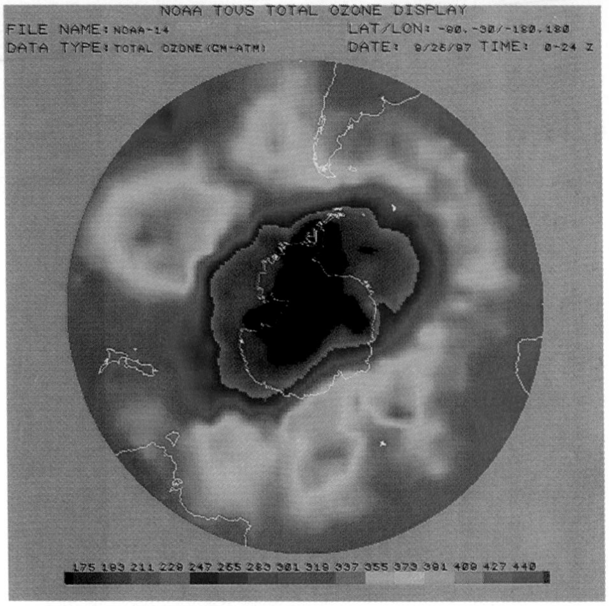

Figure 21 This satellite image shows the concentration of ozone in the air over the South Pole. The dark area shows where the ozone layer is the thinnest.

In the 1970s, scientists noticed that the ozone layer over Antarctica was growing thinner each spring. By 1992, the area of thinner ozone was more than twice as large as the continental United States. What created the ozone hole? **Chemicals produced by humans have been damaging the ozone layer.**

The main cause of ozone depletion is a group of chlorine compounds called **chlorofluorocarbons,** or CFCs. CFCs were used in air conditioners and refrigerators, as cleaners for electronic parts, and in spray cans. Most chemical compounds released into the air eventually break down. CFCs, however, can last for decades and rise all the way to the stratosphere. In the stratosphere, ultraviolet radiation breaks down the CFC molecules into atoms, including chlorine. The chlorine atoms then break ozone down into oxygen atoms.

Because ozone blocks ultraviolet radiation, a decrease in ozone means an increase in the amount of ultraviolet radiation that reaches Earth's surface. If you have ever been sunburned, you can understand one effect of stronger ultraviolet radiation! Ultraviolet radiation can also cause eye damage and several kinds of skin cancer.

In the late 1970s, the United States and many other countries banned the use of CFCs in spray cans. In 1992, more than 90 nations agreed to phase out production of CFCs. Because ozone depletion affects the whole world, such agreements must be international to be effective.

Section 4 Review

1. What human actions increase the amount of carbon dioxide in Earth's atmosphere?
2. How could increases in carbon dioxide in the air affect world temperatures?
3. What chemicals are the major cause of ozone depletion in the stratosphere?
4. **Thinking Critically** **Predicting** How might global warming change conditions where you live? How would this affect your life?

Science at Home

Visit a drugstore with your family. Compare the SPF (sun protection factor) of the various sunscreens for sale. Explain why it is important to protect your skin from ultraviolet radiation. Ask your family members to determine the best value for their money in terms of SPF rating and price.

142 ◆ I

Media and Technology

Exploring Earth Science Videodisc
Unit 6, Side 2, "Our Passion for Driving"
Chapter 1

Program Resources

◆ **Teaching Resources** 4-4 Review and Reinforce, p. 115; 4-4 Enrich, p. 116

STUDY GUIDE

CHAPTER 4 REVIEW

Section 1 What Causes Climate?

Key Ideas

- The climate of a region is determined by its temperature and precipitation.
- The main factors that influence temperature are latitude, altitude, distance from large bodies of water, and ocean currents.
- The main factors that affect precipitation are prevailing winds and the presence of mountains.
- The different seasons are a result of the tilt of Earth's axis as Earth travels around the sun.

Key Terms

climate, tropical zone, polar zone, temperate zone, marine climate, continental climate, windward, leeward, microclimate

Section 2 Climate Regions

Key Ideas

- Climates are classified according to temperature and precipitation.
- There are five main climate regions: tropical rainy, dry, temperate marine, temperate continental, and polar. Highlands are often considered to be a sixth climate region.

Key Terms

rain forest, savanna, desert, steppe, humid subtropical, subarctic, tundra, permafrost

Section 3 Long-Term Changes in Climate

Key Ideas

- Scientists assume that plants and animals in the past required the same conditions as similar plants and animals today.
- During each ice age, huge sheets of ice covered large parts of Earth's surface.
- Possible explanations for major climate changes include movement of continents, variations in the position of Earth relative to the sun, and changes in the sun's energy output.

Key Terms

ice age, sunspot

Section 4 Global Changes in the Atmosphere

INTEGRATING ENVIRONMENTAL SCIENCE

Key Ideas

- Human activities that add greenhouse gases to the atmosphere may be warming Earth's atmosphere.
- Chemicals produced by humans have been damaging the ozone layer.

Key Terms

greenhouse gas, global warming, chlorofluorocarbons

ACTIVITY USING THE INTERNET
www.science-explorer.phschool.com

Science at Home

ACTIVITY

To make sure that students can explain to their families the importance of using sunscreen, ask: **Why is it important to protect your skin from ultraviolet radiation?** *(Ultraviolet radiation can cause sunburn and several kinds of skin cancer.)* To help prepare students for comparison-shopping, suggest that they take calculators with them to the drugstore and calculate the price per ounce of the sunscreens they are comparing. After they compare the prices of equal quantities, then they can begin to determine which sunscreens are a better value based on their SPF numbers.

Program Resources

- **Teaching Resources** Chapter 4 Project Scoring Rubric, p. 100; Chapter 4 Performance Assessment, pp. 155–157; Chapter 4 Test, pp. 158–161

Media and Technology

Interactive Student Tutorial CD-ROM I-4

Computer Test Bank I–4 Test

Performance Assessment

Writing Challenge students to write a news article that describes what global warming and ozone depletion are and how human activities have affected the atmosphere.

Portfolio Students can save their news articles in their portfolios.

CHAPTER 4 REVIEW

Reviewing Content: Multiple Choice

1. b **2.** c **3.** b **4.** d **5.** a

True or False

6. precipitation **7.** winter **8.** true **9.** true
10. carbon dioxide

Checking Concepts

11. Most of the United States is in the temperate zone; Hawaii and southern Florida are in the tropical zone; much of Alaska is in the polar zone.
12. Dry climates occur where potential evaporation is greater than precipitation. The two types of dry climates differ in the amount of precipitation they receive. Steppes get more precipitation than deserts.
13. Present-day continents were once at different latitudes and had different climates. As the continents moved from their original positions, their latitudes changed, global patterns of wind and ocean currents changed, and mountains formed, all of which affect climate.
14. Ozone depletion affects the whole world, and the actions of people around the world affect the ozone. For this reason, everyone around the world must work together to prevent ozone depletion.
15. Answers should show that students have accurately observed their local climate factors and have successfully related them to the concepts in the chapter.

Thinking Visually

16. Titles may vary. *Sample Title:* Factors Affecting Climate
a. precipitation **b.** or **c.** distance from large bodies of water or ocean currents
d. mountain ranges

CHAPTER 4 REVIEW

Reviewing Content

For more review of key concepts, see the Interactive Student Tutorial CD-ROM.

Multiple Choice

Choose the letter of the best answer.

1. Temperatures are highest in the tropical zone because
a. the land is flat.
b. the sun's rays strike most directly.
c. Earth's axis is tilted toward the sun.
d. ocean currents warm the region.

2. Continental climates are found
a. on every continent.
b. only near the equator.
c. only in the Northern Hemisphere.
d. only in the Southern Hemisphere.

3. In a wet-and-dry tropical climate, the most common vegetation is
a. coniferous forests.
b. savanna grasslands.
c. tropical rain forest.
d. steppe grasslands.

4. Extremely cold periods in Earth's history have resulted in huge
a. tree rings.
b. sunspots.
c. pollen deposits.
d. glaciers.

5. Chlorofluorocarbons, or CFCs, are the main cause of
a. ozone depletion.
b. global warming.
c. the greenhouse effect.
d. ice ages.

True or False

If the statement is true, write true. If it is false, change the underlined word or words to make it true.

6. The prevailing winds affect how much sunlight falls on an area.
7. When the north end of Earth's axis is tilted toward the sun, it is summer in the Southern Hemisphere.
8. Climate regions are classified according to temperature and precipitation.
9. A thin tree ring indicates that a year was cool or dry.
10. An increase in nitrogen in the atmosphere may be making world temperatures increase.

Checking Concepts

11. Identify the parts of the United States that are located in each of the three temperature zones.
12. How are "dry" climates defined? How do the two types of dry climate differ?
13. How does the movement of continents explain major changes in climate over time?
14. In order to be effective, why must agreements aimed at preventing or reducing ozone depletion be international?
15. **Writing to Learn** In what climate region do you live? Write a description of your local climate and identify some of the things—such as latitude, bodies of water, or wind patterns—that affect the climate.

Thinking Visually

16. Concept Map Copy the concept map about climate onto a separate sheet of paper. Then complete it and add a title. (For more on concept maps, see the Skills Handbook.)

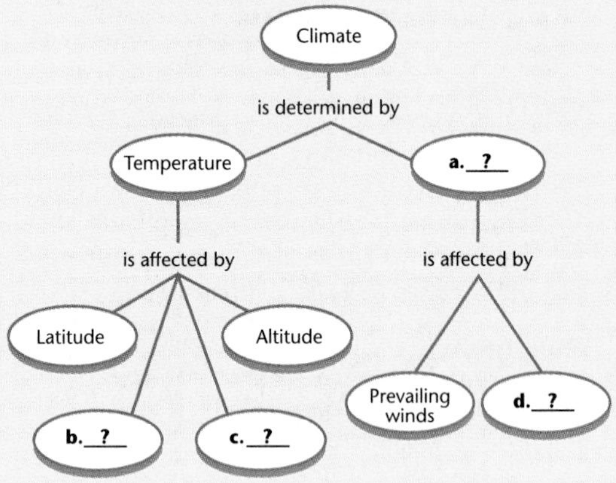

Applying Skills

17. Zone A, polar zone; Zone B, temperate zone; Zone C, tropical zone; Zone D, temperate zone; Zone E, polar zone
18. tropical zone; 47 degrees of latitude
19. Zone B

Thinking Critically

20. Answers may vary. *Sample answer:* Large bodies of water moderate the climates of nearby land; warm and cold ocean currents influence the climate of coastal areas; the amount of precipitation is a factor in wet and dry climates.
21. Global warming caused by an increase in greenhouse gases is the result of human activities and can be controlled. Earlier changes in climate were the result of natural forces.
22. Answers may vary. Some students might suggest the most important thing to do is to study the problem more to find definitive answers. Other students might say reduce the amount of carbon dioxide released into the atmosphere.
23. Air that passes over the steppe in a semiarid climate has lost its water vapor as it passed over mountain ranges, so the air is drier. Some of the air that passes over humid continental areas comes from the oceans and doesn't cross mountain ranges, so the air carries more moisture.

Applying Skills

Use the map of world temperature zones to answer Questions 17–19.

17. Interpreting Maps Name each of the five zones shown on the map.

18. Measuring What is the name of the temperature zone that includes the equator? How many degrees of latitude does this zone cover?

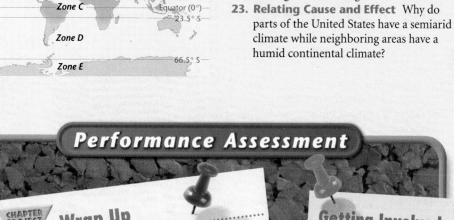

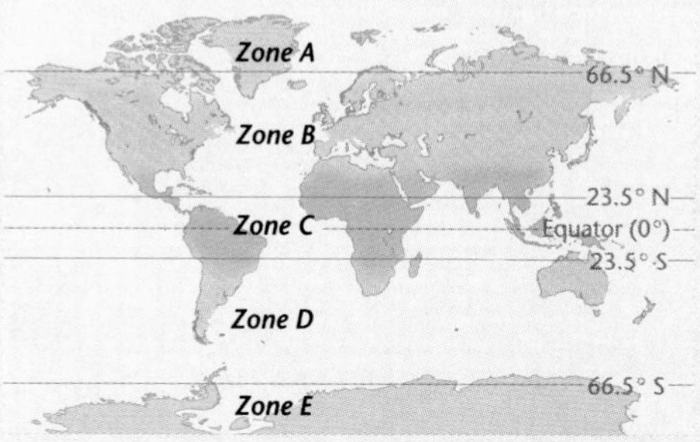

19. Interpreting Data Which of the five zones shown on the map has the greatest amount of land area suitable for people to live?

Thinking Critically

20. Relating Cause and Effect Describe three ways in which water influences climate.

21. Comparing and Contrasting How is global warming different from earlier changes in Earth's climate?

22. Making Judgments What is the most important thing that needs to be done about global warming?

23. Relating Cause and Effect Why do parts of the United States have a semiarid climate while neighboring areas have a humid continental climate?

CHAPTER 4 REVIEW

Performance Assessment

CHAPTER PROJECT 4

Wrap Up

Presenting Your Project Decide how to present your project. You could use a written report, oral presentation, or a bulletin board. Do your graphs compare the conditions in the different microclimates? What conditions favor plants or animals in some areas? After you present your project to the class, discuss what you think causes different microclimates.

Reflect and Record In your journal, describe how you could improve your investigation. Are there factors you did not study? Did you notice any organisms that live only in certain microclimates? What additional information about microclimates would you like to find?

Getting Involved

In Your Community With your classmates, investigate the agreements that various countries, including the United States, have made about CFCs and greenhouse gases. How do these agreements affect everyday products, such as automobiles and air conditioners? Create a poster that describes what individuals can do about these issues.

Program Resources

◆ **Inquiry Skills Activity Book** Provides teaching and review of all inquiry skills

Performance Assessment

CHAPTER PROJECT 4

Wrap Up

Presenting Your Project Find out from groups how they intend to present their projects. Have bulletin board space available for those groups who choose to use it. Groups giving oral presentations could use an overhead projector to display their graphs. Each group should present graphs that compare the weather conditions in the different microclimates they studied. In their presentations, groups should draw conclusions about the kinds of conditions that favor certain plants and animals. After groups have presented their reports, discuss the factors that cause different microclimates. Begin by prompting students to recall the climate factors that affect temperature and precipitation.

Reflect and Record Encourage students to be objective as they evaluate their investigations. For their journals, suggest that they reflect on the concepts they learned in this chapter and what they could have added to their investigation.

Getting Involved

In Your Community Divide the class into groups and assign groups to study either greenhouse gases or CFCs. Provide some newspaper articles, news magazine articles, or science magazine articles about these topics for students to use. Also encourage students to use encyclopedias or sources off the Internet. Students should work together to design their posters, using the information they have learned. Find places in your community to display these posters.

INTERDISCIPLINARY EXPLORATION

Antarctica

This interdisciplinary feature focuses on the weather and climate of Antarctica, the world's coldest, driest, and windiest continent. The perspectives of four different disciplines—social studies, science, mathematics, and language arts—show students how the content they are learning in *Weather and Climate* relates to other sciences and to other subjects they are studying in school. This feature is particularly suitable for team teaching and is a good springboard for extra-credit projects for students needing extra challenges.

1 Engage/Explore

Activating Prior Knowledge

Point out to students that they will be reading about Antarctica, the continent on which the South Pole is located. Help students recall what they learned in Chapter 4 about polar climates. Ask: **What would you expect the climate of Antarctica to be like?** *(Students are likely to say extremely cold; they also may say snowy.)* **What makes it so cold there?** *(The sun's rays strike the ground at a low angle year round, so it never heats up there.)* Point out that Antarctica actually receives very little snow. In fact, the continent receives less than 5 cm of precipitation each year. Ask: **Why do you think Antarctica gets so little precipitation?** *(The very cold air cannot hold much moisture.)*

Introducing the Unit

Have students look through the unit to find pictures that show the landscape of Antarctica and people exploring or doing research there. Call students' attention especially to the way the people are dressed. Then have students try to imagine being in Antarctica themselves. Ask: **What do you think it would be like to live and work in Antarctica?** *(Correct any serious misconceptions students may reveal by their comments.)* Point out to the class that, even though cruise ships now take tourists to Antarctica, it is still a difficult and dangerous place to visit because of the harshness of its climate.

Program Resources

- **Teaching Resources** Interdisciplinary Explorations, Social Studies, pp. 122–124; Science, pp. 125–128; Mathematics, pp. 129–131; Language Arts, pp. 132–133

ANTARCTICA

What kind of weather do you expect in July—hot and sunny? Brace yourself—July in Antarctica will surprise you!

On July 21, 1983, the temperature at the Russian research station Vostok dropped to a world record low: –89°C.

WELCOME TO ANTARCTICA!

Because Antarctica is in the Southern Hemisphere, July is midwinter there. But the temperature isn't very warm in summer, either. The average summer temperature at Vostok is –33°C. Antarctica's climate is unusual in other ways. It's the windiest continent as well as the coldest. Even though Antarctica is covered with snow and ice, it's also the driest continent—a snowy desert. Less than five centimeters of precipitation falls in the interior in a year. Antarctic blizzards are terrifying, but they don't bring much new snow. They just blow drifts from one place to another.

In spite of its extremes, Antarctica is both beautiful and fascinating. As you can see on the map, many countries have set up research stations there to study climate, temperature, and the atmosphere. Scientists in Antarctica also research wildlife and geology.

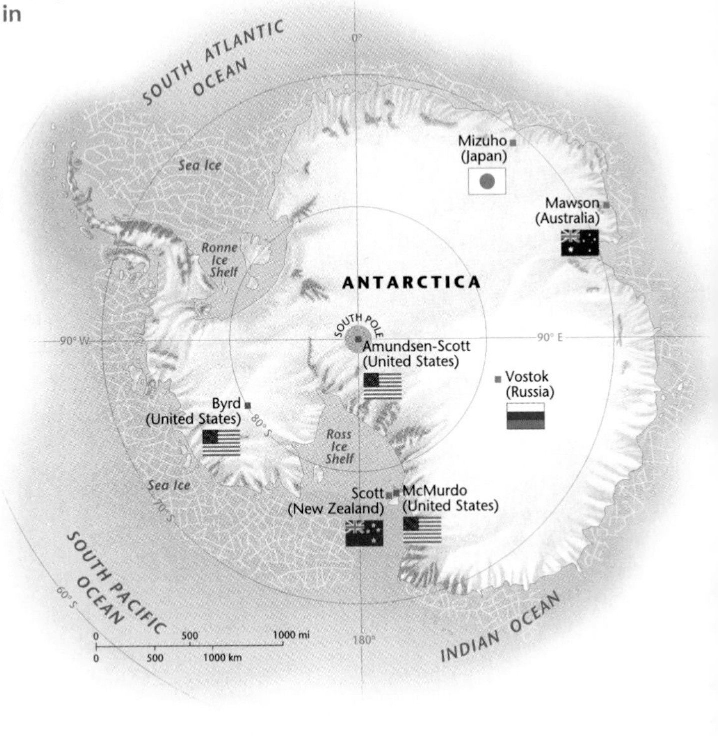

The map shows major research stations in Antarctica.

A huge dome covers buildings at the U.S. Amundsen-Scott station at the South Pole.

Race to the South Pole

Would you brave the darkness and cold of Antarctica? In the early 1900s, several famous explorers began a "race to the pole." Their attempts to reach the South Pole produced stories of heroism—and tragedy.

In October 1911, the British explorer Robert Falcon Scott traveled to the South Pole. He started overland with dog teams, motorized sleds, and ponies. He and four other explorers reached the South Pole in January 1912—only to find that a Norwegian expedition led by Roald Amundsen had beaten them there by a month! Scott's team had lost the race!

Robert F. Scott (above center) and his men reached the South Pole, but lost the race.

Soon after, Scott and his crew started back. But they were trapped in blizzards. All of them died. Searchers later found their tent, Scott's diary, and photographs. Scott's team had been only 18 kilometers from a supply camp.

A few years later, Sir Ernest Shackleton was the hero of an incredible Antarctic survival story. In 1914, Shackleton tried a new route to the South Pole. On the way, ice trapped and crushed his ship, the *Endurance.* He and his men escaped across the ice to Elephant Island. Leaving 22 men there, Shackleton and five others sailed in a small whaleboat to find help. Amazingly, everyone was rescued.

In the 1920s, airplanes brought a new way to explore Antarctica. American pilot and explorer Richard E. Byrd led the first flight over the South Pole in 1929. Later, Byrd set up research stations at Little America.

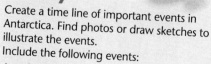

International Cooperation

In 1957–1958, during the International Geophysical Year, scientists from countries around the world established research stations in Antarctica and shared their scientific findings. In 1959, twelve nations signed the Antarctic Treaty to guarantee "freedom of scientific investigation." The original signers were (from top left) Argentina, Australia, Belgium, Chile, France, Japan, New Zealand, Norway, the Soviet Union, South Africa, the United Kingdom, and the United States.

Social Studies Activity

Create a time line of important events in Antarctica. Find photos or draw sketches to illustrate the events.

Include the following events:

- early expeditions
- "race to the pole" in the early 1900s
- International Geophysical Year
- Antarctic Treaty
- new research stations

Why did it take courage and endurance to try to reach the South Pole in the early 1900s?

2 Facilitate

- Discuss why people have been so determined to explore or do research in Antarctica. Ask: **Why would people put their lives at risk to explore Antarctica or do research there?** *(Antarctica was the last great unexplored frontier. It is of great research interest because of its uniqueness.)* Add that exploration of Antarctica began as early as 1820 and, by 1992, 17 different countries had a total of 37 research stations in Antarctica.

Social Studies Activity

Urge students to go beyond the information provided in the feature to find important events and illustrations for their time lines, such as the First (1882–1883) and Second (1932–1933) International Polar Years. You also may want to share with the class the information on early explorations given in the Background on the bottom of this page.

Teaching Resources These worksheets correlate with this page: Plotting Points on a Map, pp. 122–123, Locating Physical Features on a Map, p. 124.

3 Assess

Activity Assessment

Students' time lines should show they have mastered the content of the feature by including important events in correct chronological order. Make sure students know more than just the date of each event they include. *(For example, the International Polar Years were held to coordinate scientific research in both the Arctic and Antarctic.)* You may want to give students a place to display their time lines. In their answers, students should reveal their understanding of the rigors and dangers of working in the polar climate and remoteness of Antarctica, especially given the technological limitations of the early 1900s.

Background

History The first person to set foot on Antarctica was an American seal hunter, named John Davis, who landed a boat there in 1821. In 1823, an English seal hunter, named James Weddell, sailed even farther south, to 74°S latitude. A French expedition landed on Antarctica in 1840, and just days later a United States expedition, commanded by Charles Wilkes, reached Antarctica as well. Despite being poorly prepared, Wilkes managed to explore about 2,000 km of the eastern Antarctic coastline. The next year, an English expedition, under the leadership of James Ross, discovered the great ice barrier, now known as the Ross Ice Shelf. After that, for more than 50 years, there was little interest in Antarctica. Then, in the late 1890s, Norwegian and Swedish expeditions explored the continent. They were the first to remain there throughout the winter.

Science

2 Facilitate

- Relate the content of this page to Chapter 2. Ask: **Why does the ocean make coastal regions of Antarctica warmer than inland areas?** *(The water retains its heat longer than the land and warms the air over the coast.)* **Why does a covering of snow make most areas of Antarctica colder?** *(Snow, because it is white, reflects most of the sunlight that strikes it, so snowy areas are not heated up by the sun as much as areas of bare land, which are darker.)*
- Make sure students understand the rationale for wearing multiple layers of clothing to stay warm. Ask: **Why do many layers of clothes keep you warmer than one thick layer?** *(Each layer has a different purpose. Also, the multiple layers trap air between them, providing extra insulation.)*

Science Activity

Caution students to be very careful handling the hot water. Check students' understanding of the need to control variables by asking: **Why is it important for all the jars to start out at the same temperature?** *(So any differences in water temperature after 30 minutes will be due only to differences in the rate of cooling because of the socks)*

Teaching Resources The following worksheets correlate with this page: Designing an Experiment, page 125; Plotting Weather Station Data, pages 126–127; and Interpreting Temperature Data, page 128.

Science

Continent of Extremes

Why is Antarctica so cold? Its high latitude and months of darkness are important reasons. In addition, the broad expanses of white snow and icy glaciers reflect back sunlight before much heat is absorbed.

As on every continent, climates vary from place to place. Warmer parts of Antarctica are at lower elevations, at lower latitudes, or near the coast. Coastal areas are warmer because the nearby ocean moderates temperatures. These areas also have bare land, which absorbs heat.

Summer weather patterns in Antarctica are different from winter patterns. The short summer warm-up starts in October. The warmest temperatures are from mid-December to mid-January. Then temperatures drop suddenly. So by mid-March, the beginning of winter, the temperature has fallen to winter levels. Over the next six months Antarctica remains very cold—and dark.

Science Activity

Staying warm is essential for life in the Antarctic. Set up an experiment to test how well different materials keep heat from escaping. Use socks made of nylon, silk, cotton, and wool. You will need a jar for each material plus one jar as a control.

- Fill jars with equal amounts of very hot water. The water in each jar should be the same temperature.
- Record the temperature of each jar and screw each cap on.
- Place each jar, except the control, inside a sock. Refrigerate all the jars for 30 minutes.
- Remove the jars and record the water temperature of each.

Which jar cooled fastest? Which materials retained the heat best?

How do polar explorers and researchers stay warm? The secret is wearing layers of clothing that keep body heat from escaping. ▼

An insulated hood, a hat with earflaps, or a face mask protects against wind. Sunglasses or goggles reduce the glare of sunlight and protect eyes from freezing.

Boots and gloves are layered, too. A layer of fleece may be sealed inside a waterproof rubber layer.

- An **inner layer** of long underwear (silk, wool, or synthetic) carries moisture away from the skin.
- A fluffy **insulating layer**, such as fleece or down, traps pockets of air that are warmed by body heat.
- The **outer shell layer** protects against wind and water.

3 Assess

Activity Assessment

Students should find that the jar in the nylon sock cooled fastest, whereas the jars in the natural-fiber socks, particularly the wool sock, retained more heat.

Background

Facts and Figures Although the climate of Antarctica is too frigid for humans to live there without insulating clothing, stoves, and other technological support, that doesn't mean that there is no life in Antarctica. More than 40 different species of birds spend the summer there, including albatrosses, terns, and gulls. Sea animals are also abundant. They include seals, penguins, whales, squid, and about 100 species of fish. Many different species of animals also live on the land, although all of them are invertebrates, mostly insects. There is a greater variety of plant life on the land, with a total of about 800 plant species. Close to half of the plant species are lichens, but mosses, grasses, liverworts, and a few other types of plants are also found. In addition to animals and plants, Antarctica is home to bacteria, molds, yeast, algae, and fungi.

Sky Watch

Lingering Antarctic sunset

It's March 21—the beginning of winter—and you're watching the sun set very, very slowly. It takes 30 hours—more than a day—for the sun to disappear below the horizon. Once it's gone, you won't see sunshine again until September! April and early May aren't completely dark, but there is hardly enough light to cast a shadow. Then it's dark for two months. In August, light begins again. The sky brightens quickly until the polar sunrise.

The tilt of Earth on its axis affects the hours of daylight and darkness from season to season. At the poles, midsummer brings the "midnight sun," which circles around the sky but does not set. Midwinter brings almost total darkness.

HOURS OF DAYLIGHT IN ANTARCTICA

(sunrise to sunset, rounded to nearest hour)

Month	Mizuho Station 70° S	Amundsen-Scott Station 90° S
January	24	24
February	18	24
March	14	24
April	9	0
May	3	0
June	0	0
July	0	0
August	7	0
September	11	0
October	16	24
November	22	24
December	24	24

The table shows hours of daylight on the 15th of each month. It shows readings at two different Antarctic locations—the Amundsen-Scott station and Japan's Mizuho station. ▶

Math Activity

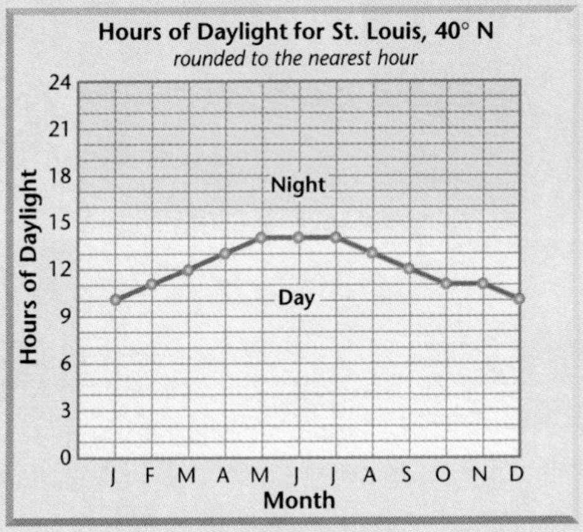

This line graph shows the year-round pattern of daylight for St. Louis, Missouri, located at about 40° north latitude. Readings were taken on the fifteenth of each month. Use the table to make another line graph that shows hours of daylight for Mizuho station, Amundsen-Scott station, and St. Louis.

- On the horizontal axis of the table, list the months.
- On the vertical axis, mark off spaces for 0 to 24 hours.
- Choose a different color marker for each latitude. Above each month for each location, place a colored dot at the correct hour mark. Connect the dots to show changes in daylight at each place during a year.
- How are the changes in darkness and daylight in Antarctica like those you see at home? How are they different?

2 Facilitate

- Check that students understand the effect of latitude on hours of daylight by asking: **How many hours of daylight do you predict a station at 80°S latitude would have in March? In November?** *(About 19 hours of daylight in March and 23 hours in November)*
- Help students appreciate the importance in their lives of a regular cycle of day and night. First have them compare the number of hours of daylight for the current month where they live with the number for the same month at 90°S latitude. Then ask: **How would your everyday life and activities be different if your location had the same number of hours of daylight as the South Pole?** *(Answers may range from trouble sleeping when it is light all night to the cancellation of outside events when it is dark all day. Accept all reasonable answers without comment.)*

Math Activity

Before students start plotting points on their graphs, check to see that they have labeled both axes correctly. You can extend the activity by asking: **How many hours of daylight do you predict there would be at the equator?** *(About 12 hours a day year round)*

Teaching Resources The following worksheets correlate with this page: Using a Model, page 129; Reading a Table, page 130; and Making a Graph, page 131.

3 Assess

Activity Assessment

Students may say that the changes in darkness and daylight both in Antarctica and at home vary in a regular way from month to month. However, in Antarctica the changes are more extreme, and the months with the most hours of daylight are different—June and July at home as compared with December and January in Antarctica.

Background

Facts and Figures Antarctica is the world's fifth-largest continent. With an area of more than 13 million km^2, it makes up almost one tenth of Earth's land surface. However, more than 98 percent of Antarctica is under a thick layer of ice, in some places 3 km thick. Because of the ice, scientists have had to learn about the shape of the land surface by beaming radio-echo soundings down through the ice.

Much of the ice-free land in Antarctica lies along the coast, but the greatest continuous stretches of ice-free land on the continent lie in three major valleys. Because extremely dry winds blow down into these valleys, no precipitation has fallen in them for over two million years. Any snow that blows into them simply evaporates because the air is so dry.

Language Arts

2 Facilitate

- Provide students with a context for Byrd's memoir by telling them that the excerpt was written during the second of five expeditions that Byrd led to Antarctica. During the second expedition, Byrd spent more than four months alone at his research station because he wanted to see what it would be like. Share the additional information provided in the background material below. Invite students who need extra challenges to research Byrd's later expeditions to Antarctica and share what they learn with the rest of the class.
- Call students' attention to the month the Byrd excerpt was written. *(April)* Point out that Little America, where Byrd set up research stations, is not the same as Byrd Station shown on the map on page 146. Little America was located in the Ross Ice Shelf at about 80°S latitude. Then have students determine from the table on page 149 about how many hours of daylight each day Byrd would have had during April at that latitude. *(From just a few hours a day to no daylight)* Ask: **How do you think long periods of darkness would have affected Byrd's solitary stay in Antarctica?** *(Students may say that long periods of darkness would have made it much harder to cope with the loneliness, barren landscape, frigid cold, and other hardships.)*

Language Arts Activity

Help students appreciate how Byrd uses concrete, sensory details to communicate to the reader the extreme cold of Antarctica. Point out that all three paragraphs describe the cold, then ask: **What images does Byrd use to convey to the reader how extremely cold it is in Antarctica?** *(Possible answers include so cold that tomato juice shatters in its bottles, your breath sounds like Chinese firecrackers, the flame of a lamp dries up on the wick, and rubber turns brittle.)* Encourage students to use similar concrete sensory details in their descriptive writing.

Language Arts

Alone in Antarctica

Admiral Richard Byrd worked in the Antarctic for nearly 30 years after his flight over the South Pole. He led several expeditions and set up research stations at Little America. Byrd's book *Alone* is based on the journal he kept while spending the winter of 1934 alone at a weather station outpost. During his four-and-a-half-month stay, Byrd nearly gave up mentally and physically. He endured, however, and kept up his weather research until help arrived in August.

In this memoir of his days in early April, 1934, Byrd describes some of the problems of working in the intense cold.

At times I felt as if I were the last survivor of an Ice Age, striving to hold on with the flimsy tools bequeathed by an easy-going, temperate world. Cold does queer things. At 50° Fahrenheit below zero a flashlight dies out in your hand. At –55° Fahrenheit kerosene will freeze, and the flame will dry up on the wick. At –60° Fahrenheit rubber turns brittle. One day, I remember, the antenna wire snapped in my hands when I tried to bend it to make a new connection. Below –60° Fahrenheit cold will find the last microscopic touch of oil in an instrument and stop it dead. If there is the slightest breeze, you can hear your breath freeze as it floats away, making a sound like that of Chinese firecrackers. . . . And if you work too hard and breathe too deeply, your lungs will sometimes feel as if they were on fire.

Cold—even April's relatively moderate cold—gave me plenty to think about. . . . Two cases of tomato juice shattered their bottles. Whenever I brought canned food inside the shack I had to let it stand all day near the stove to thaw. . . . Frost was forever collecting on the electrical contact points of

Admiral Byrd tries to keep warm in his small shack at Little America. ▸
Coastal view of Antarctica ▾

Background

History Byrd's second expedition to Antarctica in 1933–1935 is considered one of Antarctica's greatest and most adventure-filled scientific expeditions. Byrd had to be rescued from his solitary encampment in August of 1934 because of carbon monoxide fumes from his camp stove. The expedition became famous because of live radio broadcasts. This led to greater interest in Antarctica. Byrd went on to lead three more Antarctic expeditions.

Byrd founded the Little America station during his second expedition. Little America served as a research station until 1960, when it was abandoned because the ice beneath it had become unstable and the station started floating out to sea on an iceberg. Later, the United States built McMurdo, a station on McMurdo Sound. It is now the largest research station in Antarctica.

the wind vane and wind cups. Some days I climbed the twelve-foot anemometer pole two and three times to clean them. It was a bitter job, especially on blustery nights. With my legs twined around the slender pole, my arms flung over the cleats, and my free hands trying to scrape the contact point clean with a knife and at the same time hold a flashlight to see, I qualified for the world's coldest flagpole sitter. I seldom came down from that pole without a frozen finger, toe, nose, or cheek.

The shack was always freezingly cold in the morning. I slept with the door open [for ventilation]. When I arose the inside temperature (depending upon the surface weather) might be anywhere from 10° to 40° Fahrenheit below zero. Frost coated the sleeping bag where my breath had condensed during the night; my socks and boots, when I picked them up, were so stiff with frozen sweat that I first had to work them between my hands. A pair of silk gloves hung from a nail over the bunk, where I could grab them the first thing. Yet, even with their protection, my fingers would sting and burn from the touch of the lamp and stove as I lighted them.

Language Arts Activity

From this passage, what can you conclude about Byrd's attitude toward his research? Although you've probably never traveled to Antarctica, you may have had an outdoor adventure—at summer camp or even in a city park. Use descriptive writing to recapture that experience. Remember to include concrete, sensory details like those in Byrd's journal. If you prefer, write about an imaginary event or adventure in the outdoors.

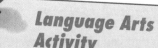

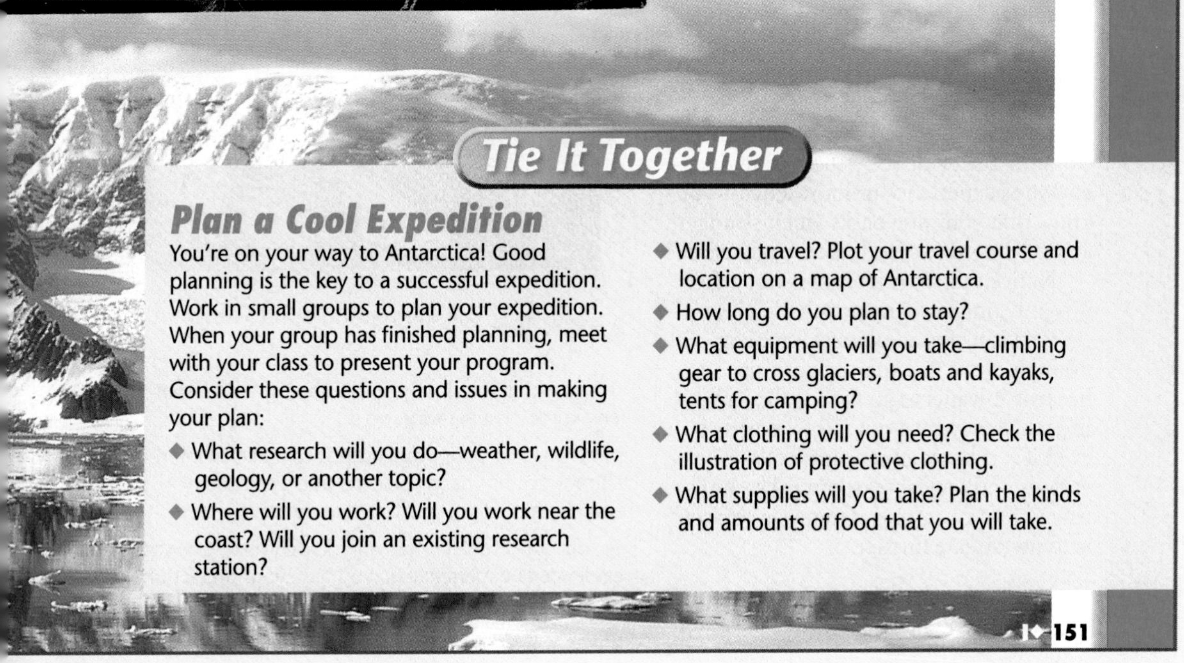

Tie It Together

Plan a Cool Expedition

You're on your way to Antarctica! Good planning is the key to a successful expedition. Work in small groups to plan your expedition. When your group has finished planning, meet with your class to present your program. Consider these questions and issues in making your plan:

- What research will you do—weather, wildlife, geology, or another topic?
- Where will you work? Will you work near the coast? Will you join an existing research station?
- Will you travel? Plot your travel course and location on a map of Antarctica.
- How long do you plan to stay?
- What equipment will you take—climbing gear to cross glaciers, boats and kayaks, tents for camping?
- What clothing will you need? Check the illustration of protective clothing.
- What supplies will you take? Plan the kinds and amounts of food that you will take.

I◆151

Teaching Resources The following worksheets correlate with these pages: Comparing Descriptive Writing, page 132, and Reading for Content, page 133.

3 Assess

Activity Assessment

Based on the hardships and dangers Byrd endured, students are likely to conclude that he was very serious about his research and very devoted to it. In their descriptive writing, students should describe an adventure, either real or imaginary, using concrete sensory details. For example, instead of saying simply that they were frightened by a bear outside their tent on a camping trip, they might describe how they imagined the bear was a monster and how the shadow it cast on their tent made it look as big as King Kong.

Tie It Together

Time 1 day for groups to develop plans, 1 day for class presentations

Tips Tell students that where they plan to work, whether they plan to travel, how long they plan to stay, and what equipment they plan to take will all depend largely on the nature of the research they plan to do. Therefore, they must first decide what their research topic will be, what data they will collect, and how they will collect it. Encourage groups to develop specific research topics. If students are having difficulty thinking of topics, you might suggest such topics as the ozone hole over Antarctica and Antarctica's active volcanoes. When groups present their plans to the class, encourage other students to suggest any items they think have been overlooked and to offer other helpful suggestions.

Extend Challenge students to pretend they have undertaken the planned expedition. Have them write journal entries to record their observations and experiences. Ask volunteers to read some of their journal entries aloud to the class.

Developing scientific thinking in students is important for a solid science education. To learn how to think scientifically, students need frequent opportunities to practice science process skills, critical thinking skills, as well as other skills that support scientific inquiry. The *Science Explorer* Skills Handbook introduces the following key science skills:

- ◆ Science Process Skills
- ◆ SI Measuring Skills
- ◆ Skills for Conducting a Scientific Investigation
- ◆ Critical Thinking Skills
- ◆ Information Organizing Skills
- ◆ Data Table and Graphing Skills

The Skills Handbook is designed as a reference for students to use whenever they need to review a science skill. You can use the activities provided in the Skills Handbook to teach or reinforce the skills.

Think Like a Scientist

Observing

ACTIVITY

Before students look at the photograph, remind them that an observation is only what they can see, hear, smell, taste, or feel. Ask: **Which senses will you use to make observations from this photograph?** *(Sight is the only sense that can be used to make observations from the photograph.)* **What are some observations you can make from the photograph?** *(Answers may vary. Sample answers: The boy is wearing sneakers, sport socks, shorts, and a tee shirt; the boy is sitting in the grass holding something blue against his knee; the boy is looking at his knee; there is a soccer ball laying beside the boy.)* List the observations on the chalkboard. If students make any inferences or predictions about the boy at this point, ask: **Can you be sure your statement is factual and accurate from just observing the photograph?** Help students understand how observations differ from inferences and predictions.

Inferring

ACTIVITY

Review students' observations from the photograph. Then ask: **What inferences can you make from your observations?** *(Students may say that the boy hurt his knee playing soccer and is holding a coldpack against his injured knee.)* **What experience or knowledge helped you make this inference?** *(Students may have experienced knee injuries from playing soccer, and they may be familiar with coldpacks like the one the boy is using.)* **Can anyone suggest another possible explanation for these observations?** *(Answers may vary. Sample answer: The boy hurt his knee jogging, and he just happened to sit beside a soccer ball his sister left in the yard.)* **How can you find out whether an inference is correct?** *(by further investigation)*

Predicting

ACTIVITY

After coming to some consensus about the inference that the boy hurt his knee, encourage students to make predictions about what will happen next. *(Students' predictions may vary. Sample answers: The boy will go to the doctor. A friend will help the boy home. The boy will get up and continue playing soccer.)*

Think Like a Scientist

Although you may not know it, you think like a scientist every day. Whenever you ask a question and explore possible answers, you use many of the same skills that scientists do. Some of these skills are described on this page.

Observing

When you use one or more of your five senses to gather information about the world, you are **observing.** Hearing a dog bark, counting twelve green seeds, and smelling smoke are all observations. To increase the power of their senses, scientists sometimes use microscopes, telescopes, or other instruments that help them make more detailed observations.

An observation must be factual and accurate—an exact report of what your senses detect. It is important to keep careful records of your observations in science class by writing or drawing in a notebook. The information collected through observations is called evidence, or data.

Inferring

When you explain or interpret an observation, you are **inferring,** or making an inference. For example, if you hear your dog barking, you may infer that someone is at your front door. To make this inference, you combine the evidence—the barking dog—and your experience or knowledge—you know that your dog barks when strangers approach—to reach a logical conclusion.

Notice that an inference is not a fact; it is only one of many possible explanations for an observation. For example, your dog may be barking because it wants to go for a walk. An inference may turn out to be incorrect even if it is based on accurate observations and logical reasoning. The only way to find out if an inference is correct is to investigate further.

Predicting

When you listen to the weather forecast, you hear many predictions about the next day's weather—what the temperature will be, whether it will rain, and how windy it will be. Weather forecasters use observations and knowledge of weather patterns to predict the weather. The skill of **predicting** involves making an inference about a future event based on current evidence or past experience.

Because a prediction is an inference, it may prove to be false. In science class, you can test some of your predictions by doing experiments. For example, suppose you predict that larger paper airplanes can fly farther than smaller airplanes. How could you test your prediction?

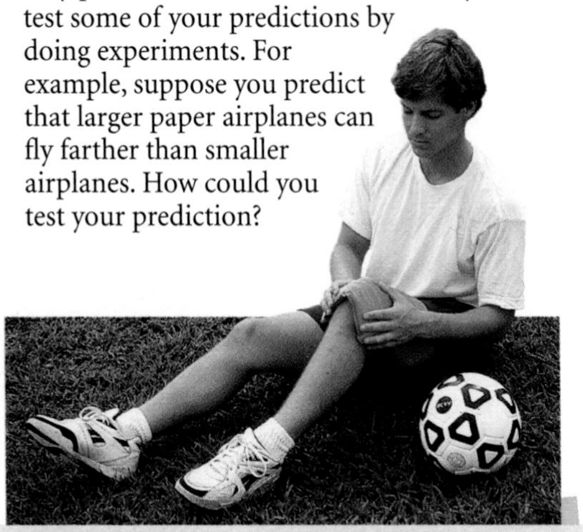

ACTIVITY Use the photograph to answer the questions below.

Observing Look closely at the photograph. List at least three observations.

Inferring Use your observations to make an inference about what has happened. What experience or knowledge did you use to make the inference?

Predicting Predict what will happen next. On what evidence or experience do you base your prediction?

SKILLS HANDBOOK

Classifying

Could you imagine searching for a book in the library if the books were shelved in no particular order? Your trip to the library would be an all-day event! Luckily, librarians group together books on similar topics or by the same author. Grouping together items that are alike in some way is called **classifying.** You can classify items in many ways: by size, by shape, by use, and by other important characteristics.

Like librarians, scientists use the skill of classifying to organize information and objects. When things are sorted into groups, the relationships among them become easier to understand.

ACTIVITY

Classify the objects in the photograph into two groups based on any characteristic you choose. Then use another characteristic to classify the objects into three groups.

Making Models

Have you ever drawn a picture to help someone understand what you were saying? Such a drawing is one type of model. A model is a picture, diagram, computer image, or other representation of a complex object or process. **Making models** helps people understand things that they cannot observe directly.

Scientists often use models to represent things that are either very large or very small, such as the planets in the solar system, or the parts of a cell. Such models are physical models—drawings or three-dimensional structures that look like the real thing. Other models are mental models—mathematical equations or words that describe how something works.

ACTIVITY

This student is using a model to demonstrate what causes day and night on Earth. What do the flashlight and the tennis ball in the model represent?

Communicating

Whenever you talk on the phone, write a letter, or listen to your teacher at school, you are communicating. **Communicating** is the process of sharing ideas and information with other people. Communicating effectively requires many skills, including writing, reading, speaking, listening, and making models.

Scientists communicate to share results, information, and opinions. Scientists often communicate about their work in journals, over the telephone, in letters, and on the Internet. They also attend scientific meetings where they share their ideas with one another in person.

ACTIVITY

On a sheet of paper, write out clear, detailed directions for tying your shoe. Then exchange directions with a partner. Follow your partner's directions exactly. How successful were you at tying your shoe? How could your partner have communicated more clearly?

On what did you base your prediction? *(Scientific predictions are based on knowledge and experience.)* Point out that in science, predictions can often be tested with experiments.

Classifying

ACTIVITY

Encourage students to think of other common things that are classified. Then ask: **What things at home are classified?** *(Clothing might be classified by placing it in different dresser drawers; glasses, plates, and silverware are grouped in different parts of the kitchen; screws, nuts, bolts, washers, and nails might be separated into small containers.)* **What are some things that scientists classify?** *(Scientists classify many things they study, including organisms, geological features and processes, and kinds of machines.)* After students have classified the different fruits in the photograph, have them share their criteria for classifying them. *(Some characteristics students might use include shape, color, size, and where they are grown.)*

Making Models

ACTIVITY

Ask students: **What are some models you have used to study science?** *(Students may have used human anatomical models, solar system models, maps, stream tables.)* **How did these models help you?** *(Models can help you learn about things that are difficult to study, either because they are too big, too small, or complex.)* Be sure students understand that a model does not have to be three-dimensional. For example, a map in a textbook is a model. Ask: **What do the flashlight and tennis ball represent?** *(The flashlight represents the sun, and the ball represents Earth.)* **What quality of each item makes this a good model?** *(The flashlight gives off light, and the ball is round and can be rotated by the student.)*

Communicating

ACTIVITY

Challenge students to identify the methods of communication they've used today. Then ask: **How is the way you communicate with a friend similar to and different from the way scientists communicate about their work to other scientists?** *(Both may communicate using various methods, but scientists must be very detailed and precise, whereas communication between friends may be less detailed and precise.)* Encourage students to communicate like a scientist as they carry out the activity. *(Students' directions should be detailed and precise enough for another person to successfully follow.)*

Making Measurements

Measuring in SI

Review SI units in class with students. Begin by providing metric rulers, graduated cylinders, balances, and Celsius thermometers. Use these tools to reinforce that the meter is the unit of length, the liter is the unit of volume, the gram is the unit of mass, and the degree Celsius is the unit for temperature. Ask: **If you want to measure the length and width of your classroom, which SI unit would you use?** *(meter)* **Which unit would you use to measure the amount of matter in your textbook?** *(gram)* **Which would you use to measure how much water a drinking glass holds?** *(liter)* **When would you use the Celsius scale?** *(To measure the temperature of something)* Then use the measuring equipment to review SI prefixes. For example, ask: **What are the smallest units on the metric ruler?** *(millimeters)* **How many millimeters are there in 1 cm?** *(10 mm)* **How many in 10 cm?** *(100 mm)* **How many centimeters are there in 1 m?** *(100 cm)* **What does 1,000 m equal?** *(1 km)*

Length ACTIVITY *(Students should state that the shell is 4.6 centimeters, or 46 millimeters, long.)* If students need more practice measuring length, have them use meter sticks and metric rulers to measure various objects in the classroom.

Liquid Volume ACTIVITY *(Students should state that the volume of water in the graduated cylinder is 62 milliliters.)* If students need more practice measuring liquid volume, have them use a graduated cylinder to measure different volumes of water.

Making Measurements

When scientists make observations, it is not sufficient to say that something is "big" or "heavy." Instead, scientists use instruments to measure just how big or heavy an object is. By measuring, scientists can express their observations more precisely and communicate more information about what they observe.

Measuring in SI

The standard system of measurement used by scientists around the world is known as the International System of Units, which is abbreviated as SI (in French, *Système International d'Unités*). SI units are easy to use because they are based on multiples of 10. Each unit is ten times larger than the next smallest unit and one tenth the size of the next largest unit. The table lists the prefixes used to name the most common SI units.

Common SI Prefixes

Prefix	Symbol	Meaning
kilo-	k	1,000
hecto-	h	100
deka-	da	10
deci-	d	0.1 (one tenth)
centi-	c	0.01 (one hundredth)
milli-	m	0.001 (one thousandth)

Length To measure length, or the distance between two points, the unit of measure is the **meter (m).** One meter is the approximate distance from the floor to a doorknob. Long distances, such as the distance between two cities, are measured in kilometers (km). Small lengths are measured in centimeters (cm) or millimeters (mm). Scientists use metric rulers and meter sticks to measure length.

Common Conversions

1 km = 1,000 m
1 m = 100 cm
1 m = 1,000 mm
1 cm = 10 mm

ACTIVITY The larger lines on the metric ruler in the picture show centimeter divisions, while the smaller, unnumbered lines show millimeter divisions. How many centimeters long is the shell? How many millimeters long is it?

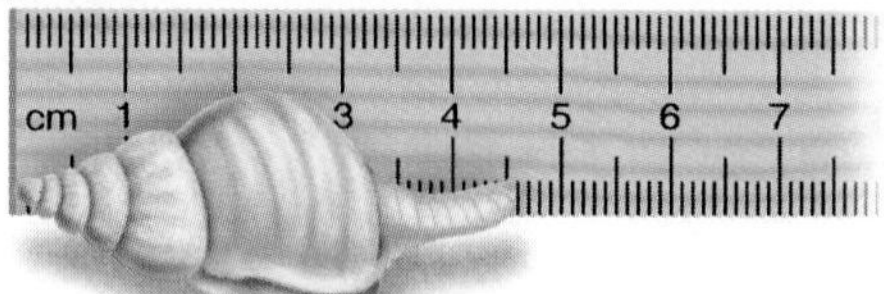

Liquid Volume To measure the volume of a liquid, or the amount of space it takes up, you will use a unit of measure known as the **liter (L).** One liter is the approximate volume of a medium-sized carton of milk. Smaller volumes are measured in milliliters (mL). Scientists use graduated cylinders to measure liquid volume.

Common Conversion

1 L = 1,000 mL

ACTIVITY The graduated cylinder in the picture is marked in milliliter divisions. Notice that the water in the cylinder has a curved surface. This curved surface is called the *meniscus*. To measure the volume, you must read the level at the lowest point of the meniscus. What is the volume of water in this graduated cylinder?

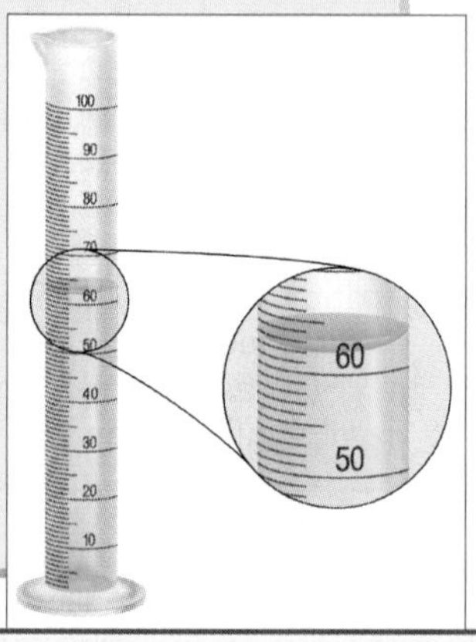

Mass To measure mass, or the amount of matter in an object, you will use a unit of measure known as the **gram (g)**. One gram is approximately the mass of a paper clip. Larger masses are measured in kilograms (kg). Scientists use a balance to find the mass of an object.

Common Conversion

1 kg = 1,000 g

ACTIVITY

The electronic balance displays the mass of an apple in kilograms. What is the mass of the apple? Suppose a recipe for applesauce called for one kilogram of apples. About how many apples would you need?

Temperature
To measure the temperature of a substance, you will use the **Celsius scale**. Temperature is measured in degrees Celsius (°C) using a Celsius thermometer. Water freezes at 0°C and boils at 100°C.

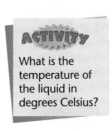

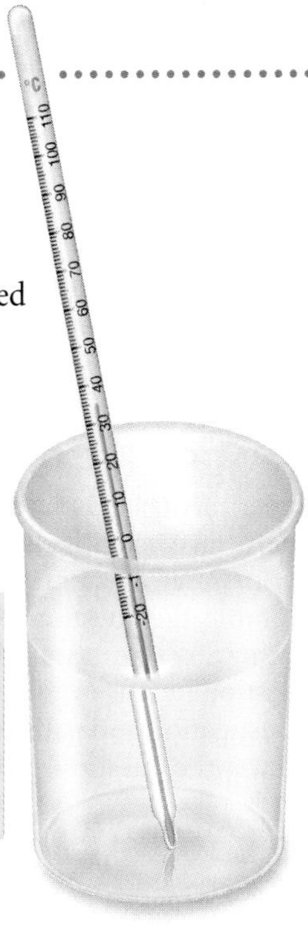

ACTIVITY

What is the temperature of the liquid in degrees Celsius?

Converting SI Units

To use the SI system, you must know how to convert between units. Converting from one unit to another involves the skill of **calculating**, or using mathematical operations. Converting between SI units is similar to converting between dollars and dimes because both systems are based on multiples of ten.

Suppose you want to convert a length of 80 centimeters to meters. Follow these steps to convert between units.

1. Begin by writing down the measurement you want to convert—in this example, 80 centimeters.
2. Write a conversion factor that represents the relationship between the two units you are converting. In this example, the relationship is *1 meter = 100 centimeters.* Write this conversion factor as a fraction, making sure to place the units you are converting from (centimeters, in this example) in the denominator.
3. Multiply the measurement you want to convert by the fraction. When you do this, the units in the first measurement will cancel out with the units in the denominator. Your answer will be in the units you are converting to (meters, in this example).

Example

80 centimeters = __?__ meters

$$80 \text{ cen}\cancel{\text{timeters}} \times \frac{1 \text{ meter}}{100 \text{ cen}\cancel{\text{timeters}}} = \frac{80 \text{ meters}}{100}$$

$$= 0.8 \text{ meters}$$

ACTIVITY

Convert between the following units.

1. 600 millimeters = __?__ meters
2. 0.35 liters = __?__ milliliters
3. 1,050 grams = __?__ kilograms

Mass *(Students should state that the mass of the apple is 0.1 kilograms. They would need 10 apples to make 1 kilogram.)* If students need practice determining mass, have them use a balance to determine the mass of various common objects, such as coins, paper clips, and books.

Temperature *(Students should state that the temperature of the liquid is 35°C.)* If students need practice measuring temperature, have them use a Celsius thermometer to measure the temperature of various water samples.

Converting SI Units

Review the steps for converting SI units and work through the example with students. Then ask: **How many millimeters are in 80 centimeters?** *(Students should follow the steps to calculate that 80 centimeters is equal to 800 millimeters.)*

Have students do the conversion problems in the activity. *(**1.** 600 millimeters = 0.6 meters; **2.** 0.35 liters = 350 milliliters; **3.** 1,050 grams = 1.05 kilograms)* If students need more practice converting SI units, have students make up conversion problems and trade with a partner.

Conducting a Scientific Investigation

Posing Questions

Before students do the activity on the next page, walk them through the steps of a typical scientific investigation. Begin by asking: **Why is a scientific question important to a scientific investigation?** *(It is the reason for conducting a scientific investigation and how every investigation begins.)* **What is the scientific question in the activity at the bottom of the next page?** *(Is a ball's bounce affected by the height from which it is dropped?)*

Developing a Hypothesis

Emphasize that a hypothesis is a prediction about the outcome of a scientific investigation, but it is *not* a guess. Ask: **On what information do scientists base their hypotheses?** *(Their observations and previous knowledge or experience)* Point out that a hypothesis does not always turn out to be correct. Ask: **In that case, do you think the scientist wasted his or her time? Explain your answer.** *(No, because the scientist probably learned from the investigation and maybe could develop another hypothesis that could be supported.)*

Designing an Experiment

Have a volunteer read the Experimental Procedure in the box. Then call on students to identify the manipulated variable *(amount of salt added to water)*, the variables that are kept constant *(amount and starting temperature of water, placing containers in freezer)*, the responding variable *(time it takes water to freeze)*, and the control *(Container 3)*.

Ask: **How might the experiment be affected if Container 1 had only 100 mL of water?** *(It wouldn't be a fair comparison with the containers that have more water.)* **What if Container 3 was not included in the experiment?** *(You wouldn't have anything to compare the other two containers to know if their freezing times were faster or slower than normal.)* Help students understand the importance of keeping all variables constant except the manipulated variable. Also be sure they understand the role of the control. Then ask: **What operational definition is used in this experiment?** *("Frozen" means the time at which a wooden stick can no longer move in a container.)*

Conducting a Scientific Investigation

In some ways, scientists are like detectives, piecing together clues to learn about a process or event. One way that scientists gather clues is by carrying out experiments. An experiment tests an idea in a careful, orderly manner. Although all experiments do not follow the same steps in the same order, many follow a pattern similar to the one described here.

Posing Questions

Experiments begin by asking a scientific question. A scientific question is one that can be answered by gathering evidence. For example, the question "Which freezes faster—fresh water or salt water?" is a scientific question because you can carry out an investigation and gather information to answer the question.

Developing a Hypothesis

The next step is to form a hypothesis. A **hypothesis** is a prediction about the outcome of the experiment. Like all predictions, hypotheses are based on your observations and previous knowledge or experience. But, unlike many predictions, a hypothesis must be something that can be tested. A properly worded hypothesis should take the form of an *If... then...* statement. For example, a hypothesis might be *"If I add salt to fresh water, then the water will take longer to freeze."* A hypothesis worded this way serves as a rough outline of the experiment you should perform.

Designing an Experiment

Next you need to plan a way to test your hypothesis. Your plan should be written out as a step-by-step procedure and should describe the observations or measurements you will make.

Two important steps involved in designing an experiment are controlling variables and forming operational definitions.

Controlling Variables In a well-designed experiment, you need to keep all variables the same except for one. A **variable** is any factor that can change in an experiment. The factor that you change is called the **manipulated variable.** In this experiment, the manipulated variable is the amount of salt added to the water. Other factors, such as the amount of water or the starting temperature, are kept constant.

The factor that changes as a result of the manipulated variable is called the responding variable. The **responding variable** is what you measure or observe to obtain your results. In this experiment, the responding variable is how long the water takes to freeze.

An experiment in which all factors except one are kept constant is a **controlled experiment.** Most controlled experiments include a test called the control. In this experiment, Container 3 is the control. Because no salt is added to Container 3, you can compare the results from the other containers to it. Any difference in results must be due to the addition of salt alone.

Forming Operational Definitions
Another important aspect of a well-designed experiment is having clear operational definitions. An **operational definition** is a statement that describes how a particular variable is to be measured or how a term is to be defined. For example, in this experiment, how will you determine if the water has frozen? You might decide to insert a stick in each container at the start of the experiment. Your operational definition of "frozen" would be the time at which the stick can no longer move.

EXPERIMENTAL PROCEDURE

1. *Fill 3 containers with 300 milliliters of cold tap water.*
2. *Add 10 grams of salt to Container 1; stir. Add 20 grams of salt to Container 2; stir. Add no salt to Container 3.*
3. *Place the 3 containers in a freezer.*
4. *Check the containers every 15 minutes. Record your observations.*

Interpreting Data

The observations and measurements you make in an experiment are called data. At the end of an experiment, you need to analyze the data to look for any patterns or trends. Patterns often become clear if you organize your data in a data table or graph. Then think through what the data reveal. Do they support your hypothesis? Do they point out a flaw in your experiment? Do you need to collect more data?

Drawing Conclusions

A conclusion is a statement that sums up what you have learned from an experiment. When you draw a conclusion, you need to decide whether the data you collected support your hypothesis or not. You may need to repeat an experiment several times before you can draw any conclusions from it. Conclusions often lead you to pose new questions and plan new experiments to answer them.

ACTIVITY

Is a ball's bounce affected by the height from which it is dropped? Using the steps just described, plan a controlled experiment to investigate this problem.

Interpreting Data

Emphasize the importance of collecting accurate and detailed data in a scientific investigation. Ask: **What if the students forgot to record the times that they made their observations in the experiment?** *(They wouldn't be able to completely analyze their data to draw valid conclusions.)* Then ask: **Why are data tables and graphs a good way to organize data?** *(They often make it easier to compare and analyze data.)* You may wish to have students review the Skills Handbook pages on Creating Data Tables and Graphs at this point.

Drawing Conclusions

Help students understand that a conclusion is not necessarily the end of a scientific investigation. A conclusion about one experiment may lead right into another experiment. Point out that in scientific investigations, a conclusion is a summary and explanation of the results of an experiment.

Tell students to suppose that for the Experimental Procedure described on this page, they obtained the following results: Container 1 froze in 45 minutes, Container 2 in 80 minutes, and Container 3 in 25 minutes. Ask: **What conclusions can you draw about this experiment?** *(Students might conclude that the more salt that is added to fresh water, the longer it takes the water to freeze. The hypothesis is supported, and the question of which freezes faster is answered—fresh water.)*

ACTIVITY

You might wish to have students work in pairs to plan the controlled experiment. *(Students should develop a hypothesis, such as "If I increase the height from which a ball is dropped, then the height of its bounce will increase." They can test the hypothesis by dropping balls from varying heights (the manipulated variable). All trials should be done with the same kind of ball and on the same surface (constant variables). For each trial, they should measure the height of the bounce (responding variable).)* After students have designed the experiment, provide rubber balls and invite them to carry out the experiment so they can collect and interpret data and draw conclusions.

Thinking Critically

Comparing and Contrasting

ACTIVITY

Emphasize that the skill of comparing and contrasting often relies on good observation skills, as in this activity. *(Students' answers may vary. Sample answer: Similarities—both are dogs and have four legs, two eyes, two ears, brown and white fur, black noses, pink tongues; Differences—smooth coat vs. rough coat, more white fur vs. more brown fur, shorter vs. taller, long ears vs. short ears.)*

Applying Concepts

ACTIVITY

Point out to students that they apply concepts that they learn in school in their daily lives. For example, they learn to add, subtract, multiply, and divide in school. If they get a paper route or some other part-time job, they can apply those concepts. Challenge students to practice applying concepts by doing the activity. *(Antifreeze lowers the temperature at which the solution will freeze, and thus keeps the water in the radiator from freezing.)*

Interpreting Illustrations

ACTIVITY

Again, point out the need for good observation skills. Ask: **What is the difference between "interpreting illustrations" and "looking at the pictures"?** *("Interpreting illustrations" requires thorough examination of the illustration, caption, and labels, while "looking at the pictures" implies less thorough examination.)* Encourage students to thoroughly examine the diagram as they do the activity. *(Students' paragraphs may vary, but should describe the internal anatomy of an earthworm, including some of the organs in the earthworm.)*

Thinking Critically

Has a friend ever asked for your advice about a problem? If so, you may have helped your friend think through the problem in a logical way. Without knowing it, you used critical-thinking skills to help your friend. Critical thinking involves the use of reasoning and logic to solve problems or make decisions. Some critical-thinking skills are described below.

Comparing and Contrasting

When you examine two objects for similarities and differences, you are using the skill of **comparing and contrasting.** Comparing involves identifying similarities, or common characteristics. Contrasting involves identifying differences. Analyzing objects in this way can help you discover details that you might otherwise overlook.

ACTIVITY — Compare and contrast the two animals in the photo. First list all the similarities that you see. Then list all the differences.

Applying Concepts

When you use your knowledge about one situation to make sense of a similar situation, you are using the skill of **applying concepts.** Being able to transfer your knowledge from one situation to another shows that you truly understand a concept. You may use this skill in answering test questions that present different problems from the ones you've reviewed in class.

ACTIVITY — You have just learned that water takes longer to freeze when other substances are mixed into it. Use this knowledge to explain why people need a substance called antifreeze in their car's radiator in the winter.

Interpreting Illustrations

Diagrams, photographs, and maps are included in textbooks to help clarify what you read. These illustrations show processes, places, and ideas in a visual manner. The skill called **interpreting illustrations** can help you learn from these visual elements. To understand an illustration, take the time to study the illustration along with all the written information that accompanies it. Captions identify the key concepts shown in the illustration. Labels point out the important parts of a diagram or map, while keys identify the symbols used in a map.

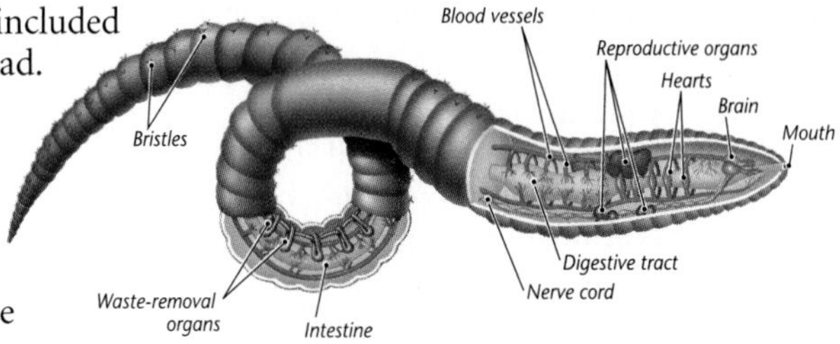

▲ Internal anatomy of an earthworm

ACTIVITY — Study the diagram above. Then write a short paragraph explaining what you have learned.

SKILLS HANDBOOK

Relating Cause and Effect

If one event causes another event to occur, the two events are said to have a cause-and-effect relationship. When you determine that such a relationship exists between two events, you use a skill called **relating cause and effect.** For example, if you notice an itchy, red bump on your skin, you might infer that a mosquito bit you. The mosquito bite is the cause, and the bump is the effect.

It is important to note that two events do not necessarily have a cause-and-effect relationship just because they occur together. Scientists carry out experiments or use past experience to determine whether a cause-and-effect relationship exists.

> **ACTIVITY**
> You are on a camping trip and your flashlight has stopped working. List some possible causes for the flashlight malfunction. How could you determine which cause-and-effect relationship has left you in the dark?

Making Generalizations

When you draw a conclusion about an entire group based on information about only some of the group's members, you are using a skill called **making generalizations.** For a generalization to be valid, the sample you choose must be large enough and representative of the entire group. You might, for example, put this skill to work at a farm stand if you see a sign that says, "Sample some grapes before you buy." If you sample a few sweet grapes, you may conclude that all the grapes are sweet—and purchase a large bunch.

> **ACTIVITY**
> A team of scientists needs to determine whether the water in a large reservoir is safe to drink. How could they use the skill of making generalizations to help them? What should they do?

Making Judgments

When you evaluate something to decide whether it is good or bad, or right or wrong, you are using a skill called **making judgments.** For example, you make judgments when you decide to eat healthful foods or to pick up litter in a park. Before you make a judgment, you need to think through the pros and cons of a situation, and identify the values or standards that you hold.

> **ACTIVITY**
> Should children and teens be required to wear helmets when bicycling? Explain why you feel the way you do.

Problem Solving

When you use critical-thinking skills to resolve an issue or decide on a course of action, you are using a skill called **problem solving.** Some problems, such as how to convert a fraction into a decimal, are straightforward. Other problems, such as figuring out why your computer has stopped working, are complex. Some complex problems can be solved using the trial and error method—try out one solution first, and if that doesn't work, try another. Other useful problem-solving strategies include making models and brainstorming possible solutions with a partner.

Relating Cause and Effect — ACTIVITY

Emphasize that not all events that occur together have a cause-and-effect relationship. For example, tell students that you went to the grocery and your car stalled. Ask: **Is there a cause-and-effect relationship in this situation? Explain your answer.** *(No, because going to the grocery could not cause a car to stall. There must be another cause to make the car stall.)* Have students do the activity to practice relating cause and effect. *(Students should identify that the flashlight not working is the effect. Some possible causes include dead batteries, a burned-out light bulb, or a loose part.)*

Making Generalizations — ACTIVITY

Point out the importance of having a large, representative sample before making a generalization. Ask: **If you went fishing at a lake and caught three catfish, could you make the generalization that all fish in the lake are catfish? Why or why not?** *(No, because there might be other kinds of fish you didn't catch because they didn't like the bait or they may be in other parts of the lake.)* **How could you make a generalization about the kinds of fish in the lake?** *(By having a larger sample)* Have students do the activity to practice making generalizations. *(The scientists should collect and test water samples from a number of different parts of the reservoir.)*

Making Judgments — ACTIVITY

Remind students that they make a judgment almost every time they make a decision. Ask: **What steps should you follow to make a judgment?** *(Gather information, list pros and cons, analyze values, make judgment)* Invite students to do the activity, and then to share and discuss the judgments they made. *(Students' judgments will vary, but should be supported by valid reasoning. Sample answer: Children and teens should be required to wear helmets when bicycling because helmets have been proven to save lives and reduce head injuries.)*

Problem Solving — ACTIVITY

Challenge student pairs to solve a problem about a soapbox derby. Explain that their younger brother is building a car to enter in the race. The brother wants to know how to make his soapbox car go faster. After student pairs have considered the problem, have them share their ideas about solutions with the class. *(Most will probably suggest using trial and error by making small changes to the car and testing the car after each change. Some students may suggest making and manipulating a model.)*

Organizing Information

Concept Maps

ACTIVITY

Challenge students to make a concept map with at least three levels of concepts to organize information about types of transportation. All students should start with the phrase *types of transportation* at the top of the concept map. After that point, their concept maps may vary. *(For example, some students might place* private transportation *and* public transportation *at the next level, while other students might have* human-powered *and* gas-powered. *Make sure students connect the concepts with linking words. Challenge students to include cross-linkages as well.)*

Compare/ Contrast Tables

ACTIVITY

Have students make their own compare/contrast tables using two or more different sports or other activities, such as playing musical instruments. Emphasize that students should select characteristics that highlight the similarities and differences between the activities. *(Students' compare/contrast tables should include several appropriate characteristics and list information about each activity for every characteristic.)*

Organizing Information

As you read this textbook, how can you make sense of all the information it contains? Some useful tools to help you organize information are shown on this page. These tools are called *graphic organizers* because they give you a visual picture of a topic, showing at a glance how key concepts are related.

Concept Maps

Concept maps are useful tools for organizing information on broad topics. A concept map begins with a general concept and shows how it can be broken down into more specific concepts. In that way, relationships between concepts become easier to understand.

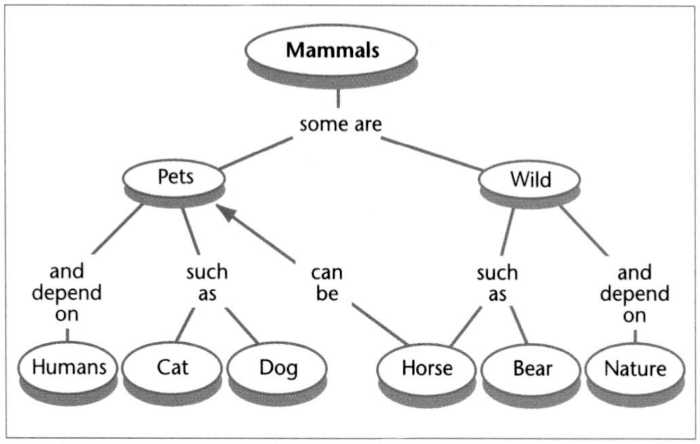

A concept map is constructed by placing concept words (usually nouns) in ovals and connecting them with linking words. Often, the most general concept word is placed at the top, and the words become more specific as you move downward. Often the linking words, which are written on a line extending between two ovals, describe the relationship between the two concepts they connect. If you follow any string of concepts and linking words down the map, it should read like a sentence.

Some concept maps include linking words that connect a concept on one branch of the map to a concept on another branch. These linking words, called cross-linkages, show more complex interrelationships among concepts.

Compare/Contrast Tables

Compare/contrast tables are useful tools for sorting out the similarities and differences between two or more items. A table provides an organized framework in which to compare items based on specific characteristics that you identify.

Characteristic	Baseball	Basketball
Number of Players	9	5
Playing Field	Baseball diamond	Basketball court
Equipment	Bat, baseball, mitts	Basket, basketball

To create a compare/contrast table, list the items to be compared across the top of a table. Then list the characteristics that will form the basis of your comparison in the left-hand column. Complete the table by filling in information about each characteristic, first for one item and then for the other.

Venn Diagrams

Another way to show similarities and differences between items is with a Venn diagram. A Venn diagram consists of two or more circles that partially overlap. Each circle represents a particular concept or idea. Common characteristics, or similarities, are written within the area of overlap between the two circles. Unique characteristics, or differences, are written in the parts of the circles outside the area of overlap.

To create a Venn diagram, draw two overlapping circles. Label the circles with the names of the items being compared. Write the unique characteristics in each circle outside the area of overlap. Then write the shared characteristics within the area of overlap.

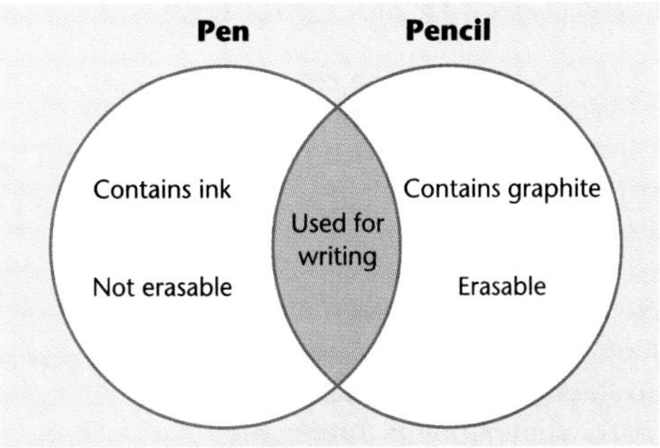

Flowcharts

A flowchart can help you understand the order in which certain events have occurred or should occur. Flowcharts are useful for outlining the stages in a process or the steps in a procedure.

To make a flowchart, write a brief description of each event in a box. Place the first event at the top of the page, followed by the second event, the third event, and so on. Then draw an arrow to connect each event to the one that occurs next.

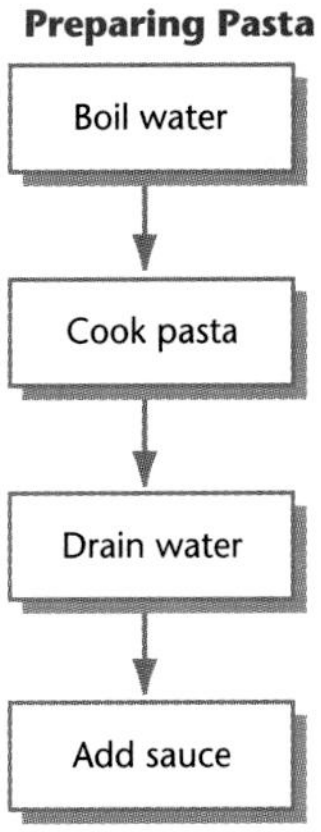

Cycle Diagrams

A cycle diagram can be used to show a sequence of events that is continuous, or cyclical. A continuous sequence does not have an end because, when the final event is over, the first event begins again. Like a flowchart, a cycle diagram can help you understand the order of events.

To create a cycle diagram, write a brief description of each event in a box. Place one event at the top of the page in the center. Then, moving in a clockwise direction around an imaginary circle, write each event in its proper sequence. Draw arrows that connect each event to the one that occurs next, forming a continuous circle.

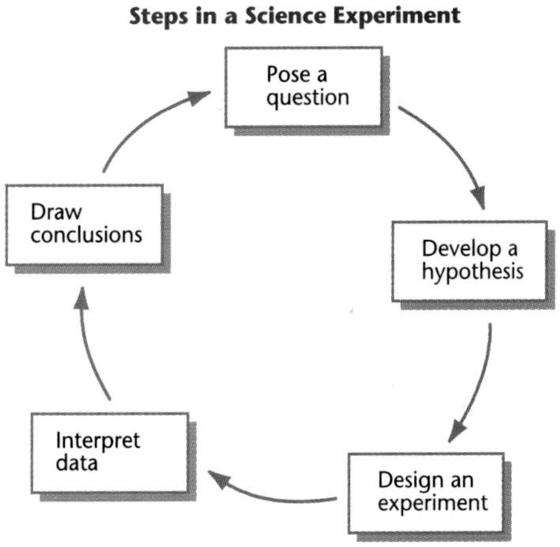

Venn Diagrams — ACTIVITY

Students can use the same information from their compare/contrast tables to create a Venn diagram. Make sure students understand that the overlapping area of the circles is used to list similarities and the parts of the circles outside the overlap area are used to show differences. If students want to list similarities and differences among three activities, show them how to add a third circle that overlaps each of the other two circles and has an area of overlap for all three circles. *(Students' Venn diagrams will vary. Make sure they have accurately listed similarities in the overlap area and differences in the parts of the circles that do not overlap.)*

Flowcharts — ACTIVITY

Encourage students to create a flowchart to show the things they did this morning as they got ready for school. Remind students that a flowchart should show the correct order in which events occurred or should occur. *(Students' flowcharts will vary somewhat. A typical flowchart might include: got up → ate breakfast → took a shower → brushed teeth → got dressed → gathered books and homework → put on jacket.)*

Cycle Diagrams — ACTIVITY

Review that a cycle diagram shows a sequence of events that is continuous. Then challenge students to create a cycle diagram that shows how the weather changes with the seasons where they live. *(Students' cycle diagrams may vary, though most will include four steps, one for each season.)*

I ◆ 161

Creating Data Tables and Graphs

Data Tables

Have students create a data table to show how much time they spend on different activities during one week. Suggest that students first list the main activities they do every week. Then they should determine the amount of time they spend on each activity each day. Remind students to give this data table a title. *(Students' data tables will vary. A sample data table is shown below.)*

Bar Graphs

Students can use the data from their data table above to make a bar graph showing how much time they spend on different activities during a week. The vertical axis should be divided into units of time, such as hours. Remind students to label both axes and give their graph a title. *(Students' bar graphs will vary. A sample bar graph is shown below.)*

Creating Data Tables and Graphs

How can you make sense of the data in a science experiment? The first step is to organize the data to help you understand them. Data tables and graphs are helpful tools for organizing data.

Data Tables

You have gathered your materials and set up your experiment. But before you start, you need to plan a way to record what happens during the experiment. By creating a data table, you can record your observations and measurements in an orderly way.

Suppose, for example, that a scientist conducted an experiment to find out how many Calories people of different body masses burn while doing various activities. The data table shows the results.

CALORIES BURNED IN 30 MINUTES OF ACTIVITY

Body Mass	Experiment 1 Bicycling	Experiment 2 Playing Basketball	Experiment 3 Watching Television
30 kg	60 Calories	120 Calories	21 Calories
40 kg	77 Calories	164 Calories	27 Calories
50 kg	95 Calories	206 Calories	33 Calories
60 kg	114 Calories	248 Calories	38 Calories

Notice in this data table that the manipulated variable (body mass) is the heading of one column. The responding variable (for Experiment 1, the number of Calories burned while bicycling) is the heading of the next column. Additional columns were added for related experiments.

Bar Graphs

To compare how many Calories a person burns doing various activities, you could create a bar graph. A bar graph is used to display data in a number of separate, or distinct, categories. In this example, bicycling, playing basketball, and watching television are three separate categories.

Calories Burned by a 30-kilogram Person in Various Activities

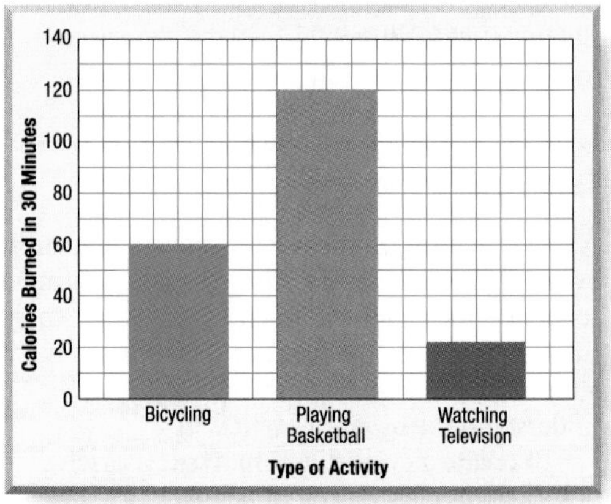

To create a bar graph, follow these steps.

1. On graph paper, draw a horizontal, or *x*-, axis and a vertical, or *y*-, axis.
2. Write the names of the categories to be graphed along the horizontal axis. Include an overall label for the axis as well.
3. Label the vertical axis with the name of the responding variable. Include units of measurement. Then create a scale along the axis by marking off equally spaced numbers that cover the range of the data collected.
4. For each category, draw a solid bar using the scale on the vertical axis to determine the appropriate height. For example, for bicycling, draw the bar as high as the 60 mark on the vertical axis. Make all the bars the same width and leave equal spaces between them.
5. Add a title that describes the graph.

Time Spent on Different Activities in a Week

	Going to Classes	Eating Meals	Playing Soccer	Watching Television
Monday	6	2	2	0.5
Tuesday	6	1.5	1.5	1.5
Wednesday	6	2	1	2
Thursday	6	2	2	1.5
Friday	6	2	2	0.5
Saturday	0	2.5	2.5	1
Sunday	0	3	1	2

Time Spent on Different Activities in a Week

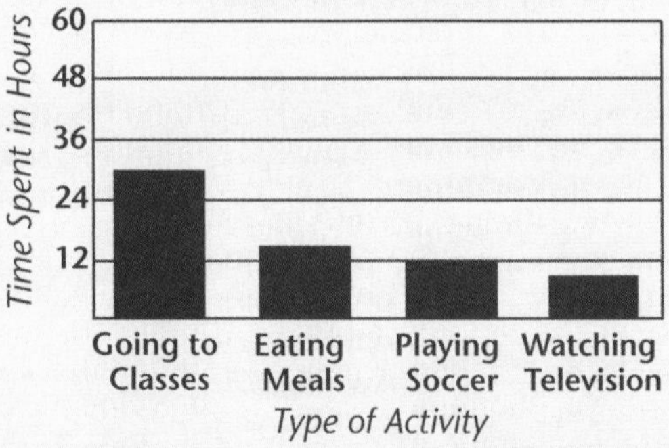

Line Graphs

To see whether a relationship exists between body mass and the number of Calories burned while bicycling, you could create a line graph. A line graph is used to display data that show how one variable (the responding variable) changes in response to another variable (the manipulated variable). You can use a line graph when your manipulated variable is *continuous*, that is, when there are other points between the ones that you tested. In this example, body mass is a continuous variable because there are other body masses between 30 and 40 kilograms (for example, 31 kilograms). Time is another example of a continuous variable.

Effect of Body Mass on Calories Burned While Bicycling

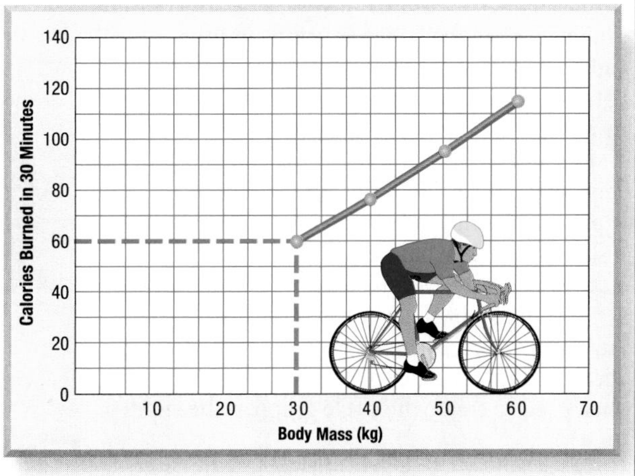

Line graphs are powerful tools because they allow you to estimate values for conditions that you did not test in the experiment. For example, you can use the line graph to estimate that a 35-kilogram person would burn 68 Calories while bicycling.

To create a line graph, follow these steps.

1. On graph paper, draw a horizontal, or *x*-, axis and a vertical, or *y*-, axis.
2. Label the horizontal axis with the name of the manipulated variable. Label the vertical axis with the name of the responding variable. Include units of measurement.
3. Create a scale on each axis by marking off equally spaced numbers that cover the range of the data collected.
4. Plot a point on the graph for each piece of data. In the line graph above, the dotted lines show how to plot the first data point (30 kilograms and 60 Calories). Draw an imaginary vertical line extending up from the horizontal axis at the 30-kilogram mark. Then draw an imaginary horizontal line extending across from the vertical axis at the 60-Calorie mark. Plot the point where the two lines intersect.
5. Connect the plotted points with a solid line. (In some cases, it may be more appropriate to draw a line that shows the general trend of the plotted points. In those cases, some of the points may fall above or below the line.)
6. Add a title that identifies the variables or relationship in the graph.

ACTIVITY

Create line graphs to display the data from Experiment 2 and Experiment 3 in the data table.

ACTIVITY

You read in the newspaper that a total of 4 centimeters of rain fell in your area in June, 2.5 centimeters fell in July, and 1.5 centimeters fell in August. What type of graph would you use to display these data? Use graph paper to create the graph.

SKILLS HANDBOOK

Line Graphs

Walk students through the steps involved in creating a line graph using the example illustrated on the page. For example, ask: **What is the label on the horizontal axis? On the vertical axis?** *(Body Mass (kg); Calories Burned in 30 Minutes)* **What scales are used on each axis?** *(3 squares per 10 kg on the x-axis and 2 squares per 20 calories on the y-axis)* **What does the second data point represent?** *(77 Calories burned for a body mass of 40 kg)* **What trend or pattern does the graph show?** *(The number of Calories burned in 30 minutes of cycling increases with body mass.)*

Have students follow the steps to carry out the first activity. *(Students should make a different graph for each experiment with different y-axis scales to practice making scales appropriate for data. See sample graphs below.)*

Have students carry out the second activity. *(Students should conclude that a bar graph would be best to display the data. A sample bar graph for these data is shown below.)*

Rainfall in June, July, and August

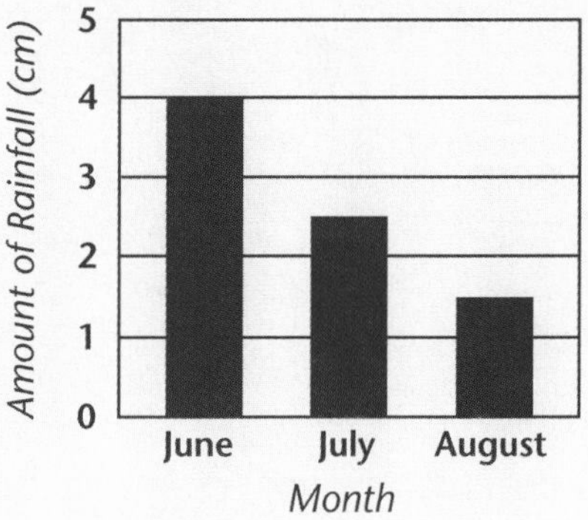

Effect of Body Mass on Calories Burned While Playing Basketball

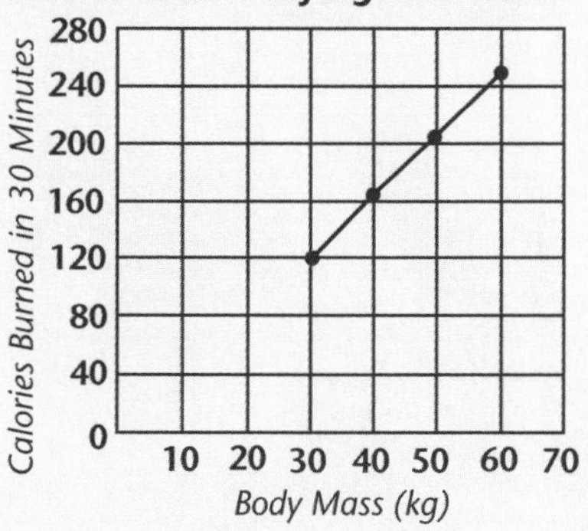

Effect of Body Mass on Calories Burned While Watching Television

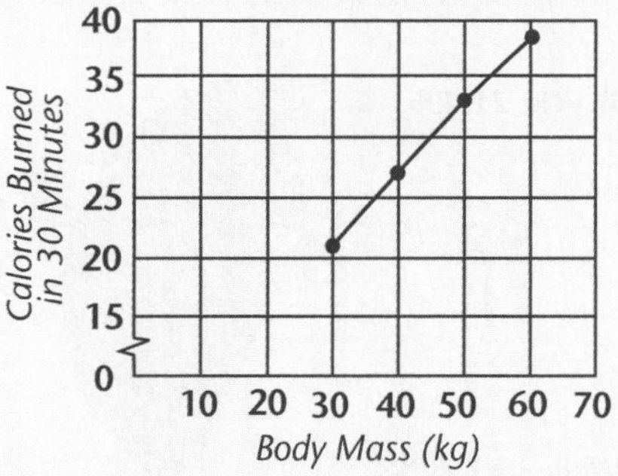

Circle Graphs

Emphasize that a circle graph has to include 100 percent of the categories for the topic being graphed. For example, ask: **Could the data in the bar graph titled "Calories Burned by a 30-kilogram Person in Various Activities" (on the previous page) be shown in a circle graph? Why or why not?** *(No, because it does not include all the possible ways a 30-kilogram person can burn Calories.)* Then walk students through the steps for making a circle graph. Help students to use a compass and a protractor. Use the protractor to illustrate that a circle has 360 degrees. Make sure students understand the mathematical calculations involved in making a circle graph.

You might wish to have students work in pairs to complete the activity. *(Students' circle graphs should look like the graph below.)*

Circle Graphs

Like bar graphs, circle graphs can be used to display data in a number of separate categories. Unlike bar graphs, however, circle graphs can only be used when you have data for *all* the categories that make up a given topic. A circle graph is sometimes called a pie chart because it resembles a pie cut into slices. The pie represents the entire topic, while the slices represent the individual categories. The size of a slice indicates what percentage of the whole a particular category makes up.

The data table below shows the results of a survey in which 24 teenagers were asked to identify their favorite sport. The data were then used to create the circle graph at the right.

Sports That Teens Prefer

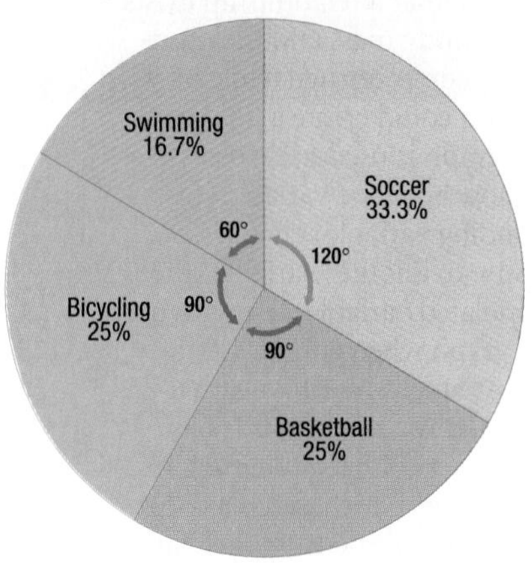

FAVORITE SPORTS

Sport	*Number of Students*
Soccer	*8*
Basketball	*6*
Bicycling	*6*
Swimming	*4*

To create a circle graph, follow these steps.

1. Use a compass to draw a circle. Mark the center of the circle with a point. Then draw a line from the center point to the top of the circle.
2. Determine the size of each "slice" by setting up a proportion where x equals the number of degrees in a slice. (NOTE: A circle contains 360 degrees.) For example, to find the number of degrees in the "soccer" slice, set up the following proportion:

$$\frac{\text{students who prefer soccer}}{\text{total number of students}} = \frac{x}{\text{total number of degrees in a circle}}$$

$$\frac{8}{24} = \frac{x}{360}$$

Cross-multiply and solve for x.

$$24x = 8 \times 360$$

$$x = 120$$

The "soccer" slice should contain 120 degrees.

3. Use a protractor to measure the angle of the first slice, using the line you drew to the top of the circle as the 0° line. Draw a line from the center of the circle to the edge for the angle you measured.
4. Continue around the circle by measuring the size of each slice with the protractor. Start measuring from the edge of the previous slice so the wedges do not overlap. When you are done, the entire circle should be filled in.
5. Determine the percentage of the whole circle that each slice represents. To do this, divide the number of degrees in a slice by the total number of degrees in a circle (360), and multiply by 100%. For the "soccer" slice, you can find the percentage as follows:

$$\frac{120}{360} \times 100\% = 33.3\%$$

6. Use a different color to shade in each slice. Label each slice with the name of the category and with the percentage of the whole it represents.
7. Add a title to the circle graph.

ACTIVITY

In a class of 28 students, 12 students take the bus to school, 10 students walk, and 6 students ride their bicycles. Create a circle graph to display these data.

Ways Students Get to School

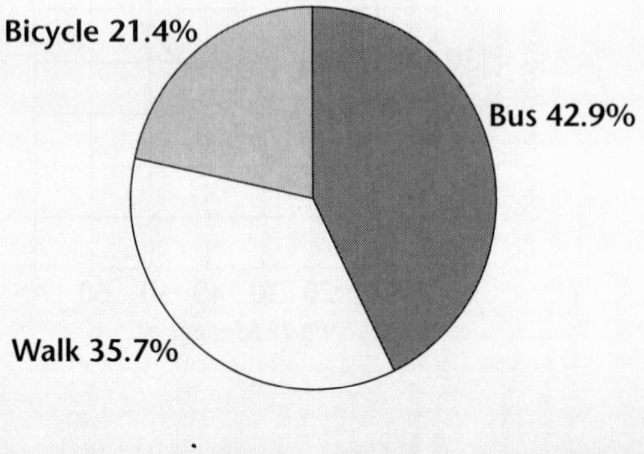

Laboratory Safety

Safety Symbols

These symbols alert you to possible dangers in the laboratory and remind you to work carefully.

Safety Goggles Always wear safety goggles to protect your eyes in any activity involving chemicals, flames or heating, or the possibility of broken glassware.

Lab Apron Wear a laboratory apron to protect your skin and clothing from damage.

Breakage You are working with materials that may be breakable, such as glass containers, glass tubing, thermometers, or funnels. Handle breakable materials with care. Do not touch broken glassware.

Heat-resistant Gloves Use an oven mitt or other hand protection when handling hot materials. Hot plates, hot glassware, or hot water can cause burns. Do not touch hot objects with your bare hands.

Heating Use a clamp or tongs to pick up hot glassware. Do not touch hot objects with your bare hands.

Sharp Object Pointed-tip scissors, scalpels, knives, needles, pins, or tacks are sharp. They can cut or puncture your skin. Always direct a sharp edge or point away from yourself and others. Use sharp instruments only as instructed.

Electric Shock Avoid the possibility of electric shock. Never use electrical equipment around water, or when the equipment is wet or your hands are wet. Be sure cords are untangled and cannot trip anyone. Disconnect the equipment when it is not in use.

Corrosive Chemical You are working with an acid or another corrosive chemical. Avoid getting it on your skin or clothing, or in your eyes. Do not inhale the vapors. Wash your hands when you are finished with the activity.

Poison Do not let any poisonous chemical come in contact with your skin, and do not inhale its vapors. Wash your hands when you are finished with the activity.

Physical Safety When an experiment involves physical activity, take precautions to avoid injuring yourself or others. Follow instructions from your teacher. Alert your teacher if there is any reason you should not participate in the activity.

Animal Safety Treat live animals with care to avoid harming the animals or yourself. Working with animal parts or preserved animals also may require caution. Wash your hands when you are finished with the activity.

Plant Safety Handle plants in the laboratory or during field work only as directed by your teacher. If you are allergic to certain plants, tell your teacher before doing an activity in which those plants are used. Avoid touching harmful plants such as poison ivy, poison oak, or poison sumac, or plants with thorns. Wash your hands when you are finished with the activity.

Flames You may be working with flames from a lab burner, candle, or matches. Tie back loose hair and clothing. Follow instructions from your teacher about lighting and extinguishing flames.

No Flames Flammable materials may be present. Make sure there are no flames, sparks, or other exposed heat sources present.

Fumes When poisonous or unpleasant vapors may be involved, work in a ventilated area. Avoid inhaling vapors directly. Only test an odor when directed to do so by your teacher, and use a wafting motion to direct the vapor toward your nose.

Disposal Chemicals and other laboratory materials used in the activity must be disposed of safely. Follow the instructions from your teacher.

Hand Washing Wash your hands thoroughly when finished with the activity. Use antibacterial soap and warm water. Lather both sides of your hands and between your fingers. Rinse well.

General Safety Awareness You may see this symbol when none of the symbols described earlier appears. In this case, follow the specific instructions provided. You may also see this symbol when you are asked to develop your own procedure in a lab. Have your teacher approve your plan before you go further.

Laboratory Safety

Laboratory safety is an essential element of a successful science class. It is important for you to emphasize laboratory safety to students. Students need to understand exactly what is safe and unsafe behavior, and what the rationale is behind each safety rule.

Review with students the Safety Symbols and Science Safety Rules listed on this and the next two pages. Then follow the safety guidelines below to ensure that your classroom will be a safe place for students to learn science.

- Post safety rules in the classroom and review them regularly with students.
- Familiarize yourself with the safety procedures for each activity before introducing it to your students.
- Review specific safety precautions with students before beginning every science activity.
- Always act as an exemplary role model by displaying safe behavior.
- Know how to use safety equipment, such as fire extinguishers and fire blankets, and always have it accessible.
- Have students practice leaving the classroom quickly and orderly to prepare them for emergencies.
- Explain to students how to use the intercom or other available means of communication to get help during an emergency.
- Never leave students unattended while they are engaged in science activities.
- Provide enough space for students to safely carry out science activities.
- Keep your classroom and all science materials in proper condition. Replace worn or broken items.
- Instruct students to report all accidents and injuries to you immediately.

Laboratory Safety

Additional tips are listed below for the Science Safety Rules discussed on these two pages. Please keep these tips in mind when you carry out science activities in your classroom.

General Precautions

- ◆ For open-ended activities like Chapter Projects, go over general safety guidelines with students. Have students submit their procedures or design plans in writing and check them for safety considerations.
- ◆ In an activity where students are directed to taste something, be sure to store the material in clean, *nonscience* containers. Distribute the material to students in *new* plastic or paper dispensables, which should be discarded after the tasting. Tasting or eating should never be done in a lab classroom.
- ◆ During physical activity, make sure students do not overexert themselves.
- ◆ Remind students to handle microscopes and telescopes with care to avoid breakage.

Heating and Fire Safety

- ◆ No flammable substances should be in use around hot plates, light bulbs, or open flames.
- ◆ Test tubes should be heated only in water baths.
- ◆ Students should be permitted to strike matches to light candles or burners *only* with strict supervision. When possible, you should light the flames, especially when working with sixth graders.
- ◆ Be sure to have proper ventilation when fumes are produced during a procedure.
- ◆ All electrical equipment used in the lab should have GFI switches.

Using Chemicals Safely

- ◆ When students use both chemicals and microscopes in one activity, microscopes should be in a separate part of the room from the chemicals so that when students remove their goggles to use the microscopes, their eyes are not at risk.

Science Safety Rules

To prepare yourself to work safely in the laboratory, read over the following safety rules. Then read them a second time. Make sure you understand and follow each rule. Ask your teacher to explain any rules you do not understand.

Dress Code

1. To protect yourself from injuring your eyes, wear safety goggles whenever you work with chemicals, burners, glassware, or any substance that might get into your eyes. If you wear contact lenses, notify your teacher.
2. Wear a lab apron or coat whenever you work with corrosive chemicals or substances that can stain.
3. Tie back long hair to keep it away from any chemicals, flames, or equipment.
4. Remove or tie back any article of clothing or jewelry that can hang down and touch chemicals, flames, or equipment. Roll up or secure long sleeves.
5. Never wear open shoes or sandals.

General Precautions

6. Read all directions for an experiment several times before beginning the activity. Carefully follow all written and oral instructions. If you are in doubt about any part of the experiment, ask your teacher for assistance.
7. Never perform activities that are not assigned or authorized by your teacher. Obtain permission before "experimenting" on your own. Never handle any equipment unless you have specific permission.
8. Never perform lab activities without direct supervision.
9. Never eat or drink in the laboratory.
10. Keep work areas clean and tidy at all times. Bring only notebooks and lab manuals or written lab procedures to the work area. All other items, such as purses and backpacks, should be left in a designated area.
11. Do not engage in horseplay.

First Aid

12. Always report all accidents or injuries to your teacher, no matter how minor. Notify your teacher immediately about any fires.
13. Learn what to do in case of specific accidents, such as getting acid in your eyes or on your skin. (Rinse acids from your body with lots of water.)
14. Be aware of the location of the first-aid kit, but do not use it unless instructed by your teacher. In case of injury, your teacher should administer first aid. Your teacher may also send you to the school nurse or call a physician.
15. Know the location of emergency equipment, such as the fire extinguisher and fire blanket, and know how to use it.
16. Know the location of the nearest telephone and whom to contact in an emergency.

Heating and Fire Safety

17. Never use a heat source, such as a candle, burner, or hot plate, without wearing safety goggles.
18. Never heat anything unless instructed to do so. A chemical that is harmless when cool may be dangerous when heated.
19. Keep all combustible materials away from flames. Never use a flame or spark near a combustible chemical.
20. Never reach across a flame.
21. Before using a laboratory burner, make sure you know proper procedures for lighting and adjusting the burner, as demonstrated by your teacher. Do not touch the burner. It may be hot. And never leave a lighted burner unattended!
22. Chemicals can splash or boil out of a heated test tube. When heating a substance in a test tube, make sure that the mouth of the tube is not pointed at you or anyone else.
23. Never heat a liquid in a closed container. The expanding gases produced may blow the container apart.
24. Before picking up a container that has been heated, hold the back of your hand near it. If you can feel heat on the back of your hand, the container is too hot to handle. Use an oven mitt to pick up a container that has been heated.

Using Glassware Safely

- ◆ Use plastic containers, graduated cylinders, and beakers whenever possible. If using glass, students should wear safety goggles.
- ◆ Use only nonmercury thermometers with anti-roll protectors.
- ◆ Check all glassware periodically for chips and scratches, which can cause cuts and breakage.

166 ◆ I

Using Chemicals Safely

25. Never mix chemicals "for the fun of it." You might produce a dangerous, possibly explosive substance.

26. Never put your face near the mouth of a container that holds chemicals. Never touch, taste, or smell a chemical unless you are instructed by your teacher to do so. Many chemicals are poisonous.

27. Use only those chemicals needed in the activity. Read and double-check labels on supply bottles before removing any chemicals. Take only as much as you need. Keep all containers closed when chemicals are not being used.

28. Dispose of all chemicals as instructed by your teacher. To avoid contamination, never return chemicals to their original containers. Never simply pour chemicals or other substances into the sink or trash containers.

29. Be extra careful when working with acids or bases. Pour all chemicals over the sink or a container, not over your work surface.

30. If you are instructed to test for odors, use a wafting motion to direct the odors to your nose. Do not inhale the fumes directly from the container.

31. When mixing an acid and water, always pour the water into the container first and then add the acid to the water. Never pour water into an acid.

32. Take extreme care not to spill any material in the laboratory. Wash chemical spills and splashes immediately with plenty of water. Immediately begin rinsing with water any acids that get on your skin or clothing, and notify your teacher of any acid spill at the same time.

Using Glassware Safely

33. Never force glass tubing or thermometers into a rubber stopper or rubber tubing. Have your teacher insert the glass tubing or thermometer if required for an activity.

34. If you are using a laboratory burner, use a wire screen to protect glassware from any flame. Never heat glassware that is not thoroughly dry on the outside.

35. Keep in mind that hot glassware looks cool. Never pick up glassware without first checking to see if it is hot. Use an oven mitt. See rule 24.

36. Never use broken or chipped glassware. If glassware breaks, notify your teacher and dispose of the glassware in the proper broken-glassware container. Never handle broken glass with your bare hands.

37. Never eat or drink from lab glassware.

38. Thoroughly clean glassware before putting it away.

Using Sharp Instruments

39. Handle scalpels or other sharp instruments with extreme care. Never cut material toward you; cut away from you.

40. Immediately notify your teacher if you cut your skin when working in the laboratory.

Animal and Plant Safety

41. Never perform experiments that cause pain, discomfort, or harm to mammals, birds, reptiles, fishes, or amphibians. This rule applies at home as well as in the classroom.

42. Animals should be handled only if absolutely necessary. Your teacher will instruct you as to how to handle each animal species brought into the classroom.

43. If you know that you are allergic to certain plants, molds, or animals, tell your teacher before doing an activity in which these are used.

44. During field work, protect your skin by wearing long pants, long sleeves, socks, and closed shoes. Know how to recognize the poisonous plants and fungi in your area, as well as plants with thorns, and avoid contact with them.

45. Never eat any part of an unidentified plant or fungus.

46. Wash your hands thoroughly after handling animals or the cage containing animals. Wash your hands when you are finished with any activity involving animal parts, plants, or soil.

End-of-Experiment Rules

47. After an experiment has been completed, clean up your work area and return all equipment to its proper place.

48. Dispose of waste materials as instructed by your teacher.

49. Wash your hands after every experiment.

50. Always turn off all burners or hot plates when they are not in use. Unplug hot plates and other electrical equipment. If you used a burner, check that the gas-line valve to the burner is off as well.

Using Sharp Instruments

- ◆ Always use blunt-tip safety scissors, except when pointed-tip scissors are required.

Animal and Plant Safety

- ◆ When working with live animals or plants, check ahead of time for students who may have allergies to the specimens.
- ◆ When growing bacteria cultures, use only disposable petri dishes. After streaking, the dishes should be sealed and not opened again by students. After the lab, students should return the unopened dishes to you. Students should wash their hands with antibacterial soap.
- ◆ Two methods are recommended for the safe disposal of bacteria cultures. *First method:* Autoclave the petri dishes and discard without opening. *Second method*: If no autoclave is available, carefully open the dishes (never have a student do this) and pour full-strength bleach into the dishes and let stand for a day. Then pour the bleach from the petri dishes down a drain and flush the drain with lots of water. Tape the petri dishes back together and place in a sealed plastic bag. Wrap the plastic bag with a brown paper bag or newspaper and tape securely. Throw the sealed package in the trash. Thoroughly disinfect the work area with bleach.
- ◆ To grow mold, use a new, sealable plastic bag that is two to three times larger than the material to be placed inside. Seal the bag and tape it shut. After the bag is sealed, students should not open it. To dispose of the bag and mold culture, make a small cut near an edge of the bag and cook in a microwave oven on high setting for at least 1 minute. Discard the bag according to local ordinance, usually in the trash.
- ◆ Students should wear disposable nitrile, latex, or food-handling gloves when handling live animals or nonliving specimens.

End-of Experiment Rules

- ◆ Always have students use antibacterial soap for washing their hands.

Glossary

A

acid rain Rain that contains more acid than normal. (p. 23)
air mass A huge body of air that has similar temperature, pressure, and humidity throughout. (p. 76)
air pressure A force that is the result of the weight of a column of air pushing down on an area. (p. 26)
altitude Elevation above sea level. (p. 28)
anemometer An instrument used to measure wind speed. (p. 53)
aneroid barometer An instrument that measures changes in air pressure without using a liquid. Changes in the shape of an airtight metal box cause a needle on the barometer dial to move. (p. 27)
anticyclone A high-pressure center of dry air. (p. 82)
atmosphere The layer of gases that surrounds Earth. (p. 14)
aurora borealis A colorful, glowing display in the sky caused when particles from the sun strike oxygen and nitrogen atoms in the ionosphere; also called the Northern Lights. (p. 36)

B

barometer An instrument used to measure changes in air pressure. (p. 26)

C

chlorofluorocarbons Chlorine compounds formerly used in air conditioners, refrigerators, and spray cans; also called CFCs. (p. 142)
cirrus Wispy, feathery clouds made mostly of ice crystals that form at high levels, above about 6 kilometers. (p. 64)
climate The average, year-after-year conditions of temperature, precipitation, winds, and clouds in an area. (p. 112)
condensation The process by which molecules of water vapor in the air become liquid water. (p. 63)
conduction The direct transfer of heat from one substance to another substance that it is touching. (p. 50)
continental (air mass) A dry air mass that forms over land. (p. 76)
continental climate The climate of the centers of continents, with cold winters and warm or hot summers. (p. 114)
controlled experiment An experiment in which all factors except one are kept constant. (p. 153)
convection The transfer of heat by the movement of a fluid. (p. 50)
Coriolis effect The way Earth's rotation makes winds in the Northern Hemisphere curve to the right and winds in the Southern Hemisphere curve to the left. (p. 57)
cumulus Clouds that form less than 2 kilometers above the ground and look like fluffy, rounded piles of cotton. (p. 64)
cyclone A swirling center of low air pressure. (p. 81)

D

density The amount of mass of a substance to a given volume. (p. 25)
desert A region that gets less than 25 centimeters of rain a year. (p. 126)
dew point The temperature at which condensation begins. (p. 63)
droughts Long periods of low precipitation. (p. 70)

E

El Niño An event that occurs every two to seven years in the Pacific Ocean, during which winds shift and push warm surface water toward the coast of South America; it can cause dramatic climate changes. (p. 104)
electromagnetic wave A form of energy that can travel through space. (p. 42)
evacuate To move away temporarily. (p. 90)
evaporation The process by which water molecules in liquid water escape into the air as water vapor. (p. 61)
exosphere The outer layer of the thermosphere, extending outward into space. (p. 36)

F

flash flood A sudden, violent flood that occurs within a few hours, or even minutes, of a heavy rainstorm. (p. 96)
front The area where air masses meet and do not mix. (p. 79)

G

global warming A gradual increase in the temperature of Earth's atmosphere. (p. 140)
global winds Winds that blow steadily from specific directions over long distances. (p. 57)
greenhouse effect The process by which heat is trapped in the atmosphere by water vapor, carbon dioxide, methane, and other gases that form a "blanket" around Earth. (p. 45)
greenhouse gases Gases in the atmosphere that trap heat. (p. 140)

H

heat The energy transferred from a hotter object to a cooler one. (p. 49)

168 ◆ I

humid subtropical A wet and warm climate area on the edge of the tropics. (p. 128)

humidity A measure of the amount of water vapor in the air. (p. 62)

hurricane A tropical storm that has winds of 119 kilometers per hour or higher; typically about 600 kilometers across. (p. 88)

hypothesis A prediction about the outcome of an experiment. (p. 152)

I

ice ages Cold time periods in Earth's history, during which glaciers covered large parts of the surface. (p. 136)

infrared radiation A form of energy with wavelengths that are longer than visible light. (p. 43)

ionosphere The lower part of the thermosphere, where electrically charged particles called ions are found. (p. 36)

isobars Lines on a map joining places that have the same air pressure. (p. 104)

isotherms Lines on a map joining places that have the same temperature. (p. 104)

J

jet streams Bands of high-speed winds about 10 kilometers above Earth's surface. (p. 60)

L

land breeze The flow of air from land to a body of water. (p. 56)

latitude The distance from the equator, measured in degrees. (p. 58)

leeward The downwind side of mountains. (p. 117)

lightning A sudden spark, or energy discharge, caused when electrical charges jump between parts of a cloud or between a cloud and the ground. (p. 84)

local winds Winds that blow over short distances. (p. 54)

M

manipulated variable The one factor that a scientist changes during an experiment. (p. 153)

marine climate The climate of some coastal regions, with relatively warm winters and cool summers. (p. 114)

maritime (air mass) A humid air mass that forms over oceans. (p. 76)

mercury barometer An instrument that measures changes in air pressure, consisting of a glass tube partially filled with mercury, with its open end resting in a dish of mercury. Air pressure pushing on the mercury in the dish forces the mercury in the tube higher. (p. 26)

mesosphere The middle layer of Earth's atmosphere; the layer in which most meteoroids burn up. (p. 32)

meteorologists Scientists who study the causes of weather and try to predict it. (p. 102)

microclimate The climate characteristic of a small, specific area; it may be different from the climate of the surrounding area. (p. 117)

monsoons Sea and land breezes over a large region that change direction with the seasons. (p. 56)

O

occluded Cut off, as the warm air mass at an occluded front is cut off from the ground by cooler air beneath it. (p. 81)

operational definition A statement that describes how a particular variable is to be measured or a term is to be defined. (p. 153)

ozone A form of oxygen that has three oxygen atoms in each molecule instead of the usual two. (p. 16)

P

permafrost Permanently frozen soil found in the tundra climate region. (p. 130)

photochemical smog A brownish haze that is a mixture of ozone and other chemicals, formed when nitrogen oxides, hydrocarbons, and other pollutants react with each other in the presence of sunlight. (p. 22)

polar (air mass) A cold air mass that forms north of 50° north latitude or south of 50° south latitude and has high air pressure. (p. 76)

polar zones The areas near both poles, from about 66.5° to 90° north and 66.5° to 90° south latitudes. (p. 113)

I ◆ 169

pollutants Harmful substances in the air, water, or soil. (p. 20)
precipitation Any form of water that falls from clouds and reaches Earth's surface. (p. 67)
pressure The force pushing on an area or surface. (p. 25)
psychrometer An instrument used to measure relative humidity, consisting of a wet-bulb thermometer and a dry-bulb thermometer. (p. 62)

R

radiation The direct transfer of energy by electromagnetic waves. (p. 42)
rain forest A forest in the tropical wet climate zone that gets plenty of rain all year. (p. 123)
rain gauge An instrument used to measure the amount of precipitation, consisting of an open-ended can topped by a collecting funnel and having a collecting tube and measuring scale inside. (p. 69)
relative humidity The percentage of water vapor in the air compared to the maximum amount the air could hold at that temperature. (p. 62)
responding variable The factor that changes as a result of changes to the manipulated variable in an experiment. (p. 153)

S

savanna A tropical grassland with scattered clumps of trees; found in the tropical wet-and-dry climate zone. (p. 126)
scattering Reflection of light in all directions. (p. 44)
sea breeze The flow of air from an ocean or lake to the land. (p. 56)
steppe A prairie or grassland found in the semiarid climate region. (p. 127)
storm A violent disturbance in the atmosphere. (p. 83)
storm surge A dome of water that sweeps across the coast where a hurricane lands. (p. 90)
stratosphere The second-lowest layer of Earth's atmosphere; the ozone layer is located in the upper stratosphere. (p. 32)
stratus Clouds that form in flat layers. (p. 64)
subarctic A climate zone that lies north of the humid continental climate zone, with short, cool summers and long, bitterly cold winters. (p. 129)
sunspots Dark, cooler regions on the surface of the sun. (p. 137)

T

temperate zones The area between the tropical and polar zones, from about 23.5° to 66.5° north and 23.5° to 66.5° south latitudes. (p. 113)
temperature The average amount of energy of motion in the molecules of a substance. (p. 49)
thermal energy The energy of motion in the molecules of a substance. (p. 49)
thermometer An instrument used to measure temperature, consisting of a thin, glass tube with a bulb on one end that contains a liquid (usually mercury or alcohol). (p. 49)
thermosphere The outermost layer of Earth's atmosphere. (p. 35)
tornado A rapidly whirling, funnel-shaped cloud that reaches down from a storm cloud to touch Earth's surface, usually leaving a destructive path. (p. 85)
tropical (air mass) A warm air mass that forms in the tropics and has low air pressure. (p. 76)
tropical zone The area near the equator, between about 23.5° north latitude and 23.5° south latitude. (p. 113)
troposphere The lowest layer of Earth's atmosphere, where weather occurs. (p. 31)
tundra A polar climate region, found across northern Alaska, Canada, and Russia, with short, cool summers and bitterly cold winters. (p. 130)

U

ultraviolet radiation A form of energy with wavelengths that are shorter than visible light. (p. 43)

V

variable Any factor that can change in an experiment. (p. 153)

W

water vapor Water in the form of a gas. (p. 17)
weather The condition of Earth's atmosphere at a particular time and place. (p. 14)
wind The horizontal movement of air from an area of high pressure to an area of lower pressure. (p. 52)
wind-chill factor Increased cooling caused by the wind. (p. 53)
windward The side of mountains that faces the oncoming wind. (p. 117)

170 ◆ I

Index

I ◆ 171

172 ◆ I

I ◆ 173

174 ◆ I

Acknowledgments

Illustration

John Edwards & Associates: 30, 44, 56t, 79, 80, 81, 89, 119, 140
GeoSystems Global Corporation: 88, 91, 92, 103t, 115, 124–125, 136, 148
Andrea Golden: 10, 151
Jared Lee: 150
Martucci Design: 15, 23, 43, 103b, 121, 132
Matt Mayerchak: 38, 72, 144
Morgan Cain & Associates: 26b, 27, 28, 45, 48, 50–51, 54, 57, 59, 67, 69, 141
Ortelius Design Inc: 17, 56b, 82, 86-87, 109, 113, 116, 138, 145
Matthew Pippin: 26t, 33, 61, 65, 96
Proof Positive/Farrowlyne Associates, Inc.: 149
John Sanderson/Horizon Design: 78
Walter Stuart: 137
J/B Woolsey Associates: 64, 97, 117

Photography

Photo Research Kerri Hoar, PoYee McKenna Oster
Cover image Tom Ives/The Stock Market

Nature of Science
Page 8, Jane Love/NASA; **9r**, Jose L. Pelaez/The Stock Market; **9l**, NASA/Photo Researchers; **10b**, NASA; **10–11t**, NASA

Chapter 1
Pages 12–13, Jay Simon/TSI; **14t**, Russ Lappa; **14b**, NASA/Photo Researchers; **16b**, Russ Lappa; **16t**, Richard Haynes; **17r**, George G. Dimijian/Photo Researchers; **18tl**, Eric Horan/Liaison International; **19**, Richard Haynes; **20t**, Russ Lappa; **20b**, Aaron Haupt/Photo Researchers; **21b**, Paul Lowe/Magnum Photos; **21t**, Biophoto Associates/Photo Researchers; **22**, Will McIntyre/Photo Researchers; **24**, Steve Casimiro/Liaison International; **25t**, Russ Lappa; **25b**, Eric A. Kessler; **27t**, Ivan Bucher/Photo Researchers; **29**, Russ Lappa; **31t**, Russ Lappa; **31b**, Steve Vidler/Superstock; **32**, Mark C. Burnett/Photo Researchers; **34b**, Corbis-Bettmann; **34t**, The Granger Collection, NY; **35b**, NASA; **35t**, The National Archives/Corbis; **36**, Jack Finch/Science Photo Library/Photo Researchers; **37**, Biophoto Associates/Photo Researchers.

Chapter 2
Pages 40–41, William Johnson/Stock Boston; **42–43**, Photo Researchers; **47**, Richard Haynes; **48**, Russ Lappa; **49**, Russ Lappa; **50–51**, Daniel Cox/Allstock/PNI; **52t**, Russ Lappa; **52bl**, Victoria Hurst/Tom Stack & Associates; **52–53**, Gary Retherford/Photo Researchers; **53r**, Richard Haynes; **55**, Richard Haynes; **56**, Steve McCurry/Magnum Photos; **58**, Scala/Art Resource, NY; **60**, Ken McVey/TSI; **61**, Russ Lappa; **62**, E.J. Tarbuck; **63**, Peter Arnold; **65t**, Michael Gadomski/GADOM/Bruce Coleman; **65tm**, Phil Degginger/Bruce Coleman; **65bm**, E.R. Degginger; **65b**, John Shaw/Bruce Coleman; **66**, Wendy Shattil/Bob Rozinski/Tom Stack & Associates; **67**, Richard Haynes; **68t**, AP/Wide World; **68b**, Nuridsany et Perennou/Photo Researchers; **68 inset**, Gerben Oppermans/TSI; **70**, Bill Frantz/TSI; **71l**, Gerben Oppermans/TSI; **71r**, Victoria Hurst/Tom Stack & Associates.

Chapter 3
Pages 74–75, Pete Turner/The Image Bank; **76t**, Russ Lappa; **76b,** Russ Lappa; **77,** Jim Corwin/TSI; **83t**, Russ Lappa; **83b**, Dirck Halstead/Liaison International; **84**, Dan Sudia/Photo Researchers; **85**, Schuster/Superstock; **86b**, The Granger Collection, NY; **86t,** The Granger Collection, NY; **87l**, North Wind Picture Archives; **88**, Sheila Beougher/Liaison International; **89**, NASA-Goddard Laboratory for Atmospheres; **90**, Clore Collection, Tate Gallery, London/Art Resource, NY; **92**, NOAA; **94**, Tony Freeman/Photo Edit; **95t**, Richard Haynes; **95bl**, Keith Kent/Science Photo Library/Photo Researchers; **95br**, Grant V. Faint/The Image Bank; **98**, AP Photo/Pool/David J. Phillip; **99t**, Larry Lawfer; **99b**, Corel Corp.; **100**, AP Photo/David Umberger; **101**, NOAA; **103**, NOAA; **104–106**, AccuWeather, Inc.; **107l**, Schuster/Superstock; **107r**, Russ Lappa.

Chapter 4
Pages 110–111, David Muench; **112t**, Richard Haynes; **112b**, Thomas D. Mangelsen/Peter Arnold; **114**, David Madison/Bruce Coleman; **116**, Duncan Wherrett/TSI; **117**, Chris Cheadle/TSI; **121**, Richard Haynes; **122t,** Russ Lappa; **122b**, Charlie Waite/TSI; **123**, Geogory G. Dimigian/Photo Researchers; **126t**, Thomas D. Mangelsen/Peter Arnold; **126b**, Alex S. MacLean/Peter Arnold; **127**, Stephen Johnson/TSI; **128t,** Ann Duncan/Tom Stack & Associates; **128b**, Margaret Gowan/TSI; **129**, Kennan Ward Photography/Corbis; **130t**, Art Wolfe/TSI; **130b**, Thomas Kitchin/Tom Stack & Associates; **131**, Photodisc, Inc.; **134**, 1996 Ira Block; **135r**, Tony Craddock/Science Photo Library/Photo Researchers; **135 inset**, George Godfrey/Animals Animals; **142**, NOAA; **143l**, Art Wolfe/TSI; **143r**, Tony Craddock/Science Photo Library/Photo Researchers.

Interdisciplinary Exploration
Page 146, Galen Rowell/Corbis; **147**, The Granger Collection, NY; **149**, AE Zuckerman/Photo Edit; **150 inset**, Corbis-Bettmann; **150–151**, AE Zuckerman/Photo Edit.

Skills Handbook
Page 152, Mike Moreland/Photo Network; **153t**, Foodpix; **153m**, Richard Haynes; **153b**, Russ Lappa; **156**, Richard Haynes; **158**, Ron Kimball; **159**, Renee Lynn/Photo Researchers.

I ◆ 175